INDUSTRIAL STATISTICS

VOLUME 1

INDUSTRIAL STATISTICS

STATISTICS

VOLUME 1

C. W. Lowe
*Manager, Operational Research Section,
Monsanto Chemicals Limited*

London

BUSINESS BOOKS LIMITED

First published 1968

Standard Book Number 220.79880.X

A 'Business Management' Book

This book has been set in 10 on 12 pt Times Roman: printed
in England by Hazell Watson & Viney Limited, Aylesbury, Bucks,
for the publishers Business Books Limited (registered office:
180 Fleet Street, London, E.C.4) publishing offices: Mercury House,
Waterloo Road, London, S.E.1

Printed and bound in Great Britain

PREFACE

MOST BOOKS on statistics have been written by statisticians who are well-trained and well-versed in statistical theory for use by statisticians who are also well-trained and well-versed in statistical theory. As one might expect, such books contain a high proportion of statistical theory and whereas these books are essential to provide the necessary background they are not very useful to the statistician who earns his living dealing with many different problems that arise in industry.

There are many statisticians working in industry who have had no formal training in mathematics or statistics, and these people have to fight their way through every problem that arises with such help as they may be able to derive from published information. Statistical theory does not help these people very much, though numbers of them accept the opportunities offered to attend various courses in statistics and learn some statistical theory.

The industrial statistician is well content to accept that the theoreticians have proved all the various bits of theory and is not interested in any further theoretical development. He, or she, needs methods, procedures, and techniques which can be used quickly and simply. Almost all the theory in this book is in Chapter 2 and other odd bits of theory are introduced only where they provide additional information of general interest. From Chapter 3 onwards, therefore, this book is a straightforward 'work' book which describes a large number of statistical methods and gives examples of their uses.

The book is not restricted to the so-called classical methods and many newer methods are described. Some of these, particularly the tests of significance, have been called 'Quick and Dirty Methods'; their simplicity makes them extremely useful. Also, the book contains some sections not usually found in statistical books, such as Chapter 3 on Charts and Graphs and some of the sampling and testing procedures in Chapters 8 and 9. No apologies are offered for these. They have been of immense benefit to many people and organizations and may be found useful to many more.

Statistical methods seem to have found greatest application in chemical industry, and many of the examples in this book are taken from chemical industry. But examples are quoted from other industries too, and many of the procedures and methods may be used in any industry where people are employed and a product is produced.

The author wishes to thank all his friends and colleagues who have supplied the examples in this book and who made suggestions regarding the subject matter to be chosen. He also wishes to thank the editors of and contributors to various statistical journals for permission to reproduce tables and other material, and Monsanto Chemicals Limited for permission to use the data in the examples.

The author is indebted to the literary executor of the late Sir Ronald A. Fisher, F.R.S., to Dr Frank Yates, F.R.S., and to Oliver and Boyd Limited, Edinburgh, for permission to reprint Table 3 from their book, *Statistical Tables for Biological, Agricultural and Medical Research.*

May, 1968   C. W. L.

CONTENTS

LIST OF FIGURES

CHAPTER ONE

INTRODUCTION TO STATISTICS

THE WORDS 'statist', 'statistics' and 'statistician' are derived from the Latin word 'status' meaning a state, particularly in the sense of a political state, and statistics began as the exposition (mostly verbal at that time) of the note-worthy characteristics of a state. These statistics permitted comparisons to be made between states. The earliest known mention of the word 'statist' occurs in *Hamlet*, Act 5, Scene 2, where it seems to refer to someone who prepares something unintelligible; *Hamlet* was written in 1602, so that statists have been in existence for quite some time.

1.1 development and uses of statistics

In 1770, Baron J. F. von Bielfield wrote a book called *The Elements of Universal Erudition* which contains a chapter entitled 'Statistics' and the definition of the subject is given as 'the science that teaches us what is the political arrangement of all the modern states of the known world'. A few years later, in 1787, E. A. W. Zimmermann in the preface to his book *A Political Survey of the Present State of Europe* wrote: 'It is about 40 years ago that that branch of political knowledge, which has for its object the actual and relative power of the several modern states, the power arising from their natural advantages, the industry and civilization of their inhabitants, and the wisdom of their governments, has been formed, chiefly by German writers, into a separate science . . . this science, distinguished by the new-coined name of Statistics, is become a favourite study in Germany.'

Sir John Sinclair wrote to the clergy of the Church of Scotland in May, 1790, saying that 'Statistical inquiries have been carried to a very great extent'. He explains that these statistical inquiries are inquiries respecting the population, the political circumstances, the productions of a country, and others matters of state.

Western civilization and modern society are pervaded – almost controlled

— by ideas of numbers and measurements, and most of the events of our daily life are bound inextricably with them. There is little difficulty in accepting that the introduction of a system of currency offers great advantages over methods of barter; just imagine trying to run the Bank of England and the Royal Mint without the ability to count and express conditions in numbers. All our business life and our sporting activities depend on measurements and numbers; even when we are affected by sleeplessness the usual remedy is to start counting.

Science is particularly dependent on numerical expression. As organized knowledge increased the necessity for precision became greater and precise statements can be formulated more easily and understandably by the use of measurement and numbers. Industry, and particularly chemical industry, is an application of science and is absolutely and utterly dependent on measurement and numbers.

Lord Kelvin in one of his enthusiastic moments stated that 'when you can measure what you are speaking about and express it in numbers, you know something about it; but when you cannot measure it, when you cannot express it in numbers, your knowledge is of a meagre and unsatisfactory kind'. This remark may be somewhat unjust to some forms of investigation such as Darwin's work on the Origin of Species, but it expresses a point of view which has been endorsed by very many people.

The Royal Statistical Society, founded in 1834 as the Statistical Society of London, set out to collect, collate and publish 'Facts calculated to illustrate the conditions and prospects of Society which can be stated numerically and arranged in tables'. Originally there were five fields of interest:

1 *Economical statistics:* dealing with agriculture, manufacturing, commerce and currency, distribution of wealth, etc.

2 *Political statistics:* dealing with legal statistics, statistics of national finance and expenditure, civil and military establishments, etc.

3 *Medical statistics:* dealing with all aspects of diseases and their treatments.

4 *Moral and intellectual statistics:* dealing with literature, education, religious instruction, institutions and crime, etc.

5 *Colonial statistics:* dealing with all aspects of colonial life.

Other equally important aspects of statistical work have been added in the course of time, among which are the development of statistical theory and methodology, and the application of statistical methods to scientific endeavour and research, industry and agriculture.

Thus 'Statistics' now covers everything dealing even remotely with the collection, analysis, interpretation and presentation of numerical data. However, in this book we are concerned only with some of the applications of statistics to industry, regardless of whether or not the applications were devised for other fields.

The theory of statistics as a distinct branch of scientific method is of comparatively recent growth. Although its beginnings may be traced back to the work of Blaise Pascal (1623–1662), Abraham de Moivre (1667–1745), Pierre Laplace (1749–1827), and Karl Gauss (1777–1845) on the theory of probability and the theory of errors of observation, the study of statistics did not really begin to flourish until the later part of the nineteenth century under Karl Pearson and Galton. These two laid secure foundations from which the study of statistics has expanded and flourished. Statistical theory and methodology are still expanding and it is not at all unusual to see the development of a statistical method which is later modified or specially adapted to the elucidation of available data of a particular kind.

There are many examples of the uses of statistical methods, but it will be sufficient to quote four from widely diverse fields of investigation:

1 *From astronomy:* in the period 1884–1911 the German astronomer, Seeliger, used the idea of a frequency distribution in the intrinsic brightness of the stars to determine the relative rate at which the stars fall off in number at increasing distances from the centre of the sidereal system. The Dutch astronomer, Kapteyn, used sampling theory to select 252 small regions of the sky in each of which star density and brightness were determined. Each of these methods permitted calculation of the diameter and thickness of the galaxy.

2 *From theoretical physics:* Maxwell and Boltzmann applied the Gaussian Law of Errors to the distribution of molecular velocities and their determinations of thermodynamical functions.

3 *From industry and agriculture:* W. S. Gosset, a chemist working for Guinness at the Park Royal Brewery, developed statistical theory and methods relating to experimental error and applied them to experimentation on sampling and analysis. As a result new types of barley were developed and still are being developed. R. A. Fisher developed statistical theory and methods on analysis of variance and applied them to the design of experiments which led to great improvements in yield from agricultural land.

4 *From medicine:* Much effort has been expended in attempting to show statistically that there is a correlation between lung cancer and smoking, which seems to be accepted or not according to whether or not one dislikes smoking. The weight of evidence points to the fact that lung cancer has killed, and is killing every year, a much larger number of smokers than non-smokers; whether or not these numbers are in the same ratio as the number of smokers to non-smokers is not known. A recent investigation dealing with stomach cancer showed that the incidence of known cases was the lowest in the chalk areas of S.E. England and increased steadily across country to a maximum in North Wales, and work was suggested to attempt to correlate this incidence with soil conditions, natural radio-activity, living and eating habits, and a number of other factors.

To illustrate these terms let us consider an exercise in which we wish to find out how many six-foot male teachers there are in this country and how they are divided into various age-groups. Here we can consider all the male teachers in the country as our population, when the six-footers among them form a sub-population. The number of teachers in the country is known; it is a definite fixed number. The six-foot teachers can be counted and they are real. So we have to deal with a real, finite population and sub-population.

If we had the time and the inclination we could speak to every male teacher in the country, ask his age and perhaps measure his height. Then we would be able to assign every six-foot teacher to one or other of our age-groups and our information would be absolute and complete. We would have examined every individual member of the sub-population and our parameters—for example the average age of the six-foot teachers—would be determined exactly. However, a procedure such as this would take a long time and require much effort; in many cases in industry complete examination of a population is either grossly uneconomic or just impossible.

For instance, if we wished to determine the yield of some chemical produced in batch manufacture we could make a large number of batches and perform the necessary measurements. But no matter how many batches were made, it would always be possible to make more and so the batches belong to a real but infinite population which has no known limit. We could consider sub-populations of this infinite population, such as those batches which were complete in a 12–13 hour time-cycle, and any such sub-population would also be real and infinite. If we wanted a lot of data in a hurry we could decide on the minimum and maximum batch yields and extract values between these limits from a table of random numbers; this would give us a hypothetical population from which our conclusions would be made.

We could draw a sample from our population of six-foot teachers by deciding to examine the teachers of say 20 towns. Then we would attempt to eliminate bias by making a random selection of 20 towns by some such method of spotting on a map or sticking pins in a gazetteer or picking 20 from a mixed heap of papers each of which carries the name of one town. This we cannot do with our manufacturing batches, so we would accept the first 20 or 30 batches completed as our random sample; this is reasonable and fair since the individual batches have no connection with each other and the final yield of each batch is the result of that batch alone and cannot be predetermined. In all cases where a number of determinations of some chemical or physical characteristic is made, or a series of manufacturing or experimental batches is run, the values obtained are regarded as a random sample of all the determinations which might have been made in infinite repetition of the procedure. From this sample a value of the relevant statistic is calculated, and that value is accepted as the best available estimate of the parameter of the population.

Let us begin our study of statistics by considering a series of values, arranged for our convenience in ascending order of magnitude. We write this series as

$$x_1, x_2, x_3, \ldots, x_i, \ldots, x_n$$

indicating that there are n values in the series and x_i represents any individual item in the series. These values may be any measured or counted values such as experimental yields from a succession of batches or the numbers of accidents that occurred in successive months. All the values in the series will be measurements of some quantity which is subject to variation, so we shall call this quantity a *variable*. Variables may be continuous or discrete: continuous variables are those which may be represented by points on a continuous scale such as weight, volume, concentration, time, distance, pH, moisture content, etc.; while discrete variables are those which do not vary continuously and whose values, therefore, cannot be expressed as points on a continuous scale — examples of discrete variables are taste, odour, smoothness, visible contamination, items of equipment, types of materials, etc.

A number of arithmetic processes can be applied to this series of values. For instance, we can subtract the smallest value (x_1) from the largest value (x_n) to give the

13 *Range*, which is defined as the difference between the largest value and he smallest value, $R = x_n - x_1$.

Next we can add all the values together to give the sum, and this is defined as

14 *Sum*, obtained by addition of all the values. $S = x_1 + x_2 + x_3 + \ldots + x_i + \ldots + x_n$. The sum may be written as $\sum_{i=1}^{n} x_i$ or just as $\sum x$.

If we divide the sum by the number of values in the series we obtain an average value defined as

15 *Sample mean*, the arithmetic mean or average of a series, usually indicated by $\bar{x}$, where

$$\bar{x} = \frac{x_1 + x_2 + x_3 + \ldots + x_i + \ldots + x_n}{n} = \frac{\sum x}{n}$$

The sample mean is an unbiased estimate of the population mean which is usually written as μ. Note that the word 'mean' is always taken to be the arithmetic mean. No confusion arises because the geometric mean and harmonic mean are always given their full titles. Most of the statistical work dealt with in this book involves samples, and the mean is probably the most important statistic calculated.

For any given sample of n values, $x_1, x_2, x_3, \ldots, x_i, \ldots, x_n$, which may be all different or not, a value can be assigned for what is called the

16 *Degrees of freedom*, which is the number of values in the sample which may be varied at will so long as the mean remains unchanged. This is, of

course, $(n - 1)$, and it is said that one degree of freedom is lost 'for the mean'. Next it is possible to calculate (if we assume the sample is drawn from a normal distribution) the

17 *Sum of Squares*, which is defined as the sum of the squares of the deviations (or differences) of each value in the sample from the sample mean

$$\text{S.S.} = (x_1 - \bar{x})^2 + (x_2 - \bar{x})^2 + (x_3 - \bar{x})^2 + \ldots + (x_i - \bar{x})^2 + \ldots$$
$$+ (x_n - \bar{x})^2 = \sum (x_i - \bar{x})^2,$$

and since this is a sum of squares, each of which is positive, the sum of squares must always be positive.

From the sum of squares and the degrees of freedom we derive the

18 *Sample variance*, which is the sum of squares divided by the degrees of freedom

$$V(\text{or } s^2) = \frac{\sum (x_i - \bar{x})^2}{n - 1}$$

and is sometimes referred to as the 'mean square'. The sample variance is an unbiased estimate of the population variance.

In calculation of the variance we use a divisor $(n - 1)$, and the variance is, of course, the quotient of the sum of squares and the number of degrees of freedom. It may be of interest to demonstrate that $(n - 1)$ is the best divisor to be used in calculating an estimate of the population variance from a sample of n observations x drawn from the population:

We wish to obtain a state in which

the average value of sample variances = the population variance

which we can write as $\quad \text{ave } (s^2) = \sigma^2$

Let the number of degrees of freedom of the sample of n values be k,

$$\text{then} \quad \text{ave } (s^2) = \text{ave } \left[\frac{\sum (x - \bar{x})^2}{k} \right] = \frac{1}{k} \text{ave } \left[\sum (x - \bar{x})^2 \right]$$

$$= \frac{1}{k} [\text{ave } (\sum x^2) - \text{ave } (n\bar{x}^2)]$$

$$= \frac{1}{k} [\sum (\text{ave } x^2) - n \text{ ave } (\bar{x}^2)]$$

$$\text{but} \quad \text{ave } (x^2) = \mu^2 + \sigma^2, \quad \text{and} \quad \text{ave } (\bar{x}^2) = \mu^2 + \frac{\sigma^2}{n}$$

$$\text{therefore} \quad \text{ave } (s^2) = \frac{1}{k} \left[n(\mu^2 + \sigma^2) - n\left(\mu^2 + \frac{\sigma^2}{n} \right) \right]$$

$$= \frac{1}{k} [n\mu^2 + n\sigma^2 - n\mu^2 - \sigma^2]$$

$$= \frac{n - 1}{k} \sigma^2$$

and so we have that $(n - 1)/k$ must equal 1 so that $k = n - 1$ and the best estimate of the population variance is obtained by dividing the sum of squares, calculated from the sample values, by a number which is one less than the number of individual observations in the sample.

The square root of the variance is known as the

19 *Standard deviation,*

$$s = \sqrt{\frac{\sum (x_i - \bar{x})^2}{n - 1}}$$

and this is sometimes called the 'root mean square'. Being a square root, the value of the standard deviation is really $\pm$, but it is always reported as positive. Note that the standard deviation is in the same units as the original measurements.

Two other statistics are sometimes of use

20 *Median,* which is the middle value of the sample and has as many of the other values lying above it as lie below it, and

21 *Mode,* which is that value which occurs most often in the sample.

If we consider the following sample of values, grouped in ascending order

11,　12, 12, 12,　13, 13, 13, 13, 13, 13, 13　14, 14, 14, 14, 14, 14,
(1)　　(3)　　　　　　(7)　　　　　　　　　(6)

15, 15, 15, 15,　16, 16, 16, 16,　17, 17, 17,
(4)　　　　　(4)　　　　　(3)

then the mean is $397/28 = 14{\cdot}1786$; the median is 14; and the mode is 13. In most of the statistical work carried out in industry it is assumed that the sample under examination has been drawn from a population which fits into a 'normal distribution' (see Chapter 2.7); for a normal distribution the mean, median, and mode are coincidental.

When a very large number of data points is available the distribution of these points approximates to a normal distribution and very little, if any, is lost in postulating a normal distribution with mean and standard deviation calculated from the data points. However, when only a few data points are available, such as four replicate analyses made from a sample

97·3, 97·6, 97·85, and 97·9

it is not wholly reasonable to calculate the mean and standard deviation from these four values and apply the parameters wholeheartedly to any and every test that may be thought of. Often it is more reasonable to use

22 *Non-parametric methods* which permit evaluation of the sample data without the assumption that the data belong to a normal distribution and therefore without the need to estimate parameters of this distribution. A number of non-parametric methods are given in this book.

1.3 averages and weighted averages

The mean, or arithmetic average, calculated from a sample (or a population) is a statistic (or a parameter) used as a measure of location. That is it helps us to decide where the sample and population are located on some reference scale compared with other samples and populations. However, in industry we must be very careful when we compute an average that we realize exactly what that average stands for, and that we are using the right average in the right way.

It is easy to see that if the profit on six different items is 2d., 3d., 4d., 5d., 6d., and 10d. each, then the average profit is 5d. per item if and only if the same number of each item is sold. If, for example, sales of these items are 6, 5, 4, 3, 2, and 1 respectively then the average profit achieved will be a little less than 4d. per item.

Sometimes difficulty arises when dealing with a variable such as plant yields. The yield declared for any month — or whatever other period of time is used — is the total of a product made divided by the total of some raw material used and thus is the average yield for all the production runs made in that month and not the arithmetic average of the yields of the individual batches made in the month. If we wish to estimate the average yield for (say) six months, the mean of the six-monthly yields would give an incorrect value; for example the figures

Product	Raw material	Yield
10,160 lb	10,000 lb	101·6
8,184	8,000	102·3
6,198	6,000	103·3
4,144	4,000	103·6
3,132	3,000	104·4
3,138	3,000	104·6

give a mean of the yields of 103·3, but the true six-month average yield is 102·8.

However, if the exercise is concerned with showing the variability of plant yields, or perhaps determining confidence limits for a control chart we would use the monthly yields as reported. Each would be compared with others and the average used would be 103·3.

Thus it is necessary to be clear before attempting any statistical clarification whether the value to be calculated is the arithmetic mean of a series of values, or the effective mean value of the process concerned. In any case where it is desirable to quote a six-monthly moving average yield, the figure to be quoted is the effective mean of the process.

1.4 methods and procedures

Perhaps this is as good a place as any to stress that the statistical calculations made in this book use only very simple arithmetic; the most difficult operation involved is that of finding a square root and with a desk calculator or even a table of logarithms, this should present no difficulty. Exhaustive proofs of the methods and theorems used need some mathematical knowledge and ability, but in this book we are not concerned with that aspect of statistics. We shall accept all theorems and the validity of all the methods as having been fully proved to everyone's satisfaction — as indeed they have been — and we shall accept all procedures as having been proved by many years of satisfactory application. Any theory necessary to the development of any procedure will be quoted and then straightway applied to the particular problem at hand.

The first problem involved in any statistical work is the collection and sorting of data. Wherever possible it is best for the analyst concerned to obtain his own data, and of course this may be done in such fields as plant control, laboratory experimentation, stores sampling, and work sampling. It is not possible to obtain one's own data when dealing with such matters as sales, accidents, durations of repairs, plant yields, etc.; the data are provided and must be accepted, though this does not imply that there will never be discussion about the inclusion or exclusion of some individuals which seem to be 'wrong' when compared with the rest of the data.

However the data are derived, it is necessary to determine their reliability before any attempt is made to base conclusions on them. This is true of all data, but particularly so of numerical data. A colour might be described as 'a sort of greeny-blue', and this might be acceptable, and indeed it might be possible to distinguish between two items whose colours are described as 'a sort of greeny-blue' and 'a kind of bluey-green'. But we could not possibly accept a value of 24, qualified as 'or it might be 23·75 or possibly a bit less'. If the reported value is 24, then the reporter has to stand by this value of 24.

Having obtained the data, and being satisfied with their reliability, it is necessary to sort (or arrange) the data into a convenient pattern for use. This may involve steps such as reducing the data to a more convenient scale of units, or deciding on the method of presentation of the data according to the work to be done on it. There are three very useful procedures which can be used in sorting data:

1 *Graphical representation:* It may be beneficial to present the data in graphical form. Often the shape and general picture of a graph or chart can be remembered long after any details of values or quantities have been forgotten.

2 *Condensation* can be used to reduce a large number of individuals to an easily managed quantity. The most frequent example of condensation occurs when individuals are arranged in groups. For instance, instead of dealing with 400 values between 1 and 100, we could assign values to the groups 1–10, 11–20, 21–30 etc. and deal with these 10 groups. The process of condensation is dependent, of course, on the permissible sacrifice in quantity for increased clarity and ease of handling; in most cases condensation results in very little loss of efficiency, and if an appreciable loss of efficiency is likely the condensation may not be wise.

3 *Correlation* can be used to describe relationships between variables. Several pages of data may be thought to look impressive in a report; if such data are an essential part of the report they should be included as an appendix and a summary table or graph included in the main body of the report. In those cases where the data refer to some relationship between two or more variables, a graph and an equation such as

$$y = ax^2 + bx + c$$

provide more enlightenment than many pages of tabulated data.

The methods or functions of statistics lie in three main fields:

1 *Estimation,* which includes such operations as calculation of means, differences of means, standard deviations and regression coefficients. It is not unusual for estimation to be converted into prediction but it must be remembered at all times that no quantity is ever measured or calculated exactly; some error is always present and it may be quite difficult to make the necessary allowance for that error.

2 *Tests of significance,* (Hypothesis Testing) where it is necessary to answer such questions as 'Is an observed difference of means real or due to chance?'; 'Is a calculated regression coefficient significantly different from zero?'; 'Are two sets of values from the same population?' These questions can be answered from the data with some probability of being correct, and this probability must be determined.

3 *Analysis of variance,* which is used to determine the effect of each of several variables all of which act on a system at the same time, but possibly to different extents.

In each of these fields both classical statistical (parametric) methods and non-parametric methods are available, and we shall deal with both kinds.

1.5 statistical evidence

An argument often put forward is that the use of mathematical methods is unjustified because the accuracy of the raw data is not sufficient to bear the weight of the mathematical treatment. This assertion is not strictly logical, because if any data are worth any analysis at all then they are worth that analysis which derives the maximum amount of information – that is, the best form of statistical analysis which may be applicable. And we define 'best' as being that which is the most convenient while still of acceptable accuracy; for example, it may be more convenient (and certainly it is a lot quicker) to do a Tukey Quadrant Test and show a 95 per cent probability that a correlation exists than to work out a linear regression and show that the probability is 97·5 per cent.

Experimental data are obtained from a sample drawn from a parent population. The sample should be obtained by some random process that gives every individual in the parent population an equal chance of appearing in the sample. Sometimes stratified sampling is necessary, in which case sampling within each stratum should be randomized. In order that generalizations may be made from the sample, the sample *must* be representative of the population from which it has been drawn; a 'selected' sample is not representative of any quantity except itself, and general conclusions may not be made from a selected sample.

What *can happen*, what *does exist*, what *is observable*, quite regardless of the frequency of occurrence and irrespective of association or causation, may be observed even on a sample of one. However large or small the sample, conclusions may be drawn from the data; all such conclusions are tentative and may need to be modified as and when new knowledge becomes available. Misuse of statistical method occurs in translation of evidence from the particular to the general. We must know that such translation is permissible, before it is done.

The following rules must be applied and adhered to, without fail, in all cases involving statistical analysis:

1 Numbers are only a shorthand convention for describing past events and forecasting trends. It is necessary to search for those facts expressed in numbers which show events and relationships most truly.
2 The doctoring of data or statistics to 'prove' a point (and in reality, to misprove the point) is immoral. If everybody did it there would be no truth or value in any figures and no one would ever be able to rely on any figures.
3 Results must not be interpreted unwarrantedly so as to appear to confirm any preconceived hypothesis. The hypothesis must emanate from the results.
4 When drawing conclusions from samples, best judgment must be used. If valid tests for probability cannot be made, or if valid tests by repetition have not been made, proper warning must be given.

Finally, two comments made by W. S. Gosset ('Student'):

   (i) 'Statistical examination in each particular case may help much, but no
statistical methods will ever replace thought as a way of avoiding pit-
falls, though they may help us to bridge them',
and

  (ii) 'Statistics are an aid to, but not a substitute for, commonsense.'

SUGGESTIONS FOR FURTHER READING

2 G. U. YULE and M. G. KENDALL, Notation and Introduction, 1958.
3 C. A. BENNETT and N. L. FRANKLIN, Chapter 1, 1954.
5 O. L. DAVIES (ed.), Chapter 1, 1958.

The numbers refer to the numbers of the references in the Bibliography, where full
references are given.

CHAPTER TWO

CHANCE, PROBABILITY, AND SOME STATISTICAL DISTRIBUTIONS

MANY OCCASIONS arise in industry where it is required to assess the probability of reaching an acceptable result by 'taking a chance' or adopting one particular sequence of events rather than any alternative sequences which may be available. Usually the probability is estimated by reference to some distribution which is built from the frequencies of occurrence obtained when random samples are drawn from the population concerned. In this chapter we shall discuss briefly the three most common distributions — Binomial, Poisson, and Normal — but we shall lead up to these by discussing chance and probability and the relationship between them.

The idea of 'taking a chance' or 'making a selection' and estimating how good a chance is being taken is best derived from consideration of permutations and combinations. These may sound complicated but they are simple and very useful, and provide the first stepping-stone in our study of industrial statistics.

2.1 permutations and combinations

First, let us define these terms and show the difference between them:

A *Permutation* is an arrangement of individuals (or objects, or items, or elements) any or all of which may be like or unlike, while

A *Combination* is a selection made from a set of like or unlike elements.

For example, if we have three different objects, A, B, and C, we can arrange them in six different ways

ABC, ACB, BCA, BAC, CAB and CBA,

and each of these arrangements is different from the others. These are the six possible arrangements of three elements.

But if all we are interested in is making a selection of three, then our selection will contain A and B and C, and it does not matter which comes first or second or third. Thus there is only one possible selection of three elements taken three at a time. We can develop these ideas a little further, retaining the names element, permutation, and combination.

2.1.1 PERMUTATIONS

Consider a set of n elements. Any arrangement of these elements such as

$$x_1, x_2, x_3, \ldots, x_i, \ldots, x_n$$

is known as a permutation. If any two (or more) elements are changed the result is a different permutation.

In deciding how many permutations can be derived from the n elements we can say that the first place can be filled in n ways, since we can choose any one of the n elements. But having chosen one, there are $(n - 1)$ elements left, so that the second place can be chosen only from these $(n - 1)$ elements; that is, it can be filled in $(n - 1)$ ways and each of these $(n - 1)$ ways can be allocated to each of the n ways of filling the first place. Thus the number of ways the first two places can be filled is $n \times (n - 1)$, and, of course, there are $(n - 2)$ elements left for the third place which therefore can be filled in $(n - 2)$ ways, each of which can be allocated to each of the $n \times (n - 1)$ ways of filling the first two places. So the number of ways in which the first three places can be filled is $n \times (n - 1) \times (n - 2)$. And we can continue this procedure until we reach the last place, the n-th, for which we have only one element left, so that the last place can be filled in only one way. Then the total number of permutations of n elements taken n at a time is called ^nP_n, and is given by

$$^nP_n = n \times (n - 1) \times (n - 2) \times (n - 3) \times \ldots \times 3 \times 2 \times 1 = n!$$

Given the necessary patience the full list of permutations can be tabulated in systematic order. As, for example, with the 24 permutations of A, B, C, and D, which are

```
A A A A A A   B B B B B B   C C C C C C   D D D D D D
B B C C D D   A A C C D D   A A B B D D   A A B B C C
C D B D B C   C D A D A C   B D A D A B   B C A C A B
D C D B C B   D C D A C A   D B D A B A   C B C A B A
```

If permutations of only part (say r elements) of the set of n elements are to be considered, then the number of permutations that can be made of the r elements is

$$n \times (n - 1) \times (n - 2) \times (n - 3) \times \ldots \times (n - r + 1)$$

and this is called the number of permutations of n elements r at a time, written as ^nP_r, where

$$^nP_r = n \times (n-1) \times (n-2) \times \ldots \times (n-r+1) = \frac{n!}{(n-r)!}$$

It follows from this relationship that

$$^nP_n = \frac{n!}{(n-n)!} = \frac{n!}{0!} = n!$$

so that $0! = 1$.

Example 1: The number of permutations of 3 letters, A, B, and C, taken 2 at a time is

$$^3P_2 = \frac{3!}{(3-2)!} = \frac{3!}{1!} = 3 \times 2 \times 1 = 6$$

and of course the permutations are AB, BA, BC, CB, CA, and AC.

Example 2: The number of groups of three different letters that can be written with the English alphabet is

$$^{26}P_3 = \frac{26!}{(26-3)!} = 26 \times 25 \times 24 = 15,600$$

If any groups of letters, not necessarily different, are required, then any one from 26 may be chosen for each place, and there are $26 \times 26 \times 26 = 17,576$ groups.

If now the set of n elements has

n_1 identical elements of one kind,
n_2 identical elements of a second kind, etc.,
up to n_k identical elements of the k-th kind

then we are in the position that of our $n!$ total permutations we have $n_1!$ arrangements of the n_1 elements of the first kind that we cannot distinguish from one another; $n_2!$ arrangements of the n_2 elements of the second kind that we cannot distinguish from one another; etc. etc., and so the total number of distinguishable permutations is ^nPn_k where

$$^nPn_k = \frac{n!}{n_1!n_2!\ldots n_k!}$$

Example 3: If in a set of 9 balls there are 4 yellow, 3 green, and 2 blue balls, then the number of different ways that these can be arranged in a line is

$$^9Pn_3 = \frac{9!}{4!3!2!} = \frac{9 \times 8 \times 7 \times 6 \times 5 \times 4 \times 3 \times 2 \times 1}{(4 \times 3 \times 2 \times 1) \times (3 \times 2 \times 1) \times (2 \times 1)} = 1,260$$

and if the reader so wishes, these arrangements can be tabulated in a systematic manner.

Sometimes the elements in a set are required to be arranged in a circle, in which case all permutations which have their elements in the same sequence, differing only by a rotation, are considered to be the same permutation. Thus to eliminate the effect of rotation one element must be considered fixed, and of course the number of permutations possible is ^nCP_n where

$$^nCP_n = (n - 1)!$$

Example 4: The number of ways in which 4 people can be arranged around a card table is

$$^4CP_4 = (4 - 1)! = 3 \times 2 \times 1 = 6.$$

2.1.2 COMBINATIONS

In most of the cases which arise we shall be interested only with the group of elements selected, and not with any particular ordering within the group, so that for our original group of three objects A, B, and C

$$ABC = ACB = BCA = BAC = CAB = CBA$$

since each of these groups contains each of the elements.

Then in any given set of n elements, the number of combinations of r of the elements which themselves have $r!$ permutations is the number of permutations of n elements taken r at a time divided by the number of permutations of r taken r at a time. This may be written as ^nC_r or C_r^n or $\binom{n}{r}$, where

$$^nC_r = \frac{n!}{(n - r)!r!}$$

Example 5: If one wished to determine the number of ways in which 3 football matches can be chosen from the 13 matches listed in the points pool for entry in the three draws pool, obviously the arrangement of the matches in each group of three is immaterial, and the number of combinations is

$$^{13}C_3 = \frac{13!}{10!3!} = \frac{13 \times 12 \times 11}{3 \times 2 \times 1} = 286$$

Example 6: When conducting planned experimentation with 5 variables, the supervisor wants to know how many interactions (effects of two or more variables) are to be determined. There are

$$^5C_1 = \frac{5!}{4!1!} = 5 \text{ main effects.}$$

$$^5C_2 = \frac{5!}{3!2!} = 10 \text{ 2-variable interactions.}$$

$$^5C_3 = \frac{5!}{3!2!} = 10 \text{ 3-variable interactions.}$$

$$^5C_4 = \frac{5!}{4!1!} = \text{5 4-variable interactions.}$$

and

$$^5C_5 = \frac{5!}{5!0!} = \text{1 5-variable interaction.}$$

Example 7: Of 6 books, 3 are mathematics books (M_1, M_2 and M_3), 2 are chemistry books (C_1 and C_2) and 1 is a physics book (P). Then the number of ways in which a selection of three books can be made from these six is

$$^6C_3 = \frac{6!}{3!3!} = \frac{6 \times 5 \times 4}{3 \times 2 \times 1} = 20$$

and this can be confirmed by a systematic tabulation

$M_1M_2M_3$	M_1M_3P	$M_2M_3C_1$	M_2PC_1	$M_1C_1C_2$
M_1M_2P	$M_1M_3C_1$	$M_2M_3C_2$	M_2PC_2	$M_2C_1C_2$
$M_1M_2C_1$	$M_1M_3C_2$	M_1PC_1	M_3PC_1	$M_3C_1C_2$
$M_1M_2C_2$	M_2M_3P	M_1PC_2	M_3PC_2	PC_1C_2

Note that every problem in permutations and combinations can be solved by tabulation given the patience to do so.

It follows, also, that the number of ways in which a selection of three books can be made so that each selection contains one mathematics book, one chemistry book and one physics book is

$$^3C_1 \times {}^2C_1 \times {}^1C_1 = 3 \times 2 \times 1 = 6.$$

And the number of ways in which a selection of books can be made so that each selection contains two mathematics books is

$$^3C_2 \times {}^3C_1 = 3 \times 3 = 9.$$

Example 6 dealt with all the possible selections that can be made from 5 elements, taking them 1, 2, 3, 4, and 5 at a time. This can be referred to as 'multiple combinations', and can be extended to the general case: the total number of selections of n unlike elements, taking any number at a time, is $2^n - 1$. This is so because for each selection each element may be selected or rejected, that is each of the elements has two chances so that there are 2^n chances of selection. But this includes the case where all elements are rejected (which is not making a selection), so that the total number of selections that can be made is $2^n - 1$.

Example 8: Continuing with the six books of Example 7, the total number of selections that can be made, any number between 1 and 6 at a time (we must exclude a zero selection) is $2^6 - 1 = 63$. These can be tabulated but an easier method is to separate the selections as done in Example 6, giving the number of selections that can be made 1 at a time is $^6C_1 = 6$

$$2 \text{ at a time is } {}^6C_2 = 15$$
$$3 \text{ at a time is } {}^6C_3 = 20$$
$$4 \text{ at a time is } {}^6C_4 = 15$$
$$5 \text{ at a time is } {}^6C_5 = 6$$
$$\text{and } 6 \text{ at a time is } {}^6C_6 = 1 \quad \text{Total} = 63.$$

The procedure of selection may be taken one stage further: Given k unlike elements, and p things alike of one kind, q things alike of a second kind, r things alike of a third kind, and so on, then the total number of selections that can be made, taking any number at a time, is

$$2^k(p + 1)(q + 1)(r + 1)(\ldots) - 1.$$

Example 9: The number of different sums of money that can be obtained from $5 \times £1$ notes, one 10/- note, four florins, 3 sixpences and one penny is

$$(5 + 1)(1 + 1)(4 + 1)(3 + 1)(1 + 1) - 1 = 6 \times 2 \times 5 \times 4 \times 2 - 1 = 479.$$

2.2 chance

If an action can have any of n possible results, and if k of these results are related to or produce some event E while the remaining $(n - k)$ results are not related to and do not produce the event E, then the chance of the occurrence of E is stated to be k/n.

For instance, reverting to Example 7, in making selections of any three from the six books, there are 20 possible selections that can be made. Then the chance of any particular selection, such as the three mathematics books, being made is $\frac{1}{20}$. Here the event E is the selection of the three mathematics books; the number of results or selections which will produce these three books, $k_1 = 1$; and the total number, n, of possible results or selections is 20.

Similarly, if a selection of three books is to contain one mathematics book, one chemistry book and one physics book, the number of selections which produces this event is 6, so that in this case $n = 20$, $k = 6$ and the chance of making a selection of this kind is $\frac{6}{20}$.

Then the chance that an event will be realized is the possibility of producing that event in a single selection. In calculating a chance we use the simple calculations of permutations and combinations, but sometimes we have to consider a compound chance, where several events are to be realized at the same time. The chance that a number of events will occur simultaneously, in a single selection, is the *product* and NOT the *sum* of their individual chances. This could be illustrated by a systematic tabulation, but can be appreciated by reference to two dice. The chance of throwing a 'two' with one die is $\frac{1}{6}$; and the chance of throwing a 'two' with a second die is $\frac{1}{6}$; but the chance of getting two 'twos' in a single throw of the two dice is $\frac{1}{6} \times \frac{1}{6} = \frac{1}{36}$, that is one throw in 36 might be a double-two (not $\frac{1}{6} + \frac{1}{6} = \frac{1}{3}$ which would lead us to believe that one-third of our throws would result in a double-two).

Now we can transform our ideas of 'taking a chance' into the concept of probability.

2.3 probability

Two more definitions are necessary before we start discussing probability. If in any system a trial or an experiment may lead to a change in state or may give a result which can change in some random manner, then the new state or the result is known as the *outcome* of the trial. The set of points representing all the possible outcomes is known as the *sample space* of the experiment.

This can be illustrated by the simple process of tossing a coin. Excluding miracles (which are not of measurable probability and so are excluded from all discussion) the coin may fall either 'heads' uppermost or 'tails' uppermost; the sample space in this experiment consists of two possible outcomes, a head and a tail. If we flip three coins at the same time, the sample space consists of 8 possible outcomes which may be illustrated by tabulation of the outcomes or by a simple sketch.

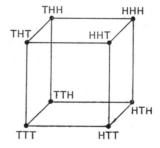

	First coin	Second coin	Third coin
Outcome 1:	H	H	H
2:	H	H	T
3:	H	T	H
4:	H	T	T
5:	T	H	H
6:	T	H	T
7:	T	T	H
8:	T	T	T

Fig. 2.3.1. SAMPLE SPACE FOR A 3-COIN FLIP

An outcome such as this is termed a simple event, and the probability that an event E_i will occur is defined as the estimate of the value approached by the ratio

$$\frac{\text{Number of occurrences of } E_i}{\text{Number of trials}} = Pr\{E_i\}$$

I.S. 1—3

as the number of trials tends to infinity. Note this difference between chance and probability: the numerical values may well be the same, but a 'chance' refers to a single trial while a 'probability' refers to a very large number (approaching infinity) of trials. Thus the chance of selecting one mathematics book, one chemistry book, and one physics book in a single selection from our set of six books is $\frac{6}{20}$; but if we make a very large number of selections of three books from our set of six the probability that our selection will consist of one mathematics book, one chemistry book, and one physics book is 0·3.

The probability that an event E occurs is written $Pr\{E\}$ or $P\{E\}$ and the probability of an event must always lie between 0 and 1. If in the trials E must occur every time, that is with certainty, then $P\{E\} = 1$; if in these trials E cannot occur, that is it is impossible for E to occur, then $P\{E\} = 0$. The two terms 'certainty' and 'impossibility' refer respectively to probability 1 and probability 0 and not to any degree of belief or disbelief. If these terms are used in any mathematical context, they must be used with their mathematical meanings.

If the outcome of the trial may be any one of $E_1, E_2, E_3, \ldots, E_n$ then

$$P\{E_1\} + P\{E_2\} + P\{E_3\} + \ldots + P\{E_n\} = 1$$

since obviously the sum of the numbers of all the occurrences must equal the number of trials. It follows that where we have situations such as tossing an unbiased coin or throwing an unbiased die, if we think that the outcomes all have equal probability, that is the estimate of the number of times outcome E_1 will appear in a large number of trials should be the same as that for E_2, and for E_3, and for each of the others, then

$$P\{E_1\} = P\{E_2\} = P\{E_3\} = \ldots = P\{E_n\} = 1/n.$$

All these simple events form the set of mutually exclusive (since the occurrence of any one of them means that all the others are excluded from consideration) and exhaustive (since together they cover all possible outcomes) states that could occur as the result of a trial. Next it is necessary to deal with the probabilities attached to composite and related events, for which we shall quote four theorems.

Theorem 1. THE ADDITION THEOREM: If A and B are mutually exclusive events, that is either A or B can occur at one time but they cannot occur together (the sample spaces for A and B have no points in common) then the probability of A *or* B occurring is given by $P\{A + B\}$, where

$$P\{A + B\} = P\{A\} + P\{B\}.$$

For example, if the probability that my wife will buy a new dress of a blue colour is 0·5, and the probability that she will buy a new dress of a red colour is 0·4, then the probability that she will buy a new dress of either a blue or a red colour is 0·5 + 0·4 = 0·9. This of course implies one of two things:

either my wife intends to buy a red or a blue dress and she is 90 per cent sure of finding something suitable, or she intends to buy a new dress which may be of any colour though 90 per cent of her preference is for red or blue.

This theorem may be extended to cover any number of events.

Theorem 2. THE MULTIPLICATION THEOREM: Where A and B are independent events, the probability of both outcomes appearing together is given by $P\{AB\}$, where

$$P\{AB\} = P\{A\}.P\{B\},$$

and again this may be extended to cover any number of events.

For example, Department 1 has 5 men and Department 2 has 4 men. Each department has one man more than 60 years old. If one man from each department is to be selected for transfer to a third department the probability that both men over 60 will be selected is

$$P\{60.60\} = P_1\{60\}.P_2\{60\} = 0.2 \times 0.25 = 0.05.$$

Remembering that $P\{A + B\}$ indicates the probability that either A or B will occur, and $P\{AB\}$ indicates the probability that both A and B will occur, the theorems dealing with related events follow easily.

Theorem 3. THE ADDITIVE THEOREM FOR RELATED EVENTS: If the probability of A occurring is $P\{A\}$, and that of B occurring is $P\{B\}$, and that of both occurring at the same time is $P\{AB\}$ then the probability of either A or B occurring is given by $P\{A + B\}$ where

$$P\{A + B\} = P\{A\} + P\{B\} - P\{AB\}.$$

This may be demonstrated by the sample spaces where it is seen that the total area of the sample spaces is $A + B - AB$.

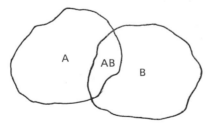

Fig. 2.3.2. SAMPLE SPACE FOR RELATED EVENTS

Theorem 4. THE MULTIPLICATION THEOREM FOR RELATED EVENTS: (also known as the theorem of conditional probability). If $P\{B|A\}$ designates the probability that if A occurs then B also occurs (but note that $P\{B|A\}$ is read as 'the probability of B given A'), then if A is the event which occurs first

$$P\{AB\} = P\{A\}.P\{B|A\}$$

and if B is the event which occurs first

$$P\{AB\} = P\{B\}.P\{A|B\}.$$

For example, a box contains 25 items of which 10 are defective and two items are to be drawn at random from the box.

a What is the probability that both items are good? Here A is the event that 'the first item drawn is a good one', B is the event that 'the second item drawn is a good one', and AB is the event that 'both items drawn are good ones', so that

$$P\{AB\} = P\{A\}.P\{B|A\} = \tfrac{15}{25}.\tfrac{14}{24} = 0.35.$$

b What is the probability that both items are defective? Now A is the event that 'the first item drawn from the box is defective', B is the event that 'the second item drawn from the box is defective', and AB is the event that 'both items drawn from the box are defective' so that

$$P\{AB\} = P\{A\}.P\{B|A\} = \tfrac{10}{25}.\tfrac{9}{24} = 0.15.$$

c What is the probability that one item is good and one item defective? Now there are three events to consider: A, that both items are good; B, that both items are defective; and C, that one item is good and one item defective. But these three events contain all the events that can happen, so that

$$P\{A + B + C\} = 1$$

and also they are mutually exclusive, so that

$$P\{A + B + C\} = P\{A\} + P\{B\} + P\{C\}$$

and it follows that

$$P\{C\} = 1 - P\{A\} - P\{B\} = 1 - 0.35 - 0.15 = 0.5.$$

This result may be obtained by considering that the probability of one item being good and the other being defective when the two items are drawn from the box is the sum of the probabilities

$P\{\text{first one Good}|\text{second one Bad}\} + P\{\text{first one Bad}|\text{second one Good}\}$

$\qquad = P\{\text{Good}\}.P\{\text{Bad}|\text{Good}\} + P\{\text{Bad}\}.P\{\text{Good}|\text{Bad}\}$

$\qquad = \quad \tfrac{15}{25} \times \tfrac{10}{24} \quad + \quad \tfrac{10}{25} \times \tfrac{15}{24} \quad = 0.5.$

2.4 probability functions

Many people are afraid of the term 'function', but there is no need for this. In mathematics a function is nothing more than a convenient method of expressing a state of existence. At some time we might be discussing (perhaps) the reactor batches run in some manufacturing department and we might decide that the yield of product depended on the time of reaction for those batches with identical charges of raw materials. After examining data from a large number of batches we might calculate that the yield was proportional to the time and to the square of the time, and this we could write as

$$\text{Yield} = a \text{ (time of reaction)} + b \text{ (time of reaction)}^2 + c$$

and we could reduce this to $y = ax + bx^2 + c$ in which a, b, and c are calculated constants. Now we have written an equation showing the dependence of y on x (yield on time of reaction) or the relationship between y and x. That is, we have expressed y in terms of x, or as a function of x, and we could write

$$y = f(x), \text{ where } f(x) = ax + bx^2 + c$$

When we have a large number of individuals in our sample so that each value occurs a number of times — and if necessary we can arrange the individuals in convenient groups so that we obtain several values in each group — then for each value or group we can calculate its frequency of occurrence. This is a straightforward division in each case:

$$\text{Relative Frequency} = \frac{\text{Number of occurrences of each value (or in each group)}}{\text{Total number of occurrences}}$$

and a plot or tabulation of these values provides a description of the *frequency function* of the individuals in the sample.

If instead of plotting individual frequencies we plot the cumulative frequency at each value, then we obtain the *cumulative distribution function* or *probability function* for the population from which our sample was taken. We know that populations may consist of discrete or continuous variables, and the difference in form between discrete and continuous distributions started a search for some means of being able to represent both by a similar form. Such a form exists in the cumulative distribution function which shows the probability that a random observation takes a value equal to or less than ($\leqq$) some assigned value, say x_0, and this we can write as

$$Pr\{x \leqq x_0\} \quad \text{or maybe, if we have two limits,} \quad Pr\{x_0 < x \leqq x_1\}$$

in which we have indicated the probability that x has some value greater than x_0 but equal to or less than some other value x_1.

The procedure involved in probability function calculations is a summation of probabilities; for discrete functions this is shown as

$$F(x) = \sum_{r=-\infty}^{\infty} P(r),$$

while for the continuous functions an integration is necessary to evaluate the corresponding distribution function

$$F(x) = \int_{-\infty}^{\infty} f(x).dx, \quad \text{in which } f(x) \text{ is the frequency function.}$$

Probability theory can be used to determine the shape of frequency distributions which will be obtained when random samples are drawn from certain types of populations. In every case the results predicted by theory can be verified by practical experiments; usually the agreement between experiment and theory is very close and the small discrepancies can be accounted for by random sampling errors. We can now consider the three most common distributions.

2.5 the binomial distribution

The binomial distribution was first postulated by James Bernouilli early in the eighteenth century, and may be stated as follows:

Where a random variable can adopt one of two values, one of which, X, occurs with probability p, so that the other occurs with probability $(1 - p)$, then the number of occurrences of X in n independent observations, which we may call x, is also a random variable and its distribution is given by

$$p(x) = {}^nC_x.p^x.(1 - p)^{n-x}$$

which may be written as ${}^nC_x.p^x.q^y]$, where $q = 1 - p$ and $y = n - x$, and of course

$$p(x) = P(0) + P(1) + P(2) + \ldots + P(n) = 1.$$

Occurrences of X may be referred to as 'successes', and the non-occurrences are 'failures'.

[Remember that the binomial expansion is

$$(a - b)^n = {}^nC_0a^n - {}^nC_1a^{n-1}b + {}^nC_2a^{n-2}b^2 + \ldots + (-1)^n.{}^nC_nb^n.]$$

Thus the probability denoted by $p(x)$ is given by the $(x + 1)$ st term in the expansion of $[(p) + (q)]^n$, and the successive values assumed by $p(x)$ are the successive terms in this expansion.

Theoretically, the binomial distribution applies only when the population sampled is an infinite population so that p remains unaltered by the sampling. In practice, the binomial distribution can be applied to finite populations as long as they are not too small.

The mean number of successes $= np$, (or the mean proportion of successes $= p$) and the variance of a binomial distribution $= np(1 - p)$, or for any proportion or sample $= [p(1 - p)]/n$, so that the standard deviation of a binomial distribution $= \sqrt{[np(1 - p)]}$, or for any proportion or sample $=$

$$\sqrt{\frac{p(1 - p)}{n}}$$

It may be demonstrated that for large values of n the binomial distribution approximates to the normal distribution, and this may be seen in Figure 2.5.1. However, the use of such an approximation attempts to impose continuity on a discrete distribution; if, at any time this is necessary then a 'correction for continuity' must be used.

2.5.1 EXAMPLE: A sampling experiment is to be made using a large number of marbles in a bag; 20 per cent of the marbles are red and the rest are blue. Random samples of 10 are to be drawn from the bag.

Then any marble drawn from the bag has a $\frac{1}{5}$ chance of being a red one and a $\frac{4}{5}$ chance of being a blue one. The number of marbles in the bag is assumed to be large enough for this chance to remain effectively unchanged when a finite sample is drawn from the bag.

The probability of drawing x red marbles and $(10 - x)$ blue marbles in any sample is

$$(0{\cdot}2)^x{\cdot}(0{\cdot}8)^{10-x}$$

and there are $^{10}C_x$ possible orders in which the sample may be drawn. Thus if $p(x)$ is the probability of drawing a sample of 10 containing x red marbles, in any order of drawing them from the bag

$$p(x) = {}^{10}C_x{\cdot}(0{\cdot}2)^x{\cdot}(0{\cdot}8)^{10-x}$$

and it is possible to work out this probability for all values of x from 0 to 10 and tabulate the results. Note that the arithmetic involved in these calculations may be simplified since

$$p(x) = {}^{10}C_x{\cdot}(0{\cdot}2)^x{\cdot}(0{\cdot}8)^{10-x} = \frac{10!}{x!(10 - x)!}{\cdot}(0{\cdot}2)^x{\cdot}(0{\cdot}8)^{10-x}$$

and $\quad p(x + 1) = {}^{10}C_{x+1}{\cdot}(0{\cdot}2)^{x+1}{\cdot}(0{\cdot}8)^{9-x}$

$$= \frac{10!}{(x + 1)!(9 - x)!}{\cdot}(0{\cdot}2)^{x+1}{\cdot}(0{\cdot}8)^{9-x}$$

$$= \frac{(10 - x)}{(x + 1)}{\cdot}\frac{10!}{x!(10 - x)!}{\cdot}\frac{0{\cdot}2}{0{\cdot}8}{\cdot}(0{\cdot}2)^x{\cdot}(0{\cdot}8)^{10-x}$$

$$= \frac{1}{4}\frac{10 - x}{x + 1}{\cdot}p(x)$$

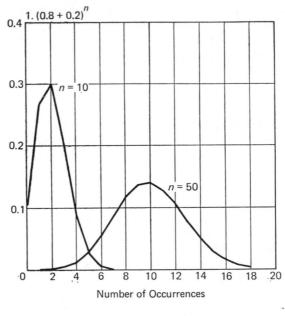

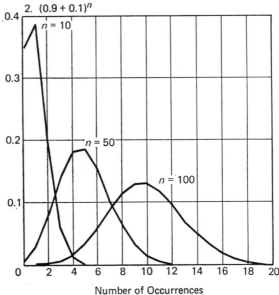

FREQUENCY POLYGONS FOR BINOMIAL DISTRIBUTIONS

and this relationship may be used to calculate all values. (A similar relationship may be deduced for any binomial distribution; the numerical value written before $p(x)$ will change according to the prevalent ratios.)

In this example, if we calculate probabilities to four places of decimals we have

$$p(0) = (0.8)^{10} \qquad\qquad\qquad = 0.1074$$
$$p(1) = \tfrac{1}{4}.\tfrac{10}{1}.p(0) = 2.5 \times 0.1074 \quad = 0.2685$$
$$p(2) = \tfrac{1}{4}.\tfrac{9}{2}.p(1) = 1.125 \times 0.2685 = 0.3021$$
$$p(3) = \tfrac{1}{4}.\tfrac{8}{3}.p(2) = \tfrac{2}{3} \times 0.3021 \quad = 0.2014$$
$$p(4) = \tfrac{1}{4}.\tfrac{7}{4}.p(3) = \tfrac{7}{16} \times 0.2014 \quad = 0.0881$$
$$p(5) = \tfrac{1}{4}.\tfrac{6}{5}.p(4) = \tfrac{3}{10} \times 0.0881 \quad = 0.0264$$
$$p(6) = \tfrac{1}{4}.\tfrac{5}{6}.p(5) = \tfrac{5}{24} \times 0.0264 \quad = 0.0055$$
$$p(7) = \tfrac{1}{4}.\tfrac{4}{7}.p(6) = \tfrac{1}{7} \times 0.0055 \quad = 0.0008$$
$$p(8) = \tfrac{1}{4}.\tfrac{3}{8}.p(7) = \tfrac{3}{32} \times 0.0008 \quad = 0.0001$$
$$p(9) = \qquad\qquad\qquad\qquad\qquad\qquad 0$$
$$p(10) = \qquad\qquad\qquad\qquad\qquad\quad 0$$

These probabilities may be translated into expected numbers of samples showing the given number of red marbles per sample. Table 2.5.1 compares the expected numbers with the experimental observations in 300 trials with 300 marbles.

Table 2.5.1 Comparison of expected numbers of red marbles with experimental observations

No. of red marbles in the sample x	Chance of obtaining a sample with x red marbles p(x)	Expected number of samples 300 × p(x)	Experimental number of samples with x red marbles
0	0.1074	32	29
1	0.2685	81	82
2	0.3021	91	88
3	0.2014	60	64
4	0.0881	26	25
5	0.0264	8	8
6	0.0055	2	3
7	0.0008	0	1
8	0.0001	0	0
9	0	0	0
10	0	0	0
	1.0003	300	300

In this experiment the agreement between theory and experimental observation is very close. Further calculations from these figures show

	Theory	*Observations*
Mean (np) = 2		2.05
Standard deviation = $\tfrac{2}{5}\sqrt{10} = 1.26$		1.30

2.5.2 APPLICATIONS FROM INDUSTRY

Of the many applications of the binomial distribution to industrial problems, four have been chosen from different fields of activity.

1 ANALYTICAL CHEMISTRY: It has been observed that an analyst will make some mistake leading to a large discrepancy in the final result once in 20 determinations. What is the probability of such an error occurring if a single analytical result is to be obtained from 4 determinations?

The probability of occurrence of a gross error is 0·05, so that the probabilities of up to 4 gross errors occurring in a set of 4 determinations are

$$
\begin{aligned}
p(0) &= {}^4C_0.(0·05)^0.(0·95)^4 = 0·8145 \\
p(1) &= {}^4C_1.(0·05)^1.(0·95)^3 = 0·1715 \\
p(2) &= {}^4C_2.(0·05)^2.(0·95)^2 = 0·0134 \\
p(3) &= {}^4C_3.(0·05)^3.(0·95)^1 = 0·0006 \\
p(4) &= {}^4C_4.(0·05)^4.(0·95)^0 = 0
\end{aligned}
$$

and the total of these is 0·1815.

The probability of at least one gross error in each set of four determinations is 0·1815, that is about one-fifth of the sets of determinations are likely to contain one gross error.

Conversely, if it had been observed that approximately 1 in 10 of the sets of four determinations contained a gross error, then we would have

$$(1 - p)^4 = 0·9 \quad \text{from which} \quad p = 0·026$$

which is the probability of occurrence of a gross error in a single determination. In this case the relative frequency of gross errors would be approximately once in every 40 determinations.

2 ACCIDENT INVESTIGATION: Following the incidence figures quoted below, the suggestion was made that men over 40 years old are more prone to accidents than men under 40. It is required to determine whether or not this is true.

	Number of accidents	Average number employed
Men over 40 years old	48	246
Men under 40 years old	127	578
Total	175	824

The proportion of men over 40 years old employed (p) is $246/824 = 0·2985$, and of course the proportion of men under 40 years old ($1 - p$) is $578/824 = 0·7015$.

Now if these two groups were equally prone to accidents, the *expected number* of accidents would be

to men over 40: $0·2985 \times 175 = 52·24$ (which is more than actually occurred)

and to men under 40: $0·7015 \times 175 = 122·76$,

and it is necessary to determine whether the ratio 48:127 differs from 52:123 more than can be attributed to chance.

The variance of the binomial distribution is $np(1 - p)$, which in this case is

$$175 \times 0.2985 \times 0.7015 = 36.65,$$

from which the standard deviation is $\sqrt{36.65} = 6.05$.

The observed deviation is $52.24 - 48 = 4.24$, so that the ratio

$$\frac{\text{observed deviation}}{\text{standard deviation}} = \frac{4.24}{6.05} = 0.7$$

As long as the numbers in each class are not too small, the binomial distribution approximates to the normal distribution. We know the probability P, that a normal variable will deviate from its mean by no more than a given number z of standard deviations, and when z is known the relevant value of P can be read from the normal probability tables. Then from the normal probability tables we find that the probability of meeting a deviation from expectation of 0.7 times the standard deviation is 0.48. Thus, on the evidence of these figures there is no reason to suppose that the accident rates are different for the two age groups.

The 95 per cent confidence limits for the number of accidents that may be expected to occur in the 'men over 40' age group, in a period of similar duration to that which produced the figures quoted above, may be obtained as follows

$$p = 48/175 = 0.2743 \quad \text{(the actual proportion of accidents)}$$

from which the variance (of a proportion) $s^2 = \dfrac{0.2743 \times 0.7257}{175} = 0.0011375$

and the standard deviation $s = 0.0337$.

Then the 95 per cent confidence limits are $0.2743 \pm (1.96 \times 0.0337)$, or 0.208 to 0.340, and these proportions correspond to 36.4 to 59.5 (say, 36 to 60) accidents.

3 WORK SAMPLING: The workmen included in any work sampling study are allocated to one of the classifications 'Working', 'Walking' or 'Waiting' each time a sample is made. However, each of these classifications may be regarded as dividing the workmen into two groups: (i) Working or Not Working; (ii) Walking or Not Walking; (iii) Waiting or Not Waiting; so that the data derived from the sample for any one group may be considered as drawn from a binomial distribution. Then if we consider a team of 30 workmen, and our interest is in the 'Working' classification, that is, in estimating how many men may be expected to be working at any moment,

if the observed probability of occurrence is 0.75
and an acceptable margin of error is ± 5 per cent, i.e. ± 0.05
then the estimated standard error is $\pm 0.75 \times 0.05 = \pm 0.0375$
so that to achieve a confidence limit of 95 per cent the standard deviation, $s = 0.0375/1.96 = 0.019133$.

The number of observations that must be made in any period is n, where n is given by

$$s^2 = \frac{p(1-p)}{n} \quad \text{or} \quad n = \frac{p(1-p)}{s^2} = \frac{0.75 \times 0.25}{(0.019133)^2} = 512$$

If each of the 30 workmen is observed in each round made of the work area, then the number of rounds to be made in each sampling period is $512/30 = 17$.

We see from this that as the value of p increases, that is as each workman becomes more fully loaded, the value of n decreases. For $p = 0.9$, $n = 178$ and 6 rounds per sampling period would be sufficient.

4 DRUG TESTING: 100 patients were each tested with two drugs. Drug A caused 18 cases of nausea, Drug B caused 10 cases of nausea, and 9 patients had nausea with both drugs. It is required to determine if there is a real difference between the two drugs.

The experimental details may be shown as

		Drug A Nausea	Drug A No nausea	Totals
Drug	Nausea	9	1	10
B	No nausea	9	81	90
	Totals	18	82	100

The 9 patients who had nausea with both drugs, and the 81 patients who had no nausea with either, provide no information. Of the other 10 patients we can tabulate the data as

1 responded favourably to A and unfavourably to B, and
9 responded unfavourably to A and favourably to B.

If there were no real difference between the drugs, these 10 patients would be expected to divide equally in favour of A and B. Then the one-sided P-value for the null hypothesis (that there was no real difference between the drugs) is given by the sum of terms in the tail of the binomial distribution

$$Pr[x \leq x_0 | n, p] = \sum_{x=0}^{x_0} {}^nC_x \cdot p^x \cdot (1-p)^{n-x}$$

in which we have $n = 10$, $x_0 = 1$, and $p = 0.5$. The probability becomes

$$Pr[x \leq 1 | 10, 0.5] = \sum_{x=0}^{1} {}^{10}C_x \cdot (0.5)^x \cdot (1-0.5)^{n-x} = 2^{1/10} \cdot \sum_{x=0}^{1} {}^{10}C_x$$

$$= 2^{1/10}\left(\frac{10!}{0!10!} + \frac{10!}{1!9!}\right) = \frac{11}{1024} = 0.01074$$

and there is almost 99 per cent probability that there was a real difference between the two drugs.

2.6 the Poisson distribution

When the probability p of the binomial distribution becomes very small, and the number of independent observations n becomes very large, and the average number of successes $np = m$ is a finite number, the binomial distribution assumes the very convenient form

$$P(x) = {}^nC_x \cdot p^x \cdot (1 - p)^{n-x} = \frac{n!}{x!(n - x)!} \cdot p^x \cdot (1 - p)^{n-x}$$

$$= \frac{n(n - 1)(n - 2)(\ldots)(n - x + 1)}{x!(1 - p)^x} \cdot p^x \cdot (1 - p)^n$$

$$= \frac{np(np - p)(np - 2p)(\ldots)(np - [x - 1]p) \cdot (1 - p)^n}{x!(1 - p)^x}$$

Now, writing $m = np$, so that $p = m/n$, we have

$$P(x) = \frac{m(m - p)(m - 2p)(\ldots)(m - [x - 1]p) \cdot (1 - m/n)^n}{x!(1 - p)^x}$$

As p becomes very small, $(1 - p)^x \rightarrow 1$; and

$$m(m - p)(m - 2p)(\ldots)(m - [x - 1]p) \rightarrow m^x.$$

And as n becomes very large,

$$\left(1 - \frac{m}{n}\right)^n \rightarrow e^{-m},$$

(the sign $\rightarrow$ means 'tends to, in the limit') so that

$$P(x) = \frac{e^{-m} \cdot m^x}{x!}$$

In this expression 'e' is the base of natural, or Napierian logarithms.

This involves only the one constant, m, and so is easier to tabulate than the binomial distribution which involves the two constants n and p. Poisson (1837) first postulated this distribution which may be described as

> 'When a large number (infinite) of possible discrete events occurs randomly over a long period of time, or over a large area, and the frequency with which these events will occur in any small interval of time or small area chosen at random is considered as the random variable, then the

probability of the occurrence of any individual event in the chosen interval will be small and is given by the Poisson distribution

$$p(x) = \frac{e^{-m} \cdot m^x}{x!}$$

where x takes the successive values 0, 1, 2, ..., and m is the expected number of events occurring on any given observation.'

The Poisson distribution assumes that it is *possible* for the number of observed events to be infinite even though the probability of occurrence of any individual event is small. It is necessary to ensure that the number of possible events which could be observed is sufficiently large and the probability of occurrence of an individual event is sufficiently small before the Poisson distribution may be applied with justification. Also, it is important that observations be made in equal time intervals or areas and that the expected value be the same for each observation.

Values of the Poisson distribution are tabulated for

$$p(x) \quad \text{and} \quad Pr(x \geq c) = \sum_{x=0}^{\infty} \frac{e^{-m} \cdot m^x}{x!} \quad \text{for} \quad m = 0{\cdot}001(0{\cdot}001)60{\cdot}0$$

and the graphs in Figure 2.6.1 show how the shape of the distribution varies as m increases. It is easily proved that both the mean value and the variance of a Poisson distribution are equal to the expected number of events m. In any particular case when the number of trials, n, is large and the probability, p, is small, the Poisson distribution with $m = np$ may be used as an approximation to the binomial distribution.

The classic examples of the application of the Poisson distribution are the number of counts recorded by a Geiger counter in one-minute intervals, or the number of white blood cells counted in small equal areas of a prepared slide.

2.6.1 EXAMPLE: In the manufacture of a certain item it has been found, over a period of years, that 8 items per thousand (0·8 per cent) will be defective. The items are packed for sale in cartons containing 200 items, and each carton may be assumed to contain a random sample of production. What is the chance of a carton containing a given number of defectives?

The Poisson distribution holds here, with $n = 200$ and $p = 0{\cdot}008$, and the average expected number of defectives per carton is given by

$$m = np = 200 \times 0{\cdot}008 = 1{\cdot}6.$$

Then the probability of a carton containing x defectives is given by

$$p(x) = \frac{e^{-1{\cdot}6} \cdot (1{\cdot}6)^x}{x!} \quad \text{for} \quad x = 0, 1, 2, 3, \text{etc.}$$

and probabilities may be tabulated as shown.

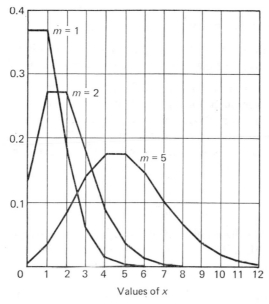

Fig. 2.6.1. FREQUENCY POLYGONS FOR MEMBERS OF THE POISSON SERIES

Table 2.6.1. Probability of Occurrence of Defectives in Cartons

No. of defectives in carton x	Probability that a carton contains x defectives $p(x)$
0	0·202
1	0·323
2	0·258
3	0·138
4	0·005
5	0·018
6	0·005
7	0·001 (total 1·000)

Usually the point of interest is not the individual probabilities of getting different numbers of defectives in a carton, but rather the probability of getting *x or more* defectives in a carton. Thus the probability of finding 5 or more defectives in a carton would be 0·018 + 0·005 + 0·001 = 0·024, or very nearly $2\frac{1}{2}$ per cent. That is, $2\frac{1}{2}$ per cent of the cartons may be expected to contain 5 or more defectives, and this would be written as $Pr(x \geq 5) = 0.024$.

Note that in an exercise such as this if we were required to determine a probability such as $Pr(x \geq 3)$ we would not make all the calculations until the total of the calculated probabilities reached 1·000. We would calculate only for $x = 0$, 1, and 2, then $Pr(x \geq 3) = 1 - p(0) - p(1) - p(2)$.

2.6.2 APPLICATIONS FROM INDUSTRY

Most of the applications of the Poisson distribution met in industry (certainly by the author) involve time, and two such applications are described here.

1 ACCIDENT INVESTIGATION: In a factory employing 210 people on a 40-hour week the average minor injury rate over a long period of time has been 3·42 minor injuries per 10,000 manhours worked. What is the probability of occurrence of 6 or more minor injuries per week?

With 8,400 manhours worked per week, the expected number of minor injuries per week would be

$$m = \frac{8,400}{10,000} \times 3\cdot42 = 2\cdot87$$

and accepting that the number of minor injuries occurring in a given week is a random variable with Poisson distribution, then the required probability distribution is given by

$$p(x) = \frac{e^{-2\cdot87}.(2\cdot87)^x}{x!} \quad \text{where} \quad x = 0, 1, 2, 3, \text{etc.}$$

The probability that in any week

No injury is likely to occur is $p(0) = \quad\quad\quad\quad e^{-2\cdot87} = 0\cdot0567$
1 injury is likely to occur is $p(1) = \quad\quad e^{-2\cdot87} \times 2\cdot87 = 0\cdot1627$
2 injuries are likely to occur is $p(2) = \quad e^{-2\cdot87} \times (2\cdot87)^2/2 = 0\cdot2335$
3 injuries are likely to occur is $p(3) = \quad e^{-2\cdot87} \times (2\cdot87)^3/6 = 0\cdot2234$
4 injuries are likely to occur is $p(4) = \quad e^{-2\cdot87} \times (2\cdot87)^4/24 = 0\cdot1603$
5 injuries are likely to occur is $p(5) = e^{-2\cdot87} \times (2\cdot87)^5/120 = 0\cdot0920$
(total 0·9286)

and the probability of occurrence of 6 or more minor injuries per week is given by

$$Pr(x \geq 6) = \sum_{x=6}^{\infty} \frac{e^{-2\cdot87}.(2\cdot87)^x}{x!} = 1 - 0\cdot9286 = 0\cdot0714.$$

That is, very slightly over 7 per cent, and in 7 weeks out of a hundred we would expect 6 or more minor injuries.

2 ENGINEERING MAINTENANCE: Two compressors, A and B, were installed at the same time and have been used continuously. By the end of the first year A had 13 breakdowns and B had three. It is required to determine which type of compressor should be installed in an expansion of the plant, and the 95 per cent confidence limits for the number of breakdowns to be expected from the compressor.

The easiest way to determine whether or not there is a real difference between the performances of the two compressors is to apply a t-test (see

Chapter 4.1.3) The t-test may be applied only to continuous distributions, so we have to apply a correction for continuity and this is done by subtracting $\frac{1}{2}$ from the larger value and adding $\frac{1}{2}$ to the smaller value. Then

$$t_{1-\alpha} = \frac{(n_1 - \frac{1}{2}) - (n_2 + \frac{1}{2})}{\sqrt{(n_1 + n_2)}} \quad [n_1 > n_2; \alpha \text{ is the probability tail}]$$

and in our example, we have for 95 per cent probability of being correct $\alpha = \frac{1}{2}(1 - 0\cdot95) = 0\cdot025$, and

$$t_{95\%} = \frac{(13 - \frac{1}{2}) - (3 + \frac{1}{2})}{\sqrt{(13 + 3)}} = \frac{9}{4} = 2\cdot25.$$

The tabulated value of t for $\alpha = 0\cdot025$ probability and 14 degrees of freedom $(13 - 1 + 3 - 1)$ is $2\cdot145$. The calculated value is greater than this, and it is probable that there is a real difference in the behaviour of the compressors leading to the numbers of breakdowns quoted. If this difference cannot be accounted for by operating conditions or requirements, then a compressor of type B should be installed in the plant expansion.

The confidence limits for a Poisson distribution may be determined by applying the χ^2-distribution (see Chapter 4.1.1), and for the 95 per cent confidence limits we have to consider the values of χ^2 at probability points $0\cdot025$ for the lower limit and $0\cdot975$ for the upper limit. Then

the upper limit is given by $\frac{1}{2}\chi^2_{0\cdot975}[2(n + 1)]$

and the lower limit is given by $\frac{1}{2}\chi^2_{0\cdot025}[2n]$

where n is the expected number of occurrences. Then for the recommended compressor of Type B

the upper limit is $\frac{1}{2}\chi^2_{0\cdot975}[8] = \frac{1}{2} \times 17\cdot5 = 8\cdot75$ (say 9)

and the lower limit is $\frac{1}{2}\chi^2_{0\cdot025}[6] = \frac{1}{2} \times 1\cdot25 = 0\cdot62$ (say 1)

so that compressors of Type B may be expected, with 95 per cent confidence to have breakdowns in the range 1 to 9 per year. Note that the required values are obtained from tabulated values of the percentage points of the χ^2-distribution. For the upper limit we wish to cover probabilities up to $0\cdot975$ and so we enter the table under the column headed $0\cdot025$, which gives a probability of exclusion of $0\cdot025$, with 8 degrees of freedom. Similarly for the lower limit we enter the table under the column headed $0\cdot975$ with 6 degrees of freedom.

2.7 the normal distribution

The development of scientific experimentation in the early eighteenth century led to the realization that repeated measurements of one and the same quantity

I.S. 1—4

showed errors which were always grouped according to a regular pattern or distribution. The observed patterns always approximated closely to a continuous distribution which was called the 'normal curve of errors', and the patterns were attributed to the laws of chance.

Blaise Pascal (1623–62) had enunciated the theory of probability, and the mathematical properties of the continuous distribution of the normal curve of errors had been investigated by Abraham de Moivre (1667–1745), Pierre Laplace (1749–1827) and Karl Gauss (1777–1855). In 1733 De Moivre showed that the continuous curve could be expressed by an equation which depends only on the mean, μ, and the standard deviation, σ, of the distribution of x. The equation may be written as

$$y = \frac{1}{\sigma\sqrt{(2\pi)}} \cdot e^{-(x-\mu)^2/2\sigma^2}$$

in which σ is chosen so that

$$\int_{-\infty}^{\infty} y \cdot dx = 1,$$

that is with unit area between the curve and the horizontal x-axis, so that the area under the curve is a probability.

The normal distribution may be derived from the binomial distribution — as indeed we derived the Poisson distribution — as n becomes very large (and in the limit approaches infinity) so that as long as p is finite and not equal to zero

$$n \to \infty, \, np = \mu \text{ and } npq = \sigma^2$$

Gauss (1833) first stated that since so many sets of data followed the curve then there must be something wrong with any set of data which did not conform. However, the accumulation of data during the second half of the nineteenth century showed that the normal distribution was no more usual than any other type. Even so, the statement has been made that 'Everybody believed in the Law of Errors: the experimenters because they think it is a mathematical theorem, the mathematicians because they think it is an experimental fact.'

The realization that the normal distribution did not correspond to any widespread natural effect did not diminish its importance in statistical theory; on the contrary, its importance has increased. Firstly, because the normal curve and the normal integral have numerous mathematical properties which make them attractive and easy to manipulate. Secondly, because the normal curve is reasonably close to many distributions of the humped type, so that where the exact nature of a humped distribution is unknown, or where its form is known but yields intractable mathematics, the assumption of a normal distribution may be made as a first approximation. Very frequently this is sufficiently accurate for the purpose in hand. In almost all cases where the distributions are unknown, or where no attempt is to be made to determine the distribution, it is assumed that a sample of values has been drawn from a normal population. A number of non-parametric or distribution-free procedures have been developed to eliminate this assumption of normality.

The normal curve is symmetrical about the mean value of the population and has the following properties:

1 The mean value ($\bar{x}$ or μ) is the mean of all the observed values.
2 The height of the curve above the base line represents the relative frequency with which the corresponding measured value would occur in a large number of measurements.
3 The area under the curve between any two given measurements represents that percentage of the measurements which fall between the two stated values in a large number of observations, and is a probability of occurrence.
4 The horizontal spread of the curve is measured by the standard deviation, σ, so that the standard deviation is a measure of the dispersion or spread of values about the mean.

It follows from the equation of the normal curve that

68·26 per cent of the area under the curve lies between -1σ and $+1\sigma$
95·46 per cent of the area under the curve lies between -2σ and $+2\sigma$
99·73 per cent of the area under the curve lies between -3σ and $+3\sigma$
99·99 per cent of the area under the curve lies between -4σ and $+4\sigma$

and, of course, these areas may be translated directly into probabilities.

An important property of the normal distribution is that where any group of independent normally distributed variables are to be considered together any linear combination of these variables is itself normally distributed. In particular, if samples are drawn at random from a normal distribution the means of these samples will form a normal distribution with the same mean but smaller variance. If we look ahead to the 208 batch yields quoted in the next section (2.7.1) and arrange these in groups of 1, 2, 4, and 8 consecutive values in turn we find that

the standard deviation of individuals, $\quad s_1 = 24{\cdot}8$
the standard deviation of the means of groups of 2, $s_2 = 17{\cdot}2$
$$= 24{\cdot}8/\sqrt{2}$$
(very nearly),
the standard deviation of the means of groups of 4, $s_4 = 12{\cdot}75$
$$= 24{\cdot}8/\sqrt{4}$$
(very nearly),
and the standard deviation of the means of groups of 8, $s_8 = 8{\cdot}6$
$$= 24{\cdot}8/\sqrt{8}$$
(very nearly)

so that the variance of the means of groups is the variance of individuals divided by the number of individuals in a group. This relationship can be very useful in such cases where groups are used to reduce the margin of error. Note that we have used s to refer to the standard deviation of a sample, keeping σ for that of a population.

In a normal distribution the mean, median, and mode are coincident. In Chapter 1.2 following the definition of 'mode' is a set of 28 values. If we assume that this set of values is a sample drawn from a normal distribution, and calculate the variance we have

$$\frac{\Sigma(x_i - \bar{x})^2}{n - 1} = \frac{5703 - (397)^2/28}{27} = \frac{74 \cdot 1072}{27} = 2 \cdot 7447$$

from which the standard deviation, s, is estimated to be $\sqrt{2 \cdot 7447} = 1 \cdot 66$.

Note that a rough estimate of the standard deviation may be obtained by

$$\hat{s} = \frac{\text{Range of values}}{\sqrt{\text{Number of values}}} = \frac{R}{\sqrt{n}} = \frac{17 - 11}{\sqrt{28}} = \frac{6}{5 \cdot 29} = 1 \cdot 13$$

and this may be used as a quick check for any standard deviation calculation to ensure that the calculated standard deviation is 'of the right order'. This set of values is assumed to belong to a normal distribution because it has been found that in chemical analysis, experimentation and control sets of results almost always conform to a normal distribution. On the other hand distributions may be assumed to be normal when they are not; a simple plot of the data on probability paper (as shown in Chapter 3.4) will show whether or not the assumption of normality is sound, as a normal distribution shows up as a straight line plot.

Frequently, a distribution which is not normal can be made approximately normal by using a transformation such as $\log x$, $\sqrt{x}$, x^2, or some other function of the observations rather than the observations themselves. Quite often the transformation to be used is indicated by a straightforward plot of the observations.

2.7.1 GROUPED FREQUENCIES

When the number of observations and the range of possible values of the observations are both large, the behaviour of the frequency of occurrence of individual measurements may be erratic and the frequency of occurrence of individual measurements may be comparatively small. In such a case the values should be grouped together, in 'cells' of equal width chosen so that 10–20 cells cover the range of values; the number of cells chosen in any case is solely a matter of convenience for establishing the groups. The frequency of occurrence of these groups of values may be tabulated as a frequency distribution.

Then, if the n values in the sample are divided into k cells having frequency f_i, with the midpoints of the cell width (or cell range) designated by x_i

$$\text{the mean is given by } \bar{x} = \frac{1}{n}\sum_1^k (x_i \cdot f_i)$$

and $$\text{the variance is given by } s^2 = \frac{\sum (x_i - \bar{x})^2 f_i}{n-1}$$

For example, Table 2.7.1 shows the weights of product obtained from 208 consecutive batches, each of which was made with the same quantities of raw material and under the same operating conditions. The reactor was emptied after each batch so there is no weight balance between batches, and the batch weights may be considered as a random variable. The mean batch weight is 764.

If we calculate from the individual values, we obtain a variance of 615, and a standard deviation of 24·8. But if the individual values are arranged in groups as shown, then

$$\begin{aligned}
207s^2 &= 3(764-704)^2 + 5(764-713)^2 + 9(764-722)^2 \\
&\quad + 8(764-731)^2 + 19(764-740)^2 + 22(764-749)^2 \\
&\quad + 22(764-758)^2 + 33(764-767)^2 + 36(764-776)^2 \\
&\quad + 20(764-785)^2 + 17(764-794)^2 + 7(764-803)^2 \\
&\quad + 3(764-812)^2 + 3(764-821)^2 + (764-830)^2 \\
&= 126{,}242.
\end{aligned}$$

From which the variance $s^2 = 609·87$ and the standard deviation $s = 24·7$ so that practically nothing is lost by using grouped frequencies.

In this example the range of batch weights is from 700 to 830. It is convenient, therefore, to divide the 208 values into 15 groups covering the range 700 to 834 so that each cell has a width of 9. Arranging matters so that the midpoint of each cell is a whole number is good practice and simplifies the arithmetic involved in the calculations.

Table 2.7.1 208 Consecutive batch weights

769	730	785	726	774	765	786	771	808	765
785	745	765	780	776	773	800	807	711	768
779	763	750	755	768	798	830	775	748	775
775	785	745	776	780	763	744	740	818	796
721	780	745	716	796	778	768	783	754	773
774	724	720	740	761	778	746	738	790	766
785	755	784	755	765	785	816	765	772	744
794	728	744	747	755	760	754	747	748	783
755	761	765	754	805	722	770	747	777	777
790	751	773	720	796	766	777	805	755	795
745	766	740	768	783	764	767	759	783	779
792	764	724	800	770	761	740	755	736	750
780	769	735	822	748	792	795	757	807	740
751	773	715	744	780	773	775	759	778	783
751	757	760	736	794	742	774	820	703	765
720	783	734	746	700	792	772	726	790	778
788	772	740	747	784	703	740	755	784	767
780	714	753	808	735	740	803	797	738	768
774	788	732	732	794	768	750	765	778	737
715	785	768	763	776	736	745	748	781	
728	783	778	763	763	760	765	798	758	

Cell midpoint	Cell range	Group frequency
704	700–708	3
713	709–717	5
722	718–726	9
731	727–735	8
740	736–744	19
749	745–753	22
758	754–762	22
767	763–771	33
776	772–780	36
785	781–789	20
794	790–798	17
803	799–807	7
812	808–816	3
821	817–825	3
830	826–834	1

The grouped frequencies may be shown diagrammatically as a frequency histogram as in Figure 2.7.1 (1), in which the height of each column is the number of occurrences in that group. Figure 2.7.1 (2) attempts to show this histogram as a smooth frequency distribution curve. Superimposed on this batch weight frequency distribution curve is a normal distribution curve for mean 764 and standard deviation 24·8. The batch weight frequency distribution curve is seen to be slightly skew, but it appears that the assumption that the batch weights are drawn from a normal distribution would not be unduly disturbing.

Many of the applications of statistics to industrial problems depend on an estimate of the standard deviation of a set of values. Sometimes, as in analytical determinations or in research work a precise estimate of the standard deviation is necessary, and in these cases a knowledge of the distribution is required. In other fields, such as plant control and investigation where there can be quite a large error in any measurements made, attempting to calculate a value for the standard deviation with a high degree of precision becomes rather meaningless. At this point, therefore, it may be advisable to consider two other methods of estimating the standard deviation.

2.7.2 THE CUMULATIVE FREQUENCY DISTRIBUTION

The cumulative frequency distribution offers a method by which the frequency distribution may be converted to a probability distribution. The cumulative frequency distribution may be plotted on a probability chart so that the probability of any specified occurrence may be read from the chart without the need for any further calculations. We start from a tabulation of the cell midpoints and frequencies of occurrence as shown at the bottom of Table 2.7.1, and from these we need to prepare cumulative frequencies or percentage frequencies which we can consider as being the equivalent of probabilities of infinite repetition of the manufacturing batches. If we cumulate the frequencies as quoted and then percentage these cumulated values we would obtain a percentage of 100 for the final value, and it is not possible to plot a value for 100 per cent probability on a probability chart. A special way of cumulating the cell frequencies has been devised and this is described in detail in Chapter 3.4 under the title 'Frequency Distribution Analysis'.

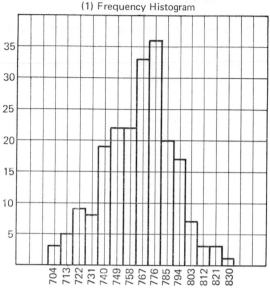

(1) Frequency Histogram

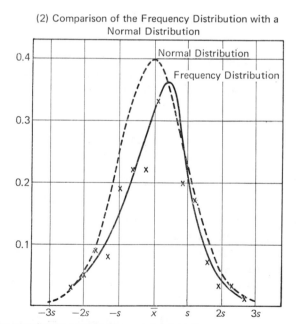

(2) Comparison of the Frequency Distribution with a Normal Distribution

Fig. 2.7.1. (1) FREQUENCY HISTOGRAM. (2) COMPARISON OF THE FREQUENCY DISTRIBUTION WITH A NORMAL DISTRIBUTION.

Briefly, another column called the Cumulator Column is added to the table. A zero is written at the head of this cumulator column and a zero is written at the head of the cell frequency column. Then each entry in the cumulator column is the sum of three values: the current cell frequency value plus the cell frequency and cumulator column values from the previous row. The final value in the cumulator column is of course double the total number of occurrences, but does not correspond to any cell or group. This final value is used as the divisor for calculation of percentage frequencies, and the cumulative percentages are obtained for each cell midpoint. The data from Table 2.7.1 are converted into

Table 2.7.2 Cumulative frequency distribution

Cell midpoint	Cell frequency	Cumulator	Cumulative percentage
	0	0	
704	3	3	0·72
713	5	11	2·6
722	9	25	6·0
731	8	42	10·1
740	19	69	16·6
749	22	110	26·4
758	22	154	37·0
767	33	209	50·2
776	36	278	66·8
785	20	334	80·3
794	17	371	89·2
803	7	395	94·95
812	3	405	97·35
821	3	411	99·0
830	1	415	99·76
		416	

Now these cumulative percentages are plotted on probability paper, with the cell midpoints entered on the arithmetic scale as the ordinate axis, as shown in Figure 2.7.2. If the plotted points lie on a straight line then the original sample values were drawn from a normal population. We can see that the values obtained in this example agree reasonably well with a straight line, and a straight line has been drawn (by inspection) to fit these points. This line enables us to estimate a number of parameters with very little effort and practically no calculation.

Firstly, we can estimate the mean. The 50 per cent probability line (which really estimates the median but is a good estimate for the mean) cuts the cumulative frequency line at approximately 763 which we take as our estimate of the mean batch weight. Secondly, we can estimate the standard deviation by taking the ordinate differences of two probabilities, and the two easiest to work with are the ranges

$$s = \frac{84\cdot13\% \text{ probability} - 15\cdot87\% \text{ probability}}{2} \quad \text{or}$$

$$= \frac{97\cdot72\% \text{ probability} - 2\cdot28\% \text{ probability}}{4}$$

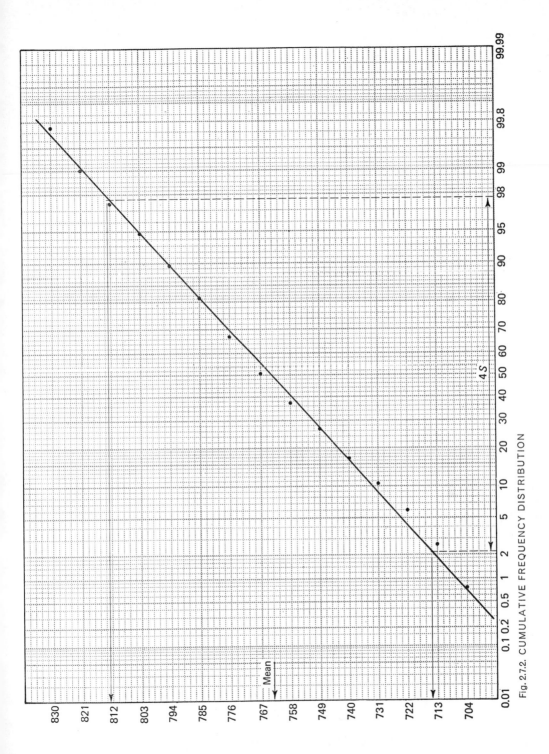

Fig. 2.7.2. CUMULATIVE FREQUENCY DISTRIBUTION

and in the latter case we have as our estimate of the standard deviation

$$\frac{813 - 715}{4} = \frac{98}{4} = 24 \cdot 5$$

which is very close to the values calculated previously, and is as good an estimate of the standard deviation as would be required, or desired, in this case. Note that the cumulative frequency line estimates the standard deviation and not the variance; if the variance is required for any purpose it must be obtained by squaring the standard deviation.

Further, the cumulative frequency distribution chart enables us to estimate various probabilities of occurrence. For example, we see that 5 per cent of batch weights would be expected to be less than 724, while at the other end of the range 5 per cent of batch weights (from probability line 95 per cent) would be expected to be greater than 803. Or we could consider the difference between the $2\frac{1}{2}$ per cent and $97\frac{1}{2}$ per cent probability lines and say that 95 per cent of batch weights would be expected to lie in the range 716–812. Considering its simplicity and ease of construction the frequency distribution chart is exceedingly useful and supplies a lot of needed information.

2.8 non-parametric estimation of the standard deviation

It was stated in Chapter 2.7 that the ratio Range/$\sqrt{n}$ gives a rough estimate of the standard deviation, and this is quite useful for small sets of values. When a large set of values is concerned this ratio gives much too small an estimate and it is necessary to use another method. The set of values, as derived and not ordered or rearranged in any way, is divided into groups of 9; some individual values may be allocated to two adjacent groups to make up the necessary number of values.

The range of each group of values is determined, and the mean of these ranges calculated. The estimate of the standard deviation is given by one-third of this mean. This method is an extension of the Range/$\sqrt{n}$, where we have

$$\frac{\text{Mean range of groups}}{\sqrt{\text{Number in each group}}} \quad \text{or} \quad \frac{\text{Mean range}}{\sqrt{n}}$$

For example, given the 60 values of Table 2.8, seven groups of 9 are necessary so that three shared values are needed, and the 60 values are divided into groups as shown

Table 2.8 A set of 60 values (last 60 values from Table 2.7.1)

807	775	740	783	738	765	747	747	805 *	759
755	757	759	820	726	755	797	**765**	748	798
808	711	748	818	754	**790**	772	748	777	755
783	736	807	**778**	703	790	784	738	778	781
758	765 *	768	775	796	773	766	744	783	777
795 *	779	750	740	783	765	778	767	768	737

(asterisks indicate group divisions, shared values are printed in bold type)

From this table we calculate as follows:

Values 1–9 have a range 738–807 = 69
10–18 have a range 726–820 = 94
18–26 have a range 711–818 = 107
26–34 have a range 736–807 = 71
34–42 have a range 703–790 = 87
43–51 have a range 744–796 = 52
52–60 have a range 738–783 = 45   Total of ranges = 525

The mean range = 525/7 = 75, and the estimate of the standard deviation is 75/3 = 25 which agrees closely with the calculated values. This method of estimating the standard deviation is very quick and fairly accurate, but does not help estimation of any other parameters.

There is another non-parametric method for the estimation of the standard deviation of a set of values which is somewhat less accurate but which may suffice in certain circumstances. The estimate is obtained by calculating 0·88 times the average difference between successive values, without regard to the sign of the differences, that is

$$\hat{s} = \frac{0 \cdot 88 \sum |d_i|}{n}$$

where n is the number of differences d_i.

For example the 60 values of Table 2.8 have differences 32, 35, 43 etc., and the estimate of the standard deviation is

$$\hat{s} = \frac{0 \cdot 88 \times 1{,}818}{59} = 27 \cdot 1$$

which is a little higher than those estimated by other methods, but which probably is a usable estimate.

SUGGESTIONS FOR FURTHER READING

2 G. U. YULE and M. G. KENDALL, Chapters 4, 5, 6, 7 and 8, 1958.
3 C. A. BENNETT and N. L. FRANKLIN, Chapters 2, 3 and 4, 1954.
5 O. L. DAVIES (ed.), Chapters 2 and 3, 1958.
6 L. M. DEBING, Chapters 1 and 2, 1957.
16 O. L. LACEY, Chapters 4, 5, 6, 7 and 8, 1953.
25 C. V. DURELL, *Advanced Algebra*, Volume 1, 1963.

CHAPTER THREE

CHARTS AND GRAPHS

MANY OF the varieties of charts and graphs have been found of great value in industrial statistics and applications are widespread. They can be used for purposes of display, for recording data, and for making calculations. In this chapter we shall discuss some of the uses and applications of charts and graphs.

3.1 the purpose of pictorial representation

Much has been written on the subject of graphical presentation. Probably one of its greatest advantages is the fact that many people have a photographic or visual memory and thus retain data presented pictorially longer than they would if the data were presented in any other form. For this reason any chart or graph intended for display must be kept simple and clear and must not contain any irrelevant details.

Graphs and charts may be used with great effectiveness in the presentation of all types of statistics. When properly constructed they readily show information that might otherwise be lost amid the details of numerical tabulations. A graph or chart shows more than just the value of a statistic; it also shows any trends that may be present and the way in which the trends change. Although this information is inherent in a table it may be quite difficult and time-consuming (and sometimes may be impossible) to determine the existence and nature of trends from a tabulation of data.

The important point that must be borne in mind at all times is that the pictorial presentation chosen for any situation must depict the true relationship and point out the proper conclusion. Use of an inappropriate chart may distort the facts and mislead the reader. Above all, the chart must be honest.

3.2 graphical representation of numerical data

Numerical data may be divided into two classes: counted data and estimated data.

Counted Data are actual occurrences over which there can be no argument. Examples are the numbers of men employed in various locations; the factory wage bill; the number of accidents that have occurred in any period of time; the quantities of each product dispatched from warehouse; the number of hours overtime worked; etc.

Estimated Data are derived from various sources and may be suspect because of possible errors or bias. Examples are the yields in chemical production departments which have a relatively large 'in process' stock where errors may arise through inaccurate measurement, sampling or analysis; analytical data on raw materials and finished products which may be in error through faulty sampling or analysis; etc.

Although estimated data may include some errors which counted data do not, instances may arise when successive points in a sequence of counted data show wide fluctuations akin to or even exceeding those shown by estimated data. There is nothing wrong in this; fluctuations in counted data are factual, however wide they may be. Figure 3.2.1 shows an example of this, where Plot A refers to the number of minor injuries reported each month of a 12-month period while Plot B shows the reported monthly yields of a large production department for the same 12-month period. Approximately the same scale is needed in each plot but the range of values covered by the counted data and the swing between values for successive months are much larger for the counted data than for the estimated data.

The common methods of graphical representation of numerical data are: 1. Straight Plot Charts; 2. Block Diagrams; 3. Moving Average Charts; 4. Shewhart Control Charts; and 5. Cumulative Sum Charts; and each of these has its own spheres of usefulness. We shall consider some of the important points of each.

3.2.1 STRAIGHT PLOT CHARTS

These are the simplest type of chart. In each case the data are plotted, in sequence as derived, on a suitable graticule; successive plotted points may be joined, or not, as required but where the scale used is such that the plotted points are relatively far apart successive points should be connected by straight lines to improve clarity. Examples of such charts are given in Figure 3.2.1, A and B.

The ordinate scale of the chart may be modified so that the plot shows variation from some pre-determined value, and a cumulator chart may be added so that the total number of occurrences at any given time may be read directly from the chart. Arrangements such as this are shown in Fig. 3.2.1, C and D. Of course, Figure 3.2.1 C is a duplicate of Figure 3.2.1.A; there is

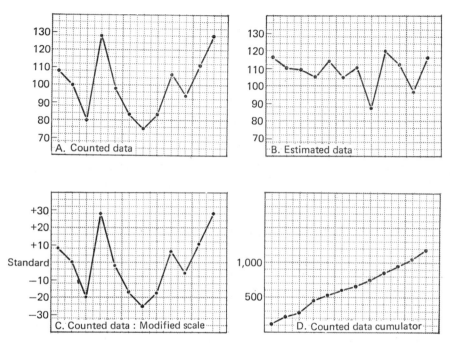

Fig. 3.2.1. STRAIGHT PLOT CHARTS

no need for duplication in practice as one chart can be drawn with both scales shown; for example the actual numerical scale can be written on the left-hand side of the chart with the difference from standard scale on the right-hand side of the chart. The cumulator chart gives an indication of the rate at which the data occur, but to be worth while must have an ordinate scale sufficiently large that the plotted points may be read; this cannot be done with the example shown in Figure 3.2.1.D.

Straight plot charts are very useful for showing the variations that occur over a period of time or the trend which may have developed in that period, and a comment about the ordinate scales used on straight plot charts may be necessary here. Like every other technique and procedure in the field of industrial statistics straight plot charts are intended to be used and should be drawn so that the maximum use may be made of them. There is no need for every ordinate scale to start from zero; if Figure 3.2.1.A had been drawn on an ordinate scale zero to 130 more than half the graticule would have been wasted. Every chart must be given an appropriate scale which will be dependent on the size of the sheet to be used, the range of values to be plotted and the actual values themselves. Further, if two or more straight plot charts are to be used for comparison they must have identical ordinate scales or the plots will be incomparable. In all cases the ordinate scale should be marked on the chart.

3.2.2 BLOCK DIAGRAMS

Block diagrams (or histograms) are a modification of straight plot charts in which a point at some ordinate value is replaced by a block drawn to the height of the observation to be recorded and of a width appropriate to the interval of sequence. The width of each block in a diagram need not be the same — in some cases the areas of the blocks are the important feature of the diagram and block widths may all be different — but whenever block diagrams are to be used to show occurrences in time, equal time intervals should be used.

Block diagrams merely give a pictorial representation of the data, and no other information is made available in such diagrams which, however, give a better visual representation of the data than the straight plot. These diagrams are better suited to counted data than to estimated data, and since the main purpose of the diagram is to indicate differences of occurrences in any intervals the blocks may be drawn to a truncated scale so that the greatest advantage is taken of the space available and differences emphasized. This is shown in Figure 3.2.2 where the actual counted data used for Figure 3.2.1.A are shown on a full scale (A) and on a truncated scale (B). Obviously the block diagram on the truncated scale (B) shows up the difference between successive intervals much more clearly than does the block diagram on the full scale (A).

Frequently an 'invert' block diagram is of more value than the simple block diagram. In an invert block diagram the blocks show the differences between the actual occurrences and some previously agreed 'acceptable' value. Figure 3.2.2.C shows the invert block diagram for Figure 3.2.2.B with 100 as the acceptable value; the construction of the blocks in the two diagrams is very similar, the only difference being that in Diagram B the blocks all stand on the horizontal axis while in Diagram C the blocks are referred to some other datum line. In this particular invert block diagram values greater than 100 show some unwelcome deficiency and so these blocks are shaded (in actual practice they would be coloured red), while values less than 100 indicate an improvement on the acceptable value and so these blocks are coloured black. In other cases values less than 100 might be unwelcome and would be coloured red; it has been found that using the colours red and black adds considerable emphasis to the presentation. In any case where an 'acceptable' value cannot be agreed, a value such as the average for the immediately previous period could be used.

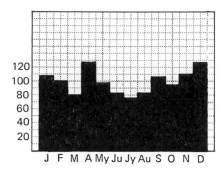

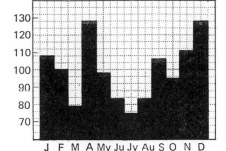

A. Counted data : Full scale

B. Counted data : Truncated scale

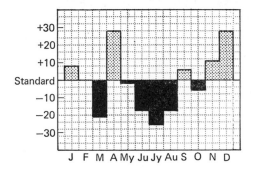

C. Counted data : Invert block diagram

Fig. 3.2.2. BLOCK DIAGRAMS

3.2.3 MOVING AVERAGE (OR MOVING MEAN) CHARTS

Moving Average charts may be constructed from weighted or unweighted data, but for graphical representation as distinct from calculation unweighted data are used. Charts such as these present the data as 'averages' or 'mean values'; each point plotted is the arithmetic average of the current value and a given number of immediately preceding values. Since most values dealt with are closed on an annual basis the averaging number chosen is usually 3, 6, or 12, so that each point plotted is an average of a run of 3, 6, or 12 successive values. Where the data under consideration refer to monthly occurrences these runs are equivalent to quarterly, half-yearly, and yearly averages. By means of this procedure the chart shows the current trend of the data.

Figure 3.2.3 shows the actual yields as reported each month for a chemical product with moving average graphs calculated on 3, 6, and 12 month runs. Each graph starts from the same point so that the moving average is not in force until the number of points plotted equals the run length. For example, in Graph C the 6-monthly average becomes effective at the sixth point plotted. These graphs show how extending the run length smooths variation between

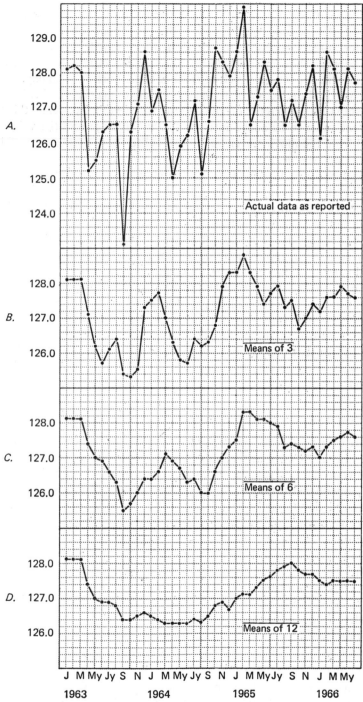

Fig. 3.2.3. MOVING AVERAGE CHARTS

ı.s. 1—5

successive monthly yields and it is obvious that if the run length be taken much beyond 12, the moving average curve will approximate closely to a straight line. Some care is necessary in selection of the run length to maintain a balance between showing the trend and showing the variation, and the degree of balance will depend on which of these is to be portrayed chiefly.

Some help in the selection of a suitable run length may be obtained from the relationship that a difference of 'run length' × 'unit of measurement' between the current value to be added into the moving average and the value to be dropped from the moving average is required to show a difference of 1 unit in the moving average. For instance, a yield graph on a 12-month run requires a yield difference of 12 units between the current value and the value to be dropped to show a change of 1 unit in the graph; if such a yield difference is likely to arise only after disastrous operation then a 12-month run for this yield will not be very informative.

Moving average charts should not be used for counted data; they are better used for suspect or approximate data with a run length sufficient to cover expected variations and no longer. Productions, production yields, and production costs, where these depend on some estimated data, with a 3-month or 4-month run would be covered very well by moving average charts and these would indicate the current trend of plant performance, with successive very good and very bad values tending to balance each other.

It is obvious that moving average charts could be used unscrupulously to obscure very good or very bad values in counted data. This should not be permitted.

3.2.4 SHEWHART CONTROL CHARTS

Shewhart Control Charts are straight plot charts on which control or comparison lines are drawn at levels decreed by some specification or deduced from previous data. In some cases both specification and deduction lines may be used, as with charts for yield data in which comparison lines for theoretical and standard yields may be drawn as well as lines indicating 95 per cent and 99·73 per cent probability of occurrence which have been calculated from previous data. This type of chart may be used for counted data and for estimated data. They are particularly useful for recording chemical analysis data, plant variable data, plant performance data, and almost all other statistics met in everyday working.

Control levels deduced from previous data are calculated from as many consecutive values as are available (or as may be convenient; 30 is a reasonable number and 12 should be regarded as the minimum number to be used). From these values the mean and standard deviation are calculated, assuming a normal distribution, and control lines are drawn at the levels indicated by

Mean ±2 standard deviations give the Inner Control or Warning Lines, and Mean ±3 standard deviations give the Outer Control or Action Lines.

Any value falling outside the Outer Control Lines may be considered to be an extraordinary value. If from estimtaed data and no valid reason is known for its occurrence, an investigation should be made to determine this reason; if from counted data the value indicates a very abnormal occurrence and here again should lead to an investigation to determine its cause.

Figure 3.2.4 shows the reported monthly yields as plotted in Figure 3.2.3.A, with the theoretical and Standard Yield levels drawn. Also drawn are the

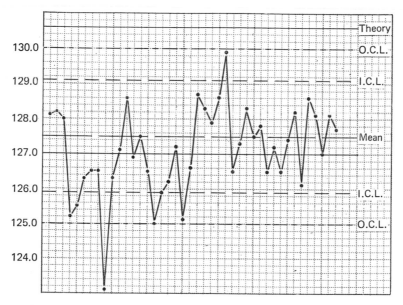

Fig. 3.2.4. SHEWHART CONTROL CHART

mean value and inner and outer control lines at levels calculated from the 36 monthly yields previous to January 1963. The chart shows one outrageously low yield value that must have been due to some assignable cause; all other values lie between the outer control limits.

3.2.5 CUMULATIVE SUM CHARTS

Figure 3.2.1.D shows a cumulative sum chart on a scale too small to be of any real use, but the worth of cumulative sum charts can be increased enormously by a minor modification to the method of constructing the graph. Instead of plotting the cumulative sums of actual values, the cumulative sums of differences between the actual values and a pre-determined 'acceptable' value are plotted. This involves a little extra arithmetic which entails no more than subtraction and addition as show below.

Consider the values plotted in Figure 3.2.1.A, referred to 100 as the 'acceptable' datum; the following tabulation is self-explanatory

Table 3.2.5 Derivation of cumulative sum

Actual value	Actual value −100	Cumulative sum
108	8	8
100	0	8
80	−20	−12
128	28	16
98	−2	14
83	−17	−3
75	−25	−28
83	−17	−45
106	6	−39
94	−6	−45
111	11	−34
128	28	−6

and the cumulative sum values are plotted as shown in Figure 3.2.5.

The usefulness of cumulative sum charts lies in the following points:

1 They are equally effective for counted or estimated data. Errors in estimated data soon balance out.
2 The trend of performance between any two points is indicated by the straight line joining those points.
3 The cumulative sum chart will detect small changes in the mean value more quickly than the Shewhart type chart.
4 Any change in trend is made obvious immediately it occurs; see points 2, 3, 4 and 10 in Figure 3.2.5.

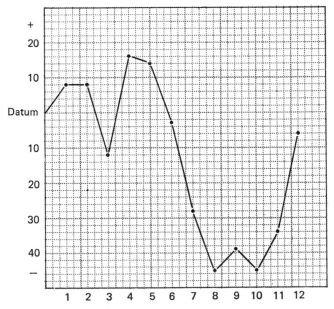

Fig. 3.2.5. CUMULATIVE SUM CHART

5 The average value at any time is determined very easily, and is merely the difference between the point considered and the datum divided by the number of points with the datum value added to convert to original values. For example, the average value of the 12 actual values in Table 3.2.5 is $-\frac{6}{12} + 100 = 99 \cdot 5$.

6 The value at each point and sum of all values up to that point are determined just as easily from the chart.

Cumulative sum charts are recommended for recording any data in which it may be important that a trend be noted at the first possible moment. These charts, however, cannot be used in conjunction with specification or comparison limits except where such a limit is taken as the datum. This type of chart is considered in more detail in the next section.

3.3 statistical control charts

Control charts are graphs in which the values of any characteristic of a process are plotted in sequence as they occur; the values are plotted as ordinates against the sequence of occurrence as abscissa. The term 'process' refers to any situation in which work is done; it includes such operations as batch and continuous operation of manufacturing units, packing and weighing, movement of materials, chemical and physical analysis, occurrence of accidents, etc.

Statistical control charts are those graphs on which 'average' and 'limit' lines are drawn to provide supervision with a guide leading to better control. The positions of these lines are determined by statistical calculations and, like all other statistics, indicate a certain degree of probability. The limit lines show the extreme values of the characteristic that are likely to occur with the indicated degree of probability. For example, 2σ (two-sigma) limit lines correspond to 0·95 probability and would be expected to include 95 per cent of all points plotted as long as no change has taken place in the process; 3σ limit lines correspond to 0·9973 probability and would be expected to include 99·73 per cent of all points plotted as long as no change has taken place in the process, so that any point lying outside the 3σ limit line should be a very unusual occurrence.

It is necessary to make a distinction between two sorts of characteristics: *variables* and *attributes*. *Variables* are those characteristics which may vary continuously and whose values, therefore, may be expressed by reference to a continuous numerical scale. Examples of such characteristics are time, weight, distance, volume, concentration, pH, moisture content, assay, temperature, pressure, etc. *Attributes* are those characteristics which do not vary continuously but occupy discrete rankings and thus cannot be expressed numerically by reference to a continuous scale. Examples of such characteristics are colour, odour, taste, smoothness, etc. (though note that some colours may be compared by numerical values). From time to time attempts are made to relate attributes on some sort of ranked scale, such as

completely acceptable = 1 (material within specification on all counts),

acceptable = 2 (material just meets specification on all counts),

acceptable (under protest) = 3 (material just outside specification on some (minor?) counts),

not generally acceptable = 4 (material outside specification on one or two major counts),

completely unacceptable = 5 (material outside specification on all counts),

but whereas attributes may be ranked in this way, it is extremely difficult to get everyone to accept the idea that the assigned numbers are merely rank indicators and are not comparative measures of badness or goodness.

3.3.1 THE VALUE OF STATISTICAL CONTROL CHARTS

Statistical control charts supply the best means of recording routine data and form a sound basis for performance review and improvement programmes. Although they are used mostly in laboratory work at present, statistical control charts are designed primarily for process control and they supply information about the process in such a form that it is immediately available as a basis for action. However, it must be remembered at all times that a control chart is not an end in itself; it is an aid to judgment additional to, but not in place of, technical knowledge of the process.

Whereas it is impossible to appreciate the significance of groups of values of various characteristics recorded on a number of loose sheets, or in several books, and while these groups of values arranged in rows and columns on one page remain barely digestible, there can be no doubt that when the values are plotted on the appropriate charts, any significant variation in values of a characteristic or correlation between values of several characteristics is immediately apparent. Table 3.3.1 and Figure 3.3.1 may lend some emphasis to this statement, especially when it is borne in mind that Table 3.3.1 is much simpler than most of the current process report sheets.

The value of statistical control charts, and the advantages of a state of statistical control may be summarized as:

1 Test results and other data can be set out clearly and concisely to provide information and a running commentary on movement of production variables which cannot be conveyed by a mass of tabulated data.

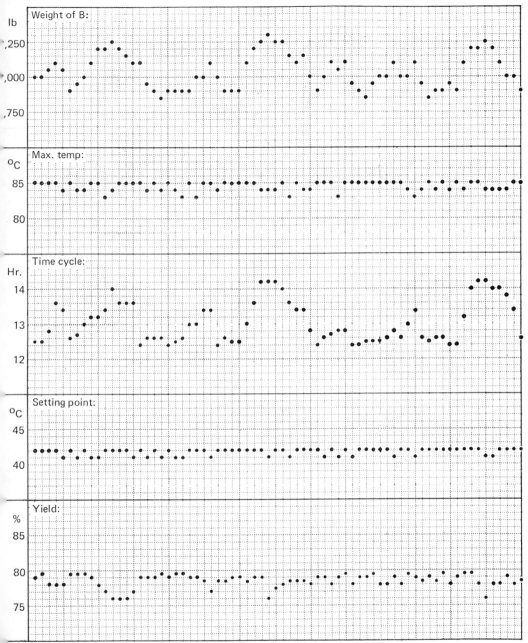

Weight of A = 3,000 lb. per batch

3.31. PLOT OF DATA IN TABLE 3.3.1

Table 3.3.1 A series of process readings

Batch	Weight of B	Max. Temp.	Batch time	Setting point	Yield	Batch	Weight of B	Max. temp.	Batch time	Setting point	Yield
	lb	°C	hr	°C	%		lb	°C	hr	°C	%
1	2,000	85	12·5	42	79·0	36	2,250	85	14·0	42	78·0
2	2,000	85	12·5	42	79·5	37	2,150	83	13·6	41	78·5
3	2,050	85	12·8	42	78·0	38	2,100	85	13·4	42	78·5
4	2,100	85	13·6	42	78·0	39	2,150	84	13·4	42	78·5
5	2,050	84	13·4	41	78·0	40	2,000	84	12·8	42	78·0
6	1,900	85	12·6	42	79·5	41	1,900	85	12·4	42	79·0
7	1,950	84	12·7	41	79·5	42	2,000	85	12·6	41	79·0
8	2,000	84	13·0	42	79·5	43	2,100	85	12·7	42	78·0
9	2,100	85	13·2	41	79·0	44	2,050	83	12·8	41	79·0
10	2,200	85	13·2	41	78·0	45	2,100	85	12·8	42	79·5
11	2,200	83	13·4	42	77·0	46	1,950	85	12·4	41	78·0
12	2,250	84	14·0	42	76·0	47	1,900	85	12·4	42	79·0
13	2,200	85	13·6	42	76·0	48	1,850	85	12·5	42	79·0
14	2,150	85	13·6	42	76·0	49	1,950	85	12·5	42	79·5
15	2,100	85	13·6	41	77·0	50	2,000	85	12·5	42	78·0
16	2,100	85	12·4	42	79·0	51	2,000	85	12·6	42	78·0
17	1,950	84	12·6	41	79·0	52	2,100	85	12·8	41	79·0
18	1,900	85	12·6	42	79·0	53	2,000	85	12·6	42	78·0
19	1,850	84	12·6	41	79·5	54	2,000	84	13·0	42	79·5
20	1,900	85	12·4	42	79·0	55	2,100	83	13·4	41	79·0
21	1,900	84	12·5	41	79·5	56	1,950	84	12·6	42	78·5
22	1,900	83	12·6	41	79·5	57	1,850	85	12·5	42	79·0
23	1,900	85	13·0	42	79·0	58	1,900	83	12·6	42	78·5
24	2,000	83	13·0	42	79·0	59	1,900	85	12·6	42	79·5
25	2,000	85	13·4	42	78·5	60	1,950	84	12·4	42	78·0
26	2,100	85	13·4	41	77·0	61	1,900	85	12·4	42	79·0
27	2,000	84	12·4	42	78·5	62	2,100	84	13·2	42	79·5
28	1,900	85	12·6	42	78·5	63	2,200	85	14·0	42	79·5
29	1,900	85	12·5	42	79·0	64	2·200	85	14·2	42	78·0
30	1,900	85	12·5	42	79·0	65	2,250	84	14·2	41	76·0
31	2,100	85	13·0	42	78·5	66	2,200	84	14·0	41	78·0
32	2,200	85	13·6	42	79·0	67	2,100	84	14·0	42	78·0
33	2,250	84	14·2	42	79·0	68	2,000	84	13·8	42	79·0
34	2,300	84	14·2	41	76·0	69	2,000	85	13·4	42	78·0
35	2,250	84	14·2	42	77·5	70	1,900	85	12·6	42	78·5

2 Unless production is controlled statistically the fact that tests on small samples comply with a given specification is no proof that the remainder of the product complies with the specification. With statistically controlled production the quality of the product which will be manufactured in the future can be predicted accurately with any given degree of probability.

3 A statistical control chart shows up any departures from statistically controlled production; steps can be taken to rectify the trouble immediately it has occurred so that a minimum quantity of reject material is manufactured. Any production troubles can be investigated by supervisors who have the quantitative data and the knowledge of when the trouble occurred.

4 The quality of the product can be specified accurately, and it can be stated with what specification limits the product complies. If the process is under statistical control then greater uniformity of product cannot be

achieved without making changes in the process itself. Hence it is known that the process is being operated as efficiently as possible as far as the particular characteristics plotted are concerned.

5 When an attempt is to be made to bring a process from an uncontrolled to a statistically controlled state, statistical control charts are indispensable. Also, they are invaluable for assessing in quantitative terms the effect of modifications in operating methods or of changes in equipment. It is not always possible for unaided judgment to decide whether or not a significant improvement has been made, and frequently opinions differ on whether a change in process or equipment has or has not made any improvement. The use of statistical control charts obviates any such differences of opinion and makes it unnecessary to attempt intricate mathematical calculations to prove the point.

6 For any degree of certainty about predictions relating to the quality characteristics of a product, the analysis and recording of test results by methods based on statistical principles are the most economical. With the process in a state of statistical control, testing may be reduced to a minimum and in some cases this itself may be an aim worthy of the effort involved in setting up control.

7 The recording of data on the statistical control charts should be done at source and as soon as the data are available. The statistical control charts provide the only record needed and the recording of data in this way will eliminate unnecessary and wasteful duplication and transcription of records.

3.3.2 THE STATISTICS USED IN STATISTICAL CONTROL CHARTS

Only three statistics are needed in the preparation of statistical control charts: the average, the range, and the standard deviation.

The *average* is the arithmetic mean of a number of values obtained immediately prior to the first value to be plotted on the chart and as defined in Chapter 1 is given by $\bar{x} = 1/n. \sum x_i$.

The *range* needed is the range of each group of 3, or 4, or 5 values plotted on the chart (or whatever convenient group size is selected) and is defined by the difference between the largest and smallest values in the group.

The *standard deviation* is calculated from the same values as the average, assuming that the values are drawn from a normal population, using the expression

$$s = \sqrt{\frac{\sum (x_i - \bar{x})^2}{n - 1}}$$

though one of the other methods for estimating the standard deviation (Chapter 2) may be used if more convenient. The standard deviation is used for calculation of the control limits to be drawn on the charts.

3.3.3 STATISTICAL CONTROL CHARTS FOR VARIABLES

Data obtained during manufacturing or analytical operations (among others) usually consist of a number of measurements of such items as time, temperature, pressure, concentration, moisture content, density, viscosity, etc. The use of statistical control charts will show whether or not the data are obtained from statistically controlled operation, that is whether or not they are consistent with the hypothesis that the data are random values from the same population, or whether changes in level and variability have taken place.

Variation in the values of any characteristic is bound to occur, and where this variation arises solely from a constant system of chance causes then the data are said to be statistically uniform and the variation is said to be statistically controlled, that is the data belong to the same population. As long as the data remain under statistical control valid predictions may be made about further data from the same source and further statistical tests may be carried out safely. Also, deductions may be made from the available data with the knowledge that all conclusions drawn from the data will apply to future data.

The variation which arises in the values of any characteristic may be due to either (or both) of two kinds of causes:

1 *Chance causes*, which are innumerable and each exercises a small effect on the total variation. These are permissible variations which cannot be identified, either because of lack of knowledge or because such identification would be uneconomic. These chance causes are inherent in the system and cannot be reduced or eliminated without modification to the system. Examples of chance causes are small variations in reaction conditions, small variations in quality of raw materials, etc.

2 *Assignable causes*, which can be identified, and which usually can be identified and eliminated economically. These causes arise from sudden or abnormal variation in properties of raw materials or reaction conditions or from mechanical faults. These give rise to difficulties during operation and interfere with smooth running of the unit. When assignable causes interfere, the process is not operating as efficiently as it might, and data obtained from the process might be unreliable.

These two terms are only relative, and the acquisition of more knowledge may result in chance causes becoming assigned. Statistical control charts will show when variation ceases to arise solely from a constant system of chance causes and when assignable causes intervene. Where assignable causes of variation are present in a set of data, the data are not statistically uniform and their value is restricted; any further statistical analysis of such data must be undertaken with care. An indication of the presence of assignable causes may be valuable as a first step in an investigation to improve the process or procedure.

3.3.4 CONSTRUCTION OF STATISTICAL CONTROL CHARTS FOR PROCESS CONTROL

The preliminary requirement is to determine the average and standard deviation of a number of values; the procedure used for estimation of the standard deviation depends on whether or not a large number (more than 50) of individual values is available. Two procedures are available and these are discussed separately.

PROCEDURE 1: WHERE A LARGE NUMBER OF READINGS IS AVAILABLE

Unless the population average and standard deviation have been defined in a specification, the first step is to obtain sufficient readings to enable good estimates to be made of these statistics. An estimate of the standard deviation is required which measures the inherent variation of the process, and 50 to 100 readings should be suitable for this purpose as long as assignable causes have not interfered with any of the data. As far as possible these readings should be obtained consecutively; no value is to be left out without absolute justification. The procedure to estimate the statistics is as follows:

1 Divide the consecutive readings into convenient subgroups, each of 4 or 5 or 6 readings.
2 Determine the average (v) and range (w) of each subgroup.
3 Determine the average of the subgroups' averages ($\bar{v}$) and of the subgroups' ranges ($\bar{w}$).
4 Determine in each subgroup the sum of the differences between the individual readings in the subgroup and the overall average $\bar{v}$. Total these sums and divide this total by the number of original readings. This final quotient is the 'variance from true' of the average $\bar{v}$ and must be added to (if positive) or deducted from (if negative) the value of $\bar{v}$ to give the true average. Often this variance figure is small and may be neglected.

Table 3.3.4 shows the percentage impurity readings obtained on 100 consecutive batches; the subgroup averages and ranges and the overall average of the subgroups' averages and ranges are given. The factor to be used in conjunction with the average range for determination of the standard deviation is merely the square root $\sqrt{n}$.

The estimate of the standard deviation, s, is obtained from the expression

$$s = \frac{\bar{w}}{\sqrt{n}}$$

and for the example of Table 3.3.4 we have $s = 0 \cdot 5 / 2 \cdot 0 = 0 \cdot 25$.

The inner control lines are drawn at the levels indicated by $\bar{v} \pm 1{\cdot}96s/\sqrt{n}$, and in this example are at $10{\cdot}7 \pm (1{\cdot}96 \times 0{\cdot}25)/\sqrt{4}$, or 10·5 and 10·9. Under normal operation almost all the *subgroup averages* should lie within these inner control lines, with a minimum probability of 95 per cent.

The upper and lower limit lines are drawn at the levels indicated by $\bar{v} \pm 3{\cdot}09s/\sqrt{n}$, which for this example are $10{\cdot}7 \pm (3{\cdot}09 \times 0{\cdot}25)/\sqrt{4}$, or 10·3 and 11·1, and a *subgroup average* outside these limits indicates a considerable deviation from normal operation which must receive immediate attention.

It is customary to prepare the statistical control chart graticule showing the average value, inner control lines and the upper and lower limit lines as estimated from the available data. Then as further data become available the individual readings (represented on the chart by a 'dot' •) and subgroup

Table 3.3.4 Estimation of standard deviation from 100 consecutive readings

Batch No.	% Impurity	Subgroup Average (v)	Range (w)	Sums of diff. from 10·7 +	−	Batch No.	% Impurity	Subgroup Average (v)	Range (w)	Sums of diff. from 10·7 +	−
1	11·2					33	10·9				
2	11·1					34	11·1				
3	11·0					35	10·5				
4	10·8	11·0	0·4	1·2	—	36	10·6	10·8	0·6	0·4	—
5	10·6					37	11·2				
6	11·0					38	10·4				
7	11·2					39	10·6				
8	10·8	10·9	0·6	0·8	—	40	10·6	10·7	0·8	—	—
9	10·9					41	10·6				
10	10·7					42	11·2				
11	10·5					43	10·7				
12	10·9	10·75	0·4	0·2	—	44	10·5	10·75	0·7	0·2	—
13	10·7					45	11·0				
14	10·7					46	11·1				
15	10·4					47	10·6				
16	10·4	10·55	0·3	—	0·6	48	11·1	10·95	0·5	1·0	—
17	10·6					49	11·0				
18	10·5					50	10·7				
19	10·9					51	11·0				
20	10·8	10·7	0·4	—	—	52	11·3	11·0	0·6	1·2	—
21	10·7					53	11·1				
22	11·2					54	11·0				
23	10·9					55	10·7				
24	10·4	10·8	0·8	0·4	—	56	10·8	10·9	0·4	0·8	—
25	10·7					57	10·4				
26	10·3					58	10·5				
27	10·7					59	10·7				
28	11·0	10·8	0·7	0·4	—	60	10·6	10·55	0·3	—	0·6
29	10·6					61	11·0				
30	10·5					62	10·4				
31	10·6					63	10·8				
32	10·7	10·6	0·2	—	0·4	64	10·6	10·7	0·6	—	—

Table 3.3.4 (cont)

Batch No.	% Impurity	Subgroup Average (v)	Range (w)	Sums of diff. from 10·7 +	−	Batch No.	% Impurity	Subgroup Average (v)	Range (w)	Sums of diff. from 10·7 +	−
65	10·9					85	10·8				
66	10·5					86	10·7				
67	10·8					87	11·0				
68	10·5	10·7	0·4	−	−	88	11·1	10·9	0·4	0·4	−
69	10·9					89	10·4				
70	11·0					90	10·7				
71	10·5					91	10·6				
72	10·4	10·7	0·6	−	−	92	10·6	10·6	0·3	−	0·4
73	10·4					93	10·9				
74	11·0					94	10·5				
75	10·6					95	10·5				
76	10·9	10·7	0·6	−	−	96	10·8	10·7	0·4	−	−
77	10·9					97	11·0				
78	10·7					98	10·4				
79	10·8					99	10·6				
80	10·8	10·8	0·2	0·4	−	100	10·6	10·65	0·6	−	0·2
81	10·3					Totals	1,070·2	268·7	12·5	7·4	3·0
82	10·4									+4·4	
83	10·9					Aver-ages	10·7	$(\bar{v})$ 10·7	$(\bar{w})$ 0·5	+0·044	
84	10·5	10·5	0·6	−	0·8					(neglect)	

averages (represented on the chart by a 'cross' ×) are plotted. Figure 3.3.4 shows such an arrangement in which the readings of Table 3.3.4 are plotted. We see that there are 6 individual readings above the upper limit line but all the subgroup average points lie within the upper and lower limit lines and 22 of the 25 points lie inside the inner control lines. In this chart the control lines have been calculated from the plotted points, but as long as the process remains unaltered all further data obtained would be expected to show a similar distribution.

For calculation of the limit lines the estimate $\bar{w}/\sqrt{n}$ has been used for the standard deviation, and in most cases this will be sufficiently accurate. A greater degree of accuracy may be achieved by replacing the divisor $\sqrt{n}$ by a mean range factor as given in *Biometrika Tables for Statisticians*, Volume 1, Table 27 'Mean Range in normal samples of size N'. Some of these divisor factors are

Number of readings in subgroup n	Factor to be used instead of $\sqrt{n}$
2	1·128
3	1·693
4	2·059
5	2·326
6	2·534
7	2·704

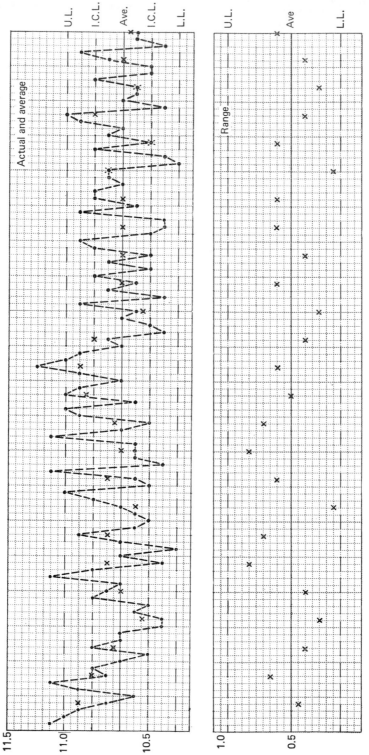

Fig. 3.3.4. CONTROL CHART FOR PERCENTAGE IMPURITY

The lower graph in Figure 3.3.4 shows a plot of the subgroup ranges with 95 per cent limits for the range. Where the statistical control chart is based on averages of groups it may be necessary, and certainly it is very useful, to control on the ranges of groups as well as the averages. In this example the 95 per cent limits are given by

$$\text{Lower limit} = 0{\cdot}59s = 0{\cdot}15; \text{Upper limit} = 3{\cdot}98s = 0{\cdot}95$$

and the factors used to multiply the standard deviation for various subgroupings and probabilities are given in *Biometrika Tables for Statisticians*, Volume 1, Table 22, 'Percentage Points of the Distribution of the Range'. Some of these multiplying factors are

Number of readings in subgroup (n)	95% Limit multipliers Lower limit	Upper limit
2	0·04	3·17
3	0·30	3·68
4	0·59	3·98
5	0·85	4·20
6	1·06	4·36
7	1·25	4·49

When both the average and range plots lie within their respective control limits, then the process is operating satisfactorily under statistical control, and improvements can be made only by modifying the process in some way. If the average plots lie within their control limits and the corresponding range plots lie outside their limits, then some assignable cause is interfering with normal operation.

PROCEDURE 2: WHERE ONLY A SMALL NUMBER OF READINGS IS AVAILABLE

Where, again, the population average and standard deviation have not been defined in a specification and insufficient readings are available to use the procedure described above, a second procedure is available for construction of the statistical control chart. Procedure 1 is used whenever control is to be exercised on *average* production values as indicated by subgroup averages, but Procedure 2 may be used in all cases where control is to be exercised on individual values.

A minimum of 12 consecutive readings is necessary, and readings should be plotted until 12 are available. Where more than 12 consecutive readings are available the most recent 24–30 consecutive readings should be used, as these may be expected to show the maximum range of random error. It is not possible to emphasize too strongly that consecutive readings must be used unless some are known to be wrong because of undoubted error in operation; there is still a tendency in some instances to discard supposedly 'bad' readings with no justification for the discard.

The standard deviation, s, of the values to be used is estimated in the usual manner assuming that the values to be used have been drawn from a normal population, that is, s is given by

$$s = \sqrt{\frac{\Sigma x^2 - (\Sigma x)^2/n}{n - 1}}$$

where n is the number of values x.

Where the individual readings are random selections from a normal population, then the range

$\bar{x} \pm s$ will cover 68 per cent of the measurements,

$\bar{x} \pm 2s$ will cover 95 per cent of the measurements, and

$\bar{x} \pm 3s$ will cover 99·73 per cent of the measurements.

These values $(\bar{x} \pm s)$, $(\bar{x} \pm 2s)$ and $(\bar{x} \pm 3s)$ are called the operating ranges, and usually are referred to as one-sigma, two-sigma and three-sigma ranges respectively. As long as the process remains under statistical control they would be expected to cover percentages of future measurements as quoted. For really good operation most of the readings will lie in the $(\bar{x} \pm s)$ range and in many cases it will be found that this range covers 90–95 per cent of the readings.

It will have been noted that this procedure gives much wider operating ranges than those obtained by Procedure 1, and of course this is because Procedure 2 deals with the actual readings as individuals whereas Procedure 1 deals with averages of groups and a large part of the range of individual readings from the mean is eliminated by considering the average of groups. Wherever desirable, such as with a very important characteristic of a product or a process, it is possible to maintain the statistical control chart in three sections showing: the individual readings and the calculated operating limits; the averages of subgroups and their calculated control limits; and the ranges of subgroups with their calculated control limits.

Applying Procedure 2 to the last 24 readings of Table 3.3.4 gives the following statistics: $\Sigma x = 256·5$, $n = 24$, $\bar{x} = 10·7$ and $s = 0·2$. From which the 2-sigma operating range is $10·7 \pm 0·4$ or 10·3 to 11·1.

For any process or product characteristic where a wide tolerance is permitted the operating control limits may be fixed at $\bar{x} \pm 3s$, but under no circumstance should a plot outside this wider range pass without a thorough investigation. In passing, we may note that all the 24 values taken to calculate the operating limits lie within the 2-sigma limits while 17 of them (70 per cent) lie within the 1-sigma limits.

3.3.5 SOME PATTERNS WHICH OCCUR REGULARLY ON STATISTICAL CONTROL CHARTS

When statistical control charts have been kept for a reasonably long period of time it may be observed that the charts show certain patterns which recur frequently. Figure 3.3.5 shows the more common of these patterns (labelled 1–6) as well as a pattern (7) which indicates a process characteristic under admirable control. The following comments refer to the individual patterns shown on Figure 3.3.5.

1 *Chart showing points above or below the operating range limits.* A chart such as this is an obvious indication that the process is out of control. Assignable causes of variation are interfering and operation of the process needs immediate investigation to rectify the situation and give the process and equipment a chance to work efficiently.

2 *Chart showing a change in the process level.* From point A to point B the process has been under control, but near B some change occurred in a process variable so that from point C onwards the process has operated at a new level. C is the seventh point on the same side of the average line, and points after C show no sign of a return below the average line.

3 *Chart showing changing conditions.* This chart shows too many points near one of the operating limits and indicates a non-normal distribution. The process requires some corrective action before it passes out of control and produces sub-specification product; action now means much less work than action later to return the process to control. Some of the more common causes for such a distribution are inadequately trained operatives, the process equipment not functioning properly — probably only one control factor is slipping — or periodic depletion of feed in a continuous process.

4 *Chart showing over-control.* This type of chart shows a bimodal, non-normal distribution. The most common cause for such a distribution is the taking of supposedly corrective action where really none is needed. Such correction applied at point A resulted in a forced counter-correction at point B and further corrections were imposed at points C, D and E. If continued, such a procedure — which really is nothing better than needless messing about with the process — would result in the process going completely out of control; and very likely the operatives would call the process 'uncontrollable'.

It must be remembered at all times that to impose 'corrections' for normal variations does nothing more than impose a man-made variation on the inherent variations of the process.

5 *Chart showing cyclical trends.* This is a very common type of chart which results from variation in one or more of the factors which control the pro-

I.S. 1—6

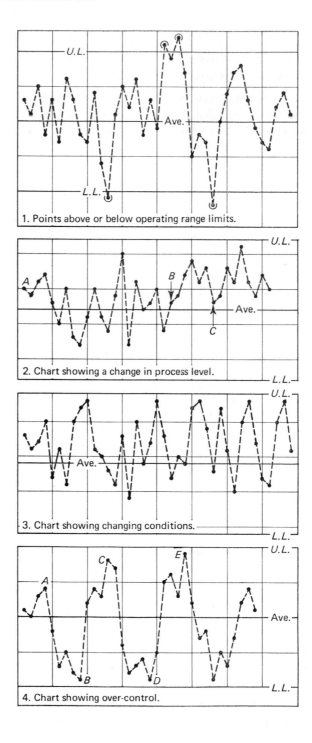

1. Points above or below operating range limits.

2. Chart showing a change in process level.

3. Chart showing changing conditions.

4. Chart showing over-control.

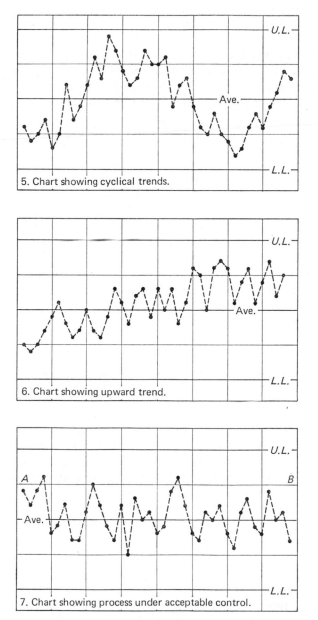

5. Chart showing cyclical trends.

6. Chart showing upward trend.

7. Chart showing process under acceptable control.

Fig. 3.3.5. SOME COMMON PATTERNS OBSERVED ON CONTROL CHARTS

cess. Such a factor may be slow changes in quality of a raw material, or the slow and unrecognized effect of time on operating procedures where these have not been constructed to deal with precise values, or cyclical supervisory pressure which usually happens following a change in management or supervision.

6 *Chart showing upward trend.* A process which is not under complete statistical control where some assignable cause is interfering will give a chart of this type, or of course its reverse showing a downward trend. Some of the factors which give rise to such trends are gradually changing raw material quality, transient production standards or procedures, catalyst poisoning which increases with time, and laboratory control solutions which are off standard.

7 *Chart showing process under acceptable control.* A chart of this type shows the process under good control, so that (*a*) all process variables controlled prior to A were controlled just as adequately in the period between A and B; and (*b*) variation is completely random, is centred about the average and is free from trends. The plotted points are more densely located near the average line, indicating a normal distribution.

This means that the equipment and process are being operated consistently, thereby producing consistent results. It does not imply that the process cannot be improved.

3.3.6 STATISTICAL CONTROL CHARTS FOR ATTRIBUTES

Statistical control charts for attributes can be constructed on any one of three bases:

1 The 'Pass or Fail' system, by which plots are made on the 'pass' side or 'fail' side of the central line as the case may be.
2 The 'Gradation' system, by which indication lines are drawn on the chart graticule to correspond with the various gradations of the attribute that are likely to be reported. For instance, if the colour of a given material is supposed to be green, then the gradations allowed on the chart for this material might be
    dark green, blue-green, green, light green, pale green, etc.
With such a system the gradations should be kept to a minimum consonant with the distinctions that have to be made. Such gradations as 'very dark green', 'almost dark green', 'fairly dark green', should not be used and all such gradations should be included in that of 'dark green'. Where colours are concerned it may be possible to use a colorimeter and convert the gradations into numerical values, but this is not always possible.
3 The 'proportion, or fraction, defective' system in which control limits are established in an attempt to control the number of defective articles or packages of product which are likely to be sent out of the manufacturing department. We have not used this system and it is not recommended

for general use as it could be argued that the sole purpose of this system is to ensure that the maximum amount of defective material per lot is approved for sale.

Figure 3.3.6 shows two charts drawn up according to systems 1 and 2. In charts such as these material which is rejected is shown as a ringed plot,

1. Showing the pass-fail system.

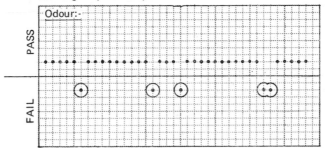

2. Showing the gradation system.

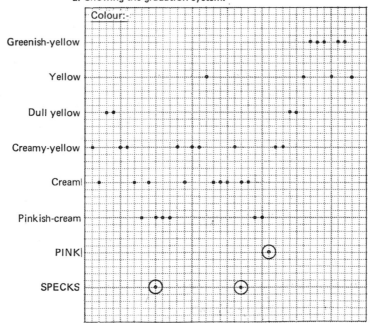

Fig. 3.3.6. CONTROL CHARTS FOR ATTRIBUTES

ensuring that these catch the eye of supervisors. In the lower chart the opportunity is taken to use the chart as an indication of contamination (specks) as well as colour.

3.3.7 DOTTOGRAPHS

The previous sections of this chapter have dealt with the construction and use of statistical control charts for control of manufacturing operations. A further use, and a very important one, of the Shewhart type chart is in the recording of data resulting from analysis where each value has to be compared with a specification limit. In all such cases as this there is no need to calculate and draw the inner and limit control lines; the quoted specification limits serve as the control limits. The graticules may be drawn as shown in Figure 3.3.7, and on each it is necessary to show

1 the sequence of occurrence (lot numbers written at the bottom of the chart),
2 the value of the test result (the ordinate value for each plot), and
3 the specification limit or limits.

Any number of data records may be made on the same sheet, the only restriction is that the scale used for each record must permit the reported value of each plotted point to be read accurately and easily. Each column of plotted points will refer to the results of analysis of a particular lot or batch of material and there is no need to consider plotting means and ranges of groups as individuals are to be compared with the specification limits.

These charts, called dottographs, provide the best and simplest method of recording routine test data. They permit runs of test values to be compared with specification and with each other, showing whether or not correlations exist between the various characteristics tested. The dottographs should be kept in the test laboratory and should be made up by the analyst who performs the test; no other record of the test values is necessary.

If desired, the data on the dottographs may be augmented to show the date, whether or not the lot met specification and was approved for sale, disposition of material, etc. In so far as it is possible and convenient the dottographs should remain simple and clear so that the information made available on them is not obscured by unnecessary trivia.

3.3.8 CUMULATIVE SUM CHARTS

Cumulative sum charts were mentioned briefly in Chapter 3.2.5 as aids in recording numerical data where it is important that development of a trend or of a change in trend be indicated immediately. Additionally cumulative sum (Cusum) charts may be used in process control and in recording ana-

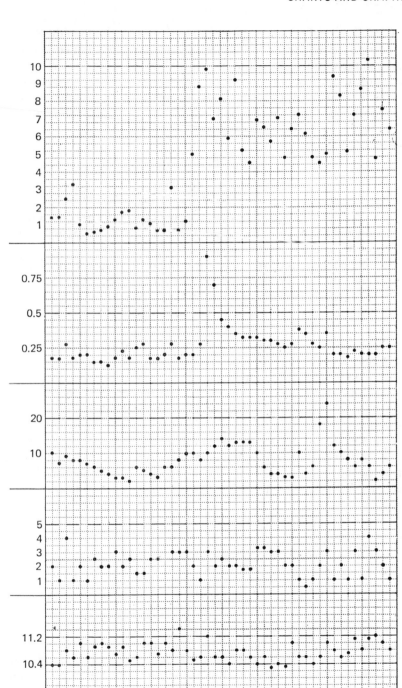

Fig. 3.3.7. DOTTOGRAPH

lytical test data, and for some applications are more useful than the Shewhart type charts. The arithmetic involved in calculating the cumulative values is trivial and there is no calculation of control limit levels for cusum charts.

A cusum chart plots the cumulative sum of the differences between the actual values observed, (x_i), and some reference value (the datum, k). At the point when n values have been obtained, the cusum value plotted is given by S_n, where

$$S_n = \sum_{i=1}^{n} (x_i - k).$$

Any change in the average value of the characteristic concerned is shown immediately it occurs, since there is a change in the slope of the cusum line at that point; this may vary from a small change in slope to a major alteration in direction and the slope of the cusum line over a series of points indicates the level of departure from the datum.

Where the main purpose of analytical routines is to ensure that a process is operating satisfactorily and is producing product of acceptable quality, and to indicate when a departure from satisfactory operation or quality occurs, the use of cusum charts rather than the Shewhart type charts is preferable. The need is to develop a procedure for determining whether a change in direction of the cusum line represents a significant variation in the characteristic under test, and this is reasonably simple. As long as the cusum line continues to deviate from the datum line, the values of the characteristic show the same sign of difference from the datum; the need, therefore, is to determine whether or not a reversal in direction is significant.

Usually a cusum chart is arranged so that the cusum line tends downwards for acceptable quality (better than some standard) and upwards for acceptable quantity. A change in direction of the cusum line means that an interval must be calculated – the decision interval – so that, for example, necessary corrections may be applied to the process before the quality deteriorates too far.

In Chapter 2.8 it was shown how an estimate of the standard deviation of a set of values can be obtained by considering the sum of successive differences between the values and this method can be applied very easily to cusum charts as in many cases the successive differences will be summed already. Using the estimate

$$s = \frac{0 \cdot 88 \sum |d_i|}{n}$$

for the standard deviation of the plotted points, then a significant change in direction of the cusum line occurs when the cusum line passes a distance $2s$ (95 per cent) or $3s$ (99·73 per cent) from the lowest point (or maybe the highest point) reached.

The only rule we have enforced when setting up a cusum chart is that the vertical and horizontal scales are to be fixed so that the plotted points are likely to be near each other. This does away with the necessity of joining points. Cusum charts have a variety of uses and three examples are given.

Example 1. CUSUM CHART FOR ANALYTICAL DATA

The specification for an important characteristic of a finished product is 3·0 per cent (max.), and an internal control specification of 2·0 per cent (max.) is in force. Thus for a Shewhart type control chart the warning limit would be drawn at 2·0 per cent and the action limit at 3·0 per cent.

Recorded values for 44 successive samples are

1·2	0·9	1·2	1·5	1·2	1·5	1·9	2·3	2·9
1·3	1·5	1·1	0·9	1·2	1·5	2·1	2·5	2·7
0·4	1·2	0·9	1·5	0·6	1·8	1·9	2·5(A)	2·9
0·7	1·8	1·2	1·5	1·2	1·8	2·1	2·7	3·0
0·7	1·5	0·6	1·8	1·3	1·9	2·3	3·0	

and taking a datum of 2·0, the cusum chart for these values is shown in Figure 3.3.8.

The change in direction takes place at A, the 33rd point plotted, although point 31 gives an indication that a change in direction is likely; from point 27 onwards the slope of the cusum line has been reduced progressively. However, at point 33 the sum of successive differences between points 1 and 33 is $(22·7 − 0·8) + 0·1 + 0·1 = 22·1$, for 32 differences, and the estimate of the standard deviation is $0·88 × 22·1/32 = 0·6$, and confidence lines for a change in direction may be drawn as shown. Point 37 lies on the 2-sigma confidence line and the necessary corrective action was initiated at this point although some time elapsed and more inter-specification product was made before the action became effective.

Example 2. CUSUM CHART FOR PLANT CONTROL

Figure 3.2.4 shows a Shewhart-type control chart on which the yields of an operating department are plotted and it is rather obvious that some changes have occurred at various times. It is not quite so obvious exactly when those changes occurred and what effect they had.

Figure 3.3.9 shows the cusum chart prepared from the data of Figure 3.2.4, using a datum of 127·0. The data refer to plant yields so that the desired direction of the cusum line is upwards; any downward movement indicates a loss of yield below standard. In a chart such as this there is usually no need to calculate and draw limit lines as any downward trend in the graph indicates unfavourable operation with consequent need for action.

The cusum line shows major reversal of trend at points (a) and (b), and a period of unsteadiness at (c). Action for improvement should have been taken after the 8th point plotted; had this been done the steep downward trend to point (b) might never have occurred.

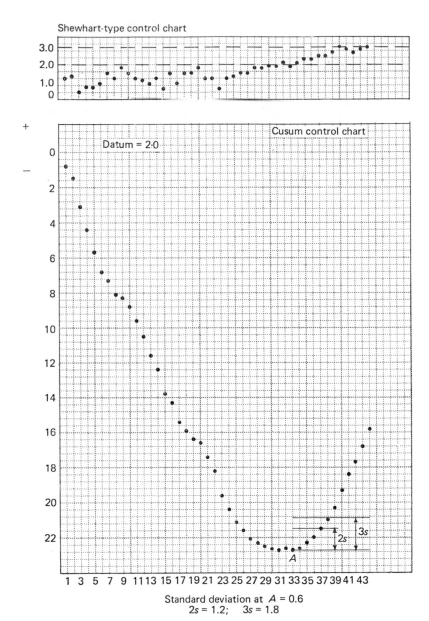

Fig. 3.3.8. CUSUM CHART FOR ANALYTICAL CONTROL

Example 3. CUSUM CHART FOR ACCIDENT REPORTING

Figure 3.3.10 shows a series of cusum graphs based on monthly records of minor accidents reported in a works. Since it is hoped that accidents will show

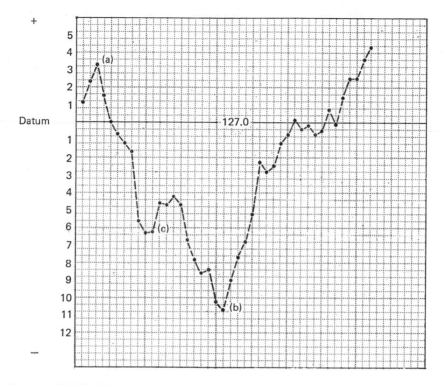

Fig. 3.3.9. CUMULATIVE SUM CHART FROM DATA OF FIGURE 3.2.4

a continued reduction in occurrence the datum for each year is the arithmetic monthly average for the previous year. Here again calculation of limit lines is not of importance. The purpose of the chart is to provide a comparison of the monthly incidence of accidents in any one year with that of the preceding year. Each annual cusum line should tend downwards; if it does not do so there is cause for concern and an investigation into a rise in the incidence of accidents is indicated.

There are, of course, many other instances where cusum charts are useful. Generally, a cusum chart is the best type of chart to use where development of a trend should be indicated at the first possible moment.

3.4 frequency distribution analysis

When a large number of values of a variable has been obtained it is seldom possible to determine any significance attaching to these values, individually or in bulk, and it is necessary to condense the record by some method of ranking or classification so that its characteristics may be appreciated and understood. The simplest way to perform this classification is to divide the

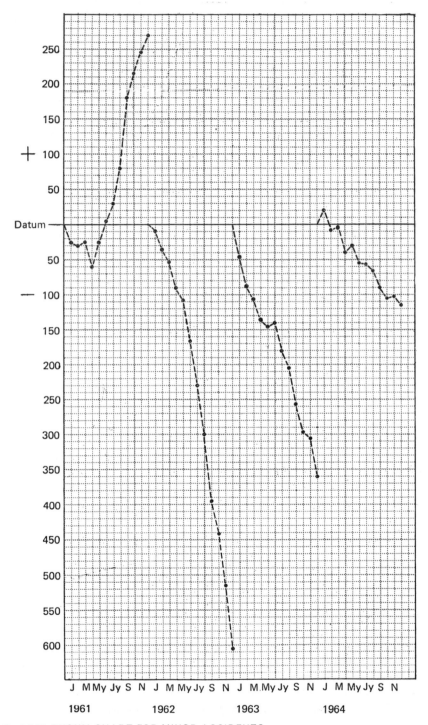

Fig. 3.3.10. CUSUM CHART FOR MINOR ACCIDENTS

entire range of values into intervals and allocate the individual values to these intervals. Usually the intervals are called *class-intervals* and the number of values allocated into each interval is called the *frequency* or *class frequency* of that interval. Values of the variable chosen to define the successive classes should be equidistant so that the numbers of observations in different classes are comparable.

The manner in which the class frequencies are distributed over the class intervals is called the frequency distribution of the variable. The frequency distribution can be represented by a block diagram or histogram which provides useful information of the general run of observations. In a histogram the *area* of each block is proportional to the frequency of the class it represents; where the class intervals are equal, the areas and frequencies are proportional to the height of the blocks and this simplifies matters. But a general rule that class intervals should be equal must not be held to bar the analysis by smaller intervals of a portion of the range over which the frequency varies rapidly.

As the width of the class intervals becomes smaller the histogram approximates to a smooth curve which is called the *frequency curve*. Very often the heights of the blocks in the histogram are used for the construction of a frequency curve, and we saw in Figure 2.7.1 that the frequency curve for a large number of values approximates closely to the frequency curve for a normal distribution. Figure 2.7.2 showed how a cumulative plot of the frequencies on probability graph paper could be used to estimate some parameters of the sample, and we shall now consider this method of estimation a little more closely under the title of frequency distribution analysis.

The graphical technique of frequency distribution analysis provides a quick and simple method of estimating statistics from a large amount of data. Only very simple calculations are used in this procedure and significant errors are not likely to occur as the arithmetic has a built-in check for accuracy. If the data are not normally distributed the fact is made obvious, but the procedure permits estimation of the mean, standard deviation, and any limits (such as the upper $2\frac{1}{2}$ per cent and the lower $2\frac{1}{2}$ per cent for 95 per cent control limits) that may be desired regardless of the type of distribution involved.

The procedure is quite simple and was carried out for Figure 2.7.2. The detailed instructions are:

1 The range of values is divided into convenient intervals so that the frequency of each interval gives some idea of the distribution of values. For a small amount of data, say up to 50 values, 7 or 8 intervals should be used; 15 to 20 intervals may be used for larger quantities of data, and 30 intervals should be the maximum used. Within the range 7 to 30 intervals the number finally chosen may depend on the convenience of using whole numbers. In some cases, such as the example which follows, there is no need to bother with intervals as the actual values reported can act perfectly well as their own intervals.

2 Remember that at all times
the intervals chosen (also called classes, cells or groups) for any set of data must be of equal width;
there must be no missing cells, even if some cells have no data;
each cell is designated by its *midpoint* and not by the highest, the lowest, or any other value in the cell.

3 The cell midpoints and frequencies are tabulated and FDA cumulators are calculated. A zero is added to the head of the cell frequency column and to the head of the cumulator column. Then each successive value in the cumulator column is the sum of the current row cell frequency value plus the cell frequency and cumulator values from the previous row. The last value in the cumulator column is of course double the total of the values in the cell frequency column, but this total does not correspond to any cell.

4 The FDA cumulator values are expressed as percentages of the column final value and these percentages are plotted on a linear-probability chart as shown in Figure 3.4. If there is an empty cell in the cell frequency column there must be a corresponding empty cell in the FDA column, and there will be no percentage quoted in any such row.

5 If the plotted points follow a reasonably straight line then the distribution is a normal distribution and a straight line may be drawn to fit the plotted points. This line becomes the *working line* for the graphical analysis which follows.

If the plotted points appear not to follow a straight line, indicating that the data are not normally distributed, then successive points are joined by straight lines and the end lines are extended as required. The disjoint line so formed becomes the working line for the graphical analysis which follows.

6 The mean, or average value, $(\bar{x})$, is given at that point where the working line crosses the 50 per cent probability line and the value of $\bar{x}$ is read from the linear scale. It should be remembered that this measures the median rather than the mean; if the data are normally distributed these two statistics are identical, and if not then the median is a more useful measure of central tendency than the mean.

7 The standard deviation is estimated from the relationships

$$s = \frac{84\cdot13\% \text{ probability} - 15\cdot87\% \text{ probability}}{2} \quad \text{or}$$

$$s = \frac{97\cdot72\% \text{ probability} - 2\cdot28\% \text{ probability}}{4}$$

where the linear scale readings are inserted for the appropriate probability values. If these two relationships give different values for s, it is customary to accept the larger value as the best available estimate of the standard deviation.

8 Limits may be obtained from the intersection of the working line with the required probability lines. For instance the 95 per cent limits ($\pm 1.96s$) may be taken as the 84 per cent and 16 per cent probability lines. Specification lines may be drawn on the FDA chart, and the points of intersection of these limits with the working line show the percentages of values over and under specification to be expected.

For example, Table 3.4 gives the set-points obtained from 116 successive batches from which it is required to estimate the standard deviation and 95 per cent limits.

Table 3.4 Set-points from 116 batches

82·3, 81·3, 84·6, 84·4, 83·3, 82·3, 82·2, 82·4, 84·0, 82·6, 82·7, 81·9, 83·3, 82·4, 83·0, 82·8, 83·9, 83·2, 83·2, 83·6, 83·9, 81·9, 82·6, 83·1, 83·1, 81·9, 85·0, 83·4, 83·8, 82·6, 82·5, 82·6, 85·1, 81·8, 83·2, 82·8, 84·4, 83·4, 84·2, 82·6, 83·0, 82·3, 83·6, 84·3, 84·0, 83·0, 84·0, 82·9, 84·3, 82·5, 81·7, 83·1, 83·3, 85·1, 82·4, 83·6, 83·6, 82·5, 84·7, 82·6, 82·6, 82·9, 83·6, 85·1, 82·2, 82·0, 82·7, 83·4, 82·9, 82·3, 83·3, 83·0, 82·9, 82·6, 84·8, 82·1, 82·5, 83·2, 82·9, 83·0, 82·1, 83·0, 82·7, 82·9, 83·3, 82·1, 82·3, 81·8, 83·1, 82·0, 81·8, 83·6, 83·3, 82·9, 81·8, 82·9, 84·7, 84·0, 82·2, 81·9, 83·1, 84·8, 83·0, 82·4, 83·3, 83·1, 82·0, 82·4, 81·8, 83·1, 82·2, 83·7, 82·9, 82·5, 83·2, 83·3.

The range of these values is from 81·3 to 85·1 so that a convenient division of these values is into 14 cells of cell width 0·3; the midpoint of the lowest value cell will be 81·2, and that of the highest value cell will be 85·1. The cumulator table is compiled as follows:

Cell midpoint	Cell frequency	FDA cumulator	FDA percentage
	0	0	
85·1	4	4	1·7
84·8	4	12	5·2
84·5	3	19	8·2
84·2	3	25	10·8
83·9	7	35	15·1
83·6	7	49	21·1
83·3	16	72	31·0
83·0	23	111	47·8
82·7	13	147	63·4
82·4	15	175	75·4
82·1	10	200	86·2
81·8	10	220	94·8
81·5	—	—	—
81·2	1	231	99·6
	116	232	

The FDA percentages are plotted on a linear probability chart as shown in Figure 3.4. The plotted values are not very far from a normal distribution, but

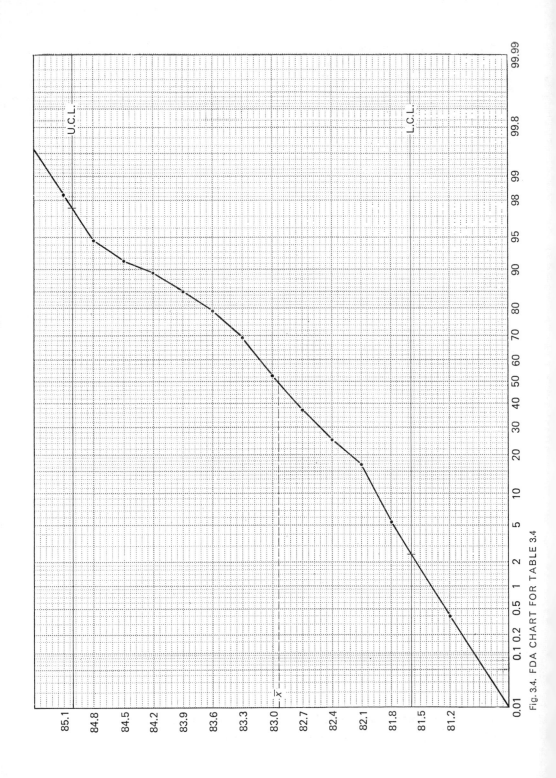

Fig. 3.4. FDA CHART FOR TABLE 3.4

successive points are joined by straight lines and the disjoint line forms the working line from which all estimates are made. Note that there are no values in the 81·5 cell, and so there is no reading in either the FDA cumulator or the FDA percentage column corresponding to this value of the variable, and no point plotted on the FDA chart.

From the chart the standard deviation is found to be $(85·0 - 81·6)/4 = 0·85$, and the 95 per cent limits for lower and upper control limits are, of course 81·6 and 85·0. We see that these limits agree, as expected, with the values of Table 3.4.

3.5 miscellaneous charts

Circular charts and bar charts have some uses for displaying information and some of the uses to which they have been put are described briefly.

3.5.1 CIRCULAR PERCENTAGE, SECTOR, OR PIE CHARTS

The pie chart is a popular means of presenting data. The chart is simple to construct and is widely used in business, technical, and popular publications. It is not of importance or accuracy for purely analytical or other precise presentations of data. This kind of chart is merely a graphic symbolic device to give the reader a quick semi-quantitative or comparative assessment of the component parts of a whole. The relative sizes of the parts into which the whole quantity is divided may be expressed in absolute values (when they must add up to the total available), in percentages (when they must add up to 100), or in fractions (when they must add up to 1).

This form of chart has been criticized because it is difficult to compare the relative sizes of the sectors, but this is not a serious fault because the principal uses of the chart are in such fields as publicity, public relations, and advertising, etc., where rigorous and precise comparisons of data are neither necessary nor desirable.

The chart may be constructed using a protractor to divide the circle in the required proportions, or, for percentages, the usual geometric construction to divide a circle into 20 equal sectors may be used. Normally 4 to 8 sectors should be used to avoid crowding and illegibility, and too many small sectors should not be used. Where small sectors are to be used some sort of shading or colour scheme should be considered to permit easy identification of the separate sectors. Subdivisions of a sector should be avoided — it is much better to group sectors — but if this is thought to be advantageous to presentation of the data subdivision should be made by radial lines and not by arcs cut across the sector.

Figure 3.5.1 shows a pie chart used to illustrate the number of accidents due to various causes in a six-month period in one factory, where there were

I.S. 1—7

Accidents due to 1. falling objects 8 = 20
2. falls 4 = 10
3. fumes 7 = $17\frac{1}{2}$
4. foreign bodies in eyes 5 = $12\frac{1}{2}$
5. burns 6 = 15
6. cuts and bruises 10 = 25

—— ——

40 = 100

Figure 3.5.2 shows a pie chart used to illustrate the division of manufacturing costs of a product into its major components, as follows:
Raw materials: 55 per cent of total product cost split between

R.M. A 20 per cent
B 18 per cent
C 7 per cent
and other raw materials 10 per cent

Direct conversion expenses: 40 per cent of total product cost split between

Labour and supervision 15 per cent
Engineering and maintenance 15 per cent
other direct expenses 10 per cent

Indirect conversion expenses: 5 per cent of the total product cost, and this is not allocated to individuals.

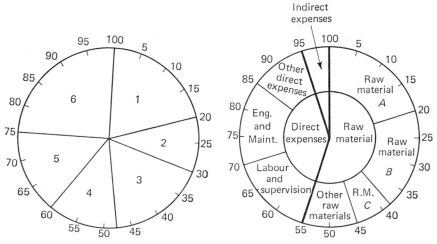

Fig 3.5.1. PIE CHART FOR ACCIDENTS

Fig. 3.5.2. PIE CHART FOR MANUFACTURING COSTS

3.5.2 COLUMN CHARTS, BAR CHARTS AND GANTT CHARTS

Column charts are block diagrams with the blocks drawn separately. That is, they are charts in which a series of separate columns is drawn to the appropriate heights to represent the quantities involved. The values used may be absolute values or percentages (except that if the total of component quantities is not known, percentages cannot be calculated and this is one instance where a column chart would be used instead of a pie chart).

Column charts are used to illustrate variations among different things at one time or variations in one thing at different times. By shading or colouring the various columns different time periods can be illustrated on the same chart. Columns may be subdivided to show component parts but under normal circumstances columns should not be broken as a broken column gives an erroneous impression of height; the heights of all columns on a chart should be comparable. However, exceptions are permitted, and if one column on a chart is relatively unimportant, or the height of one column is much greater than any of the others, the column may be broken to avoid an excessively large chart. Whenever a column is broken, its numerical value and the numerical value of every other column on the chart should be written on or alongside the column.

Where columns are connected we get the usual block diagram and, as with block diagrams, the column chart can be split at some datum to show deviations from that datum. Other common arrangements of column charts are

1 *High and low value charts* in which each column is drawn between the maximum and minimum value of the variable under study. This form of chart is very useful for illustrating ranges of temperatures, humidities, selling prices, etc.

2 *Floating column charts*, which are variations of the subdivided column chart in which each column has two components. Each component has a positive value and the components are shown on either side of the zero line.

3 *100 per cent column charts* in which all columns are drawn to the same height, each to represent 100 per cent of the item concerned, and subdivisions of the columns show variations in composition. This is a very effective form of chart to illustrate the change in composition of a variable or the changing effect of a catalyst over a period of time.

Examples of the use made of these charts are shown in Figure 3.5.3. For added effect three-dimensional column charts may be drawn but these require very great care in their construction.

The bar chart is the simplest form of chart to construct; it is the easiest chart to draw and is the most readily understood. It is used mostly to compare different items under specified conditions such as time period, operational

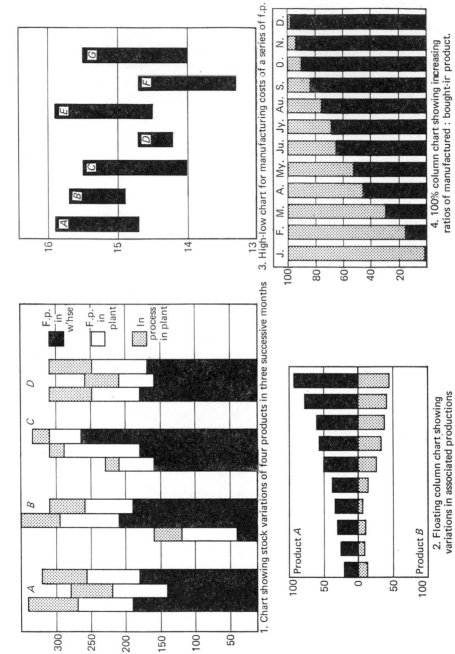

1. Chart showing stock variations of four products in three successive months

F.p. in w'hse

F.p. in plant

In process in plant

3. High-low chart for manufacturing costs of a series of f.p.

4. 100% column chart showing increasing ratios of manufactured : bought-in product.

Product A

Product B

2. Floating column chart showing variations in associated productions

Fig. 3.5.3. COLUMN CHARTS

restrictions, etc. The bars of a bar chart are drawn to the right of a common vertical base line, and the horizontal lengths of the bars are referred to common vertical measured distances or scales at both the top and bottom edges of the chart. Vertical rulings of these scales may be drawn through the bars and the whole vertical height of the chart. For improved clarity and appearance a border or frame may be drawn around the chart and this border should include any legends or footnotes that may be necessary. [Note that a column chart is a bar chart with vertical bars.]

In a bar chart the space between bars should be one-half the width of a bar and this should be constant over the whole chart. Numerical values associated with bars may be placed near the right-hand end of the bar, or may be written within the bar near the right-hand end, and where bars are identified numerically there is no need to provide an overall scale. Any labelling of bars should be written at the left-hand side of the base line.

As with the columns of a column chart, bars should not be broken, and bars should be arranged in that sequence which provides the best illustration; usually this means arranging the bars so that they decrease in length from top downwards or from bottom upwards. Generally the bars should not be arranged haphazardly, but in certain applications it may be necessary to show differences between bars in different locations in the chart and shading or colouring may help in these cases.

Gantt charts are bar charts whose horizontal scale is a time scale, so that the chart may be used as an activity chart. Each bar refers to some work being done or to be done, or to the workman or unit which is to do the work, and the length of the bar is proportional to the activity. It is customary to draw a framework or graticule with activities listed from top to bottom, but this is not necessary and in order to reduce the size of the chart several independent activities may be shown on the same horizontal line as long as their expected performance times do not overlap.

Where Gantt charts are to be used as activity control charts, narrow hollow rectangles should be drawn, and these should be shaded in at appropriate intervals so that completion of the activities may be compared with the passage of time.

SUGGESTIONS FOR FURTHER READING

5 O. L. DAVIES (ed.), Chapter 10, 1958.
6 L. M. DEBING, Chapters 3 and 4, 1957.
7 FREUND and WILLIAMS, Chapter 2 and Appendix 2, 1959.
17 W. A. SHEWHART, 1941.
18 E. S. PEARSON, 1935.
19 B. P. DUDDING and W. J. JENNETT, 1955.

CHAPTER FOUR

TESTS OF SIGNIFICANCE

IN INDUSTRY there are many occasions when a test of significance is applied to some data, as for example the chemical analysis of a sample by different analytical methods or by different analysts; the performance of different items of equipment; the performance of a single item of equipment or a whole manufacturing plant in different periods of time; etc. The test of significance is required to indicate whether or not some of the data are different from the other data at some level of probability, so that the necessary action may be taken to bring about improved performance.

Tests of significance may be divided into two classes: in the first class are those tests which are carried out when numerical values of the variables are used, and in the second class are those tests which are carried out on the order or ranking of the numerical values of the variables. Tests in the first class are widely used; but often tests from the second class are the easier to use and these tests are recommended for use whenever a test of significance is required even if only to determine whether or not the longer tests are worth doing. Before making any test of significance it is good practice to make sure that the data are acceptable, and where there is any doubt of this Dixon's test for outliers should be used.

4.1 Dixon's test for inclusion or exclusion of extreme values (outliers)

Experimentation very often ends in a set of values one of which seems to be widely separated from the others, either above or below; these 'wild' values are called outliers. Where an outlier is known to have resulted from some aberration in control, then obviously it should be ignored though in some circumstances it may be possible to repeat the run and either confirm or replace the value. Where no known reason exists to account for the outlier it must be retained as a valid value and the outlier must not be dropped to provide a neat set of results. However, it is necessary to decide whether or not the outlier properly belongs to the set of values under consideration; the outlier can be discarded only if it can be shown that there is some acceptably low degree of probability that it belongs to the set, and this probability can be determined by means of Dixon's test.

Where the values in a set are ranked, so that

x_n is the suspect value (the outlier),
x_{n-1} is the nearest value to x_n,
x_{n-2} is the next-but-one value to x_n, and so on until
x_1 is the furthest value from x_n

then the criterion to be applied to the set of values depends upon the number of values in the set and is selected from Table 1 (Appendix), which quotes the critical values at various probabilities for inclusion of the outlier. Table 1 gives the critical values for sets of 3 to 25 values; a calculated value less than the tabulated critical value indicates that there is less than the appropriate probability that the outlier does not properly belong to the set of values.

For example, five experimental plant batches gave yields of

541, 547, 551, 559 and 579, and these would be ranked
x_1, x_2, x_3, x_4 and x_5

where the yield 579 is considered suspect. Before making any statistical analysis of these results it is necessary to determine whether or not the yield 579 properly belongs to the set.

The criterion to be applied here is that of r_1

$$r_1 = \frac{x_5 - x_4}{x_5 - x_1} = \frac{579 - 559}{579 - 541} = \frac{20}{38} = 0.527$$

The tabulated values for $n = 5$ are 0·451 at 0·2 probability and 0·557 at 0·1 probability, so the probability that x_5 belongs to the set is greater than 0·1, or there is less than 90 per cent probability that we would be correct if we assumed that x_5 did not belong to the set and discarded it. Therefore x_5 is retained in the set.

If in any set of values there are two or more suspect values, these must be tested separately, first testing the most extreme value. If the two suspect values lie at opposite ends of the set then the one should be excluded from the set when the other is being tested.

Now that the validity of the values can be assessed we can consider the various tests of significance that may be performed on the values.

4.2 the χ^2 (chi-squared)-test

If a sample of n values, $x_1, x_2, \ldots, x_i, \ldots, x_n$, is drawn at random from a normal population, then χ^2 is defined as the sum of the squares of the deviations of the observed quantities from the expected quantity, divided by the expected quantity, and has $(n - 1)$ degrees of freedom.

$$\chi^2 = \frac{(x_1 - E)^2}{E} + \frac{(x_2 - E)^2}{E} + \ldots + \frac{(x_i - E)^2}{E} + \ldots + \frac{(x_n - E)^2}{E}$$

The distribution of χ^2 was worked out by Karl Pearson, and Table 2 (Appendix) gives values of χ^2 for various probabilities and 1 to 30 degrees of freedom.

For example, the tabulated value of χ^2 for 8 d.f. and 0·01 probability is 20·09, so that the probability that a calculated value of χ^2 for 8 d.f. will exceed 20·09 is 0·01, or, a calculated value in excess of 20·09 would be expected once in a hundred trials. If the calculated value does exceed 20·09 there is a probability of 0·99 (99 in a hundred trials) that there is a real difference between the observations.

Thus, whereas Dixon's test shows whether or not extreme values of a set properly belong in the set, the χ^2-test shows whether or not the values of a set are compatible with each other and with an expected value.

EXAMPLE 4.1: The failure rates of piston rings on four supposedly similar compressors in some given time-interval are

$$(1)\ 46; \quad (2)\ 33; \quad (3)\ 38; \quad (4)\ 49;$$

and it is required to determine whether or not these failure rates indicate any real difference in wear of the compressors.

The expectancy of failure is the average failure rate, i.e. $(46 + 33 + 38 + 49)/4 = 41·5$, and the calculated value of χ^2 is

$$\frac{(46 - 41·5)^2 + (33 - 41·5)^2 + (38 - 41·5)^2 + (49 - 41·5)^2}{41·5} = \frac{161·00}{41·5} = 3·88.$$

The set contains 4 values and so has 3 degrees of freedom. Table 2 shows that the value of χ^2 for 3 d.f. and 0·15 probability is 7·81. The calculated value is less than this so that it is more than 95 per cent probable that there is no significant difference between the compressors in their probabilities of failure of piston rings, and there is no point in wasting time looking for explanations of the apparent differences. Interpolating in the table for 3 d.f. shows that $\chi^2 = 3·879$ corresponds to about 28 per cent probability.

When χ^2 is to be calculated with equal expectation for all items, the alternative formula

$$\chi^2 = \frac{\Sigma x_i^2}{E} - \Sigma x_i$$

may be used. In Example 1 the value calculated by this formula is

$$\chi^2 = \frac{46^2 + 33^2 + 38^2 + 49^2}{41·5} - 166 = 169·88 - 166 = 3·88$$

which agrees exactly with the value calculated previously.

EXAMPLE 4.2: Trials with three new drugs resulted in the following mortality data

Drug	Percentage recovered	Percentage died
A	65	35
B	90	10
C	85	15

It is required to determine whether or not these figures indicate a real difference in the behaviour of the drugs.

The expectancy of recovery is $(65 + 90 + 85)/3$ per 100, i.e. 80 per 100, and the expectancy of dying is $(35 + 10 + 15)/3$ per 100, i.e. 20 per 100,

and the data must be tested to determine whether or not they are compatible with these expectancies.

For these trials

$$\chi^2 = \frac{(65 - 80)^2 + (90 - 80)^2 + (85 - 80)^2}{80}$$

$$+ \frac{(35 - 20)^2 + (10 - 20)^2 + (15 - 20)^2}{20} = 21 \cdot 875$$

Although there are six squares in this calculation, there are only three trials each of which provided two squares to the value of χ^2 and the calculated value of χ^2 has 2 degrees of freedom.

For 2 d.f. the χ^2-table (Table 2) quotes a value of 9·21 at the 0·01 level of probability, so that it is more than 99 per cent probable that there is a difference between the effects of the drugs and that there exists a relationship between the drug used and the recovery rate. Inspection of the data suggests that drug A is much less efficient than drugs B and C, but that there is little to choose between B and C, any preference being for drug B.

The χ^2-distribution is a continuous frequency function where $0 \leq \chi^2 \leq \infty$, and it is most useful in dealing with discrete quantities. With fairly large expectations the approximation to continuity is quite good, but it fails somewhat for expectations below (about) 5; in some cases where this occurs it may be convenient to pool or combine cells to give expectations higher than 5. Yates showed that in a number of cases reducing the absolute value $|x_i - E|$ by $\frac{1}{2}$ will result in a closer approximation to a normal distribution, and it is wise to make this check.

An important property of χ^2 follows from its definition: the sum of χ_1^2 with n_1 degrees of freedom and χ_2^2 with n_2 degrees of freedom is a value χ^2 with $(n_1 + n_2)$ degrees of freedom.

4.3 the F-test

The F-test is used to compare two variances or mean squares. That is, it compares the dispersions of two sets of values and so determines whether or not the two sets or samples have been drawn from the same population. The relationship may be shown as

$$F = \frac{s_1^2}{s_2^2} = \frac{[\Sigma(x_1 - \bar{x}_1)^2]/(n_1 - 1)}{[\Sigma(x_2 - \bar{x}_2)^2]/(n_2 - 1)}$$

in which s_1^2 and s_2^2 are the variances belonging respectively to set x_1 of n_1 values and set x_2 of n_2 values.

Use of the F-test will indicate whether or not two variances are significantly different. It will not show that the variances are alike, but merely indicates that the evidence available is such that the variances are, or are not, significantly different.

When calculating the value of F the larger variance is always placed as the numerator so that calculated values of F are always greater than 1. Values of F are tabulated according to probability and the degrees of freedom of each of the variances concerned, and Appendix Table 3 gives a selection of F-tables.

F is defined as χ^2 divided by the number of degrees of freedom. Thus the F-table for 0·01 probability entered for 8 and ∞ degrees of freedom [8 d.f. for the numerator] quotes a value of 2·51, which is the corresponding value of χ^2 for 8 degrees of freedom divided by this number of degrees of freedom, $20·09/8 = 2·51$.

EXAMPLE 4.3. Analysis of a sample of product by two methods gave the following results:

Method 1: 25·02, 25·04, 24·98, 25·00, 25·06, 25·02.
Method 2: 25·02, 24·98, 24·97, 24·99, 25·01, 24·97.

The range of results obtained by Method 1 is 0·08, while that of Method 2 is 0·05 and it is required to determine whether or not the spread of results obtained by Method 1 is significantly greater than that of Method 2.

From the results obtained by Method 1, the variance is calculated to be 0·0008; and from the results obtained by Method 2 the variance is calculated to be 0·00044. For these two methods, therefore, the F-ratio is

$$F = 8/4·4 = 1·81.$$

Each set of values has 5 degrees of freedom, and the F-table for 0·05 probability quotes a value for 5 and 5 degrees of freedom of 5·05. The calculated value is less than this so that it may be stated, with 95 per cent probability of being correct, that there is no significant difference in the variability (dispersion, or spread) of results obtained by the two methods. Note that this does not purport to indicate that one method is more accurate than the other.

EXAMPLE 4.4. Sets of batches in two reactors gave the following reaction times to reach specification:

Reactor 1: 60, 60, 62, 64, 62, 64.
Reactor 2: 50, 52, 52, 54, 55, 55, 58, 60, 63, 65 (ranked to show the wide range).

Then assuming these values to have been drawn from normal populations, we have

$$\text{for Reactor 1: } s_1^2 = \frac{23{,}080 - (376)^2/6}{5} = 3{\cdot}2$$

and

$$\text{for Reactor 2: } s_2^2 = \frac{32{,}032 - (564)^2/10}{9} = 24{\cdot}71$$

For the two reactors, therefore, the F-ratio is

$$F = 24{\cdot}71/3{\cdot}2 = 7{\cdot}7 \text{ with 9 and 5 degrees of freedom.}$$

The tabulated value at the 0·05 level of probability is 6·68. The calculated value is greater than this so that it is more than 95 per cent probable that the two variances are different, i.e. the two sets of values are drawn from different populations, and the two reactors are not behaving in the same way.

4.4 the Student t-distribution

Where $\bar{x}$ is the mean and s is the standard deviation of a random sample of n values from a population whose true mean is μ and whose distribution approximates to a normal distribution, then the statistic

$$t = \frac{(\bar{x} - \mu){\cdot}\sqrt{n}}{s}$$

has a distribution which closely follows the normal distribution, but which is dependent only on the number of degrees of freedom of the sample.

W. S. Gosset ('Student', 1908) worked out the theory of the distribution of t, and tabulated the probability (or frequency) with which a calculated value of t could occur from chance causes. Since the t-distribution is symmetric then for any given probability α, $100(1 - 2\alpha)$ per cent of the area under the t-curve will lie between the values $-t_\alpha$ and $+t_\alpha$. Thus it can be stated with a probability of $100(1 - 2\alpha)$ per cent of being correct that the given value of t will lie between $-t_\alpha$ and $+t_\alpha$. That is

$$-t_\alpha < t < +t_\alpha \quad \text{or} \quad -t_\alpha < \frac{(\bar{x} - \mu)\sqrt{n}}{s} < +t_\alpha$$

which may be re-arranged as

$$\frac{-t_\alpha . s}{\sqrt{n}} < (\bar{x} - \mu) < \frac{+t_\alpha . s}{\sqrt{n}} \quad \text{or} \quad \bar{x} - \frac{t_\alpha . s}{\sqrt{n}} < \mu < \bar{x} + \frac{t_\alpha . s}{\sqrt{n}}.$$

That is, $\bar{x} \pm t_\alpha . s/\sqrt{n}$ are the $100(1 - 2\alpha)$ per cent confidence limits, calculated from the set of observations which formed the sample, for the population mean μ, where t_α is the appropriate value of t at $(n - 1)$ degrees of freedom and probability 2α. Table 4 (Appendix) gives the values of t for various probabilities and degrees of freedom that must be exceeded to indicate significance. Note that tabulated values of χ^2 for 1 degree of freedom are the squares of the normal deviates (value of t for ∞ d.f.) at the same levels of probability.

The values $(\bar{x} \pm t_\alpha . s/\sqrt{n})$ are called the confidence limits for a (single) mean, and the value $s/\sqrt{n}$ is often called 'the standard error of the mean'.

EXAMPLE 4.5. Over a long period of time the standard deviation of an analysis for assay has been found to be 0·12 per cent. Six replicate determinations of assay on a sample gave an average assay of 32·56 and it is required to determine the true assay of the sample.

It must be stated straightaway that the true assay of the sample cannot be determined. All that can be determined are the limits within which the true assay will lie.

Assuming that the replicate determinations belong to a normal population, then since the tabulated value of t for infinite degrees of freedom and 0·05 probability is 1·96 (written as $t_{\infty,0·05} = 1·96$), the 95 per cent confidence interval for the true assay of the sample is given by

$$\left(32·56 - \frac{1·96 \times 0·12}{\sqrt{6}}\right) < \mu < \left(32·56 + \frac{1·96 \times 0·12}{\sqrt{6}}\right)$$

$$\text{that is, } 32·46 < \mu < 32·66.$$

And the true value of the assay of the sample lies somewhere between 32·46 and 32·66.

The Student t-test can be extended to provide a comparison between the means of two sets of observations, since

$$t_{f,\alpha} = \frac{\bar{x}_1 - \bar{x}_2}{s} \sqrt{\frac{n_1 n_2}{n_1 + n_2}}$$

where s^2 is the combined variance of the two sets n_1 and n_2 whose means are $\bar{x}_1$ and $\bar{x}_2$ respectively. This may be written as

$$t_{f,\alpha} = \frac{\bar{x}_1 - \bar{x}_2}{\sqrt{\left[\frac{\Sigma(\bar{x}_1 - x_1)^2 + \Sigma(\bar{x}_2 - x_2)^2}{n_1 + n_2 - 2} . \frac{n_1 + n_2}{n_1 n_2}\right]}}$$

and where there is the same number of observations in each set, i.e. where $n_1 = n_2$, the relationship simplifies to

$$t_{f,\,\alpha} = \frac{\sum x_1 - \sum x_2}{\sqrt{\left[\dfrac{n \sum x^2 - (\sum x_1)^2 - (\sum x_2)^2}{n - 1}\right]}}$$

in which $x = x_1 + x_2$ and $n = n_1 = n_2$.

If a value of t calculated from either of these identities is greater than the tabulated value of t for $f\,(=n_1 + n_2 - 2)$ degrees of freedom at the chosen level of probability (2α), then we may say with $100(1 - 2\alpha)$ per cent confidence of being correct, that the means of the two series are really different; usually these means are said to be significantly different at $100(1 - 2\alpha)$ per cent confidence.

EXAMPLE 4.6: The monthly yields obtained in a manufacturing department for 1965 and the first seven months of 1966 were

1965: 132·5, 134·3, 131·6, 132·0, 130·6, 130·4, 132·8, 131·7, 130·8, 130·2, 130·2, 134·8;
1966: 132·0, 134·1, 127·7, 134·0, 127·4, 131·1, 135·1;

and we require to determine whether or not the yields obtained in 1966 are consistent with those for 1965.

Then, if the 1965 yields are labelled series 1, and the 1966 yields series 2, we have

$$\Sigma(\bar{x}_1 - x_1)^2 = 16\cdot3424 \quad \text{and} \quad \Sigma(\bar{x}_2 - x_2)^2 = 57\cdot6286,$$
$$\bar{x}_1 = 131\cdot825 \quad \text{and} \quad \bar{x}_2 = 131\cdot614$$

whence
$$t = \frac{131\cdot825 - 131\cdot614}{\sqrt{\left(\dfrac{16\cdot3424 + 57\cdot6286}{12 + 7 - 2} \times \dfrac{12 + 7}{12 \times 7}\right)}} = 0\cdot2127.$$

But the tabulated value of t for 0·05 probability and 17 degrees of freedom is 2·11. Since the calculated value is very much less than this, it is more than 95 per cent probable that there is no real difference between the mean values of the two series of yields.

If we were to consider the 1965 series of yields as our 'standard', then we have the sum of squares $\sum (\bar{x}_1 - x_1)^2 = 16\cdot3424$ and the standard deviation is $\sqrt{(16\cdot3424/11)} = 1\cdot22$. The tabulated value of t for 11 degrees of freedom and 0·05 probability is 2·201, so that the true yield of the process may be expected, with 95 per cent probability, to lie in the range

$$131\cdot825 \pm \frac{2\cdot201 \times 1\cdot22}{\sqrt{12}}, \quad \text{.e.} \quad 131\cdot825 \pm 0\cdot775, \quad \text{or} \quad 131\cdot05 \text{ to } 132\cdot6.$$

Further, the tabulated value of t for 0·05 probability and infinite degrees of freedom (all the trials that will ever be made) is 1·96, so that if no assignable cause interferes with the process, yields would be expected to lie in the range

$$131·825 \pm (1·96 \times 1·22), \text{ i.e. } 131·825 \pm 2·391, \text{ or } 129·43 \text{ to } 134·21.$$

Any yield lying outside this range must be considered suspect unless an assignable cause is known. The 1965 series of yields has two values just outside the upper limit of this range, but the 1966 series has two values well below the lower limit, with two values just inside and one value outside the upper limit. The 1966 series, therefore, is suspect. If we apply an F-test to the two series of yields, putting the larger variance as the numerator, we have

$$F = \frac{57·6284}{6} \bigg/ \frac{16·3424}{11} = \frac{9·605}{1·484} = 6·472.$$

The tabulated value of F at the 0·01 level of probability for 6 and 11 degrees of freedom is 5·07. The calculated value is greater than this so that it is 99 per cent probable that there is a real difference between the dispersions of the two series and it is very probable that the two series belong to different populations.

Thus although there is no significant difference between the means of the two series, there is a real difference in the dispersion of values about those means. Unless assignable causes are known the inescapable conclusion is that the process is doing its best but either was under less strict control in 1966 than it was in 1965 or some of the yields for 1966 were calculated wrongly.

When the means of two series are to be examined to determine the probability of there being a real difference between them, Student's t-test is applicable only when the variances of the two series do not differ significantly when examined by an F-test. Where the variances differ significantly it is possible to use the t-test by a suitable adjustment to the number of degrees of freedom available in the two series. It has been suggested by Satterthwaite that the number of degrees of freedom to be used in such a case is given by the relationship

$$\text{d.f.} = \frac{(s_1^2/n_1 + s_2^2/n_2)^2}{[(s_1^2/n_1)^2/(n_1 - 1)] + [(s_2^2/n_2)^2/(n_2 - 1)]}$$

in which s_1^2 is the variance of the n_1 values in one series, and s_2^2 is the variance of the n_2 values in the other series.

Usually, this formula results in a lesser number of degrees of freedom than the $n_1 + n_2 - 2$ of the straightforward t-test, so that any test which is not significant on $n_1 + n_2 - 2$ degrees of freedom is likely to remain not significant on the adjusted degrees of freedom. For example, with the two series of Example 4.6 we have: $s_1^2 = 9·605$, $n_1 = 7$; $s_2^2 = 1·484$, $n_2 = 12$, so that the number of degrees of freedom to use when testing for t should be

$$\text{d.f.} = \frac{(9 \cdot 605/7 + 1 \cdot 484/12)^2}{[(1 \cdot 372)^2/6 + (0 \cdot 124)^2/11]} = \frac{2 \cdot 238}{0 \cdot 315} = 7,$$

compared with the 17 degrees of freedom used previously. The tabulated value of t for 7 degrees of freedom and $0 \cdot 05$ probability is $2 \cdot 365$, slightly higher than the $2 \cdot 11$ quoted for 17 degrees of freedom so that by using the adjusted number of degrees of freedom a more stringent demand is made than that of the straightforward t-test.

4.5 non-parametric tests of significance

The F-test and t-test are widely used in industrial statistics, but often the assumption that the data under examination belong to a normal distribution is not justified. Also, there may be very little need to determine the probability of a real difference as $0 \cdot 99$ when a simple 'better than $0 \cdot 95$' will meet requirement. A number of statistical tests have been developed which enable the necessary comparisons to be made without assuming that the data are drawn from a normal population and thus without the necessity to calculate parameters of this normal population.

These tests are grouped together as 'non-parametric' or 'distribution-free' tests. They are quick and easy to use, and though they have been referred to in terms of endearment such as 'Quick and Dirty Methods', the dirtiness (the loss of statistical efficiency compared with the classical tests) is seldom enough to prevent their use.

4.5.1 TUKEY'S TEST FOR THE DIFFERENCE BETWEEN TWO MEANS

Common examples of the use of this test are the comparisons made between two sets of values, where the two sets may be derived from

> chemical analysis of samples by two analytical methods,
> analytical test results obtained by two analysts,
> the performance of two items of equipment, or
> the performance of a plant in two periods of time, etc.

The values in each set are arranged in order of magnitude, and the total number of observations in the non-overlapping portions of each set is counted. If this total exceeds 7 (or 8 if the sample sizes are very unequal) then the difference between the means of the two sets of values is judged to be significant.

For example, in the two sets of values

A: 325, 328, 330, 332, 335, 336, 338, 340, 340, 341   (10 values)
B: 338, 339, 340, 341, 345, 346, 347, 350

                                                 (8 values)

Set A has 6 values below the lowest value of Set B, and
Set B has 4 values above the highest value of Set A.

The count, therefore, is $6 + 4 = 10$, which is greater than 7 (or 8) and the conclusion is that there is a significant difference between the mean values of the two sets.

The total count of 7 indicates a probability of 95 per cent that there is a real difference between the two means. Counts corresponding to other probabilities are

	Probability that a
Total count	*difference exists*
4	90 per cent
7	95 ,, ,,
10	99 ,, ,,
14	99·9 ,, ,,

The three rules which control the application of this test are:

1 The number of values in each set should be between 4 and 20. We have used this test when one set contains more than 20 values by considering only the last 20 values (before ordering) if the remaining values of the set lie within the range of the last 20.

2 Obviously, the two non-overlapping portions must not belong to the same set, as would be the case with the two sets of values quoted in Example 4.6. A significant difference between the means may be indicated with a non-overlapping portion of one set on one side only.

3 Sample sizes are considered to be very unequal if they are each less than 10 values and differ by 3 values, or if either is more than 10 values and they differ by 4 values.

4.5.2 LORD'S TEST FOR THE DIFFERENCE BETWEEN TWO MEANS

This test requires a small amount of arithmetic. It is necessary to calculate the value of the statistic

$$u = \frac{|\bar{x}_1 - \bar{x}_2|}{w_1 + w_2}$$

in which $\bar{x}_1$ is the mean and w_1 the range of the n_1 values in Set 1,
$\bar{x}_2$ is the mean and w_2 the range of the n_2 values in Set 2,
and $n_1 \geqq n_2$.

The calculated value of u is compared with the tabulated value of u for the given n_1 and n_2 at the appropriate probability. If the calculated value is greater than the tabulated value then the difference between the means of the two sets of values is significant at the stated level of probability.

Tables 5 (i, ii, iii and iv) (Appendix) quote the minimum values of u to indicate 99, 98, 95, and 90 per cent probability respectively that a real difference exists between the means of two sets of values. The number of values in either set may lie between 2 and 20.

For example, using the two sets of values quoted in section 4.5.1, we have

for Set A: $n_1 = 10$; $\bar{x}_1 = 334.5$; $w_1 = 341 - 325 = 16$; and
for Set B: $n_2 = 8$; $\bar{x}_2 = 343.25$; $w_2 = 350 - 338 = 12$; so that

$$u = \frac{|334.5 - 343.25|}{16 + 12} = \frac{8.75}{28} = 0.312$$

The tabulated value for $n_1 = 10$, $n_2 = 8$ at 0.01 probability is 0.235. The calculated value is greater than this so there is less than 1 per cent probability that the two means are the same, or, we can say with 99 per cent probability of being correct that there is a real difference between the two means.

If we wish to check this conclusion by a classical statistical test, a t-test for the means of these two sets of values gives

$$t = \frac{334.5 - 343.25}{\sqrt{\left(\dfrac{276.5 + 131.5}{16} \times \dfrac{18}{80}\right)}} = \frac{8.75}{2.395} = 3.653$$

which is significant at the 99.5 per cent level of probability.

The difference between the 99 per cent significance obtained by Lord's test (or the statement that the means are significantly different by Tukey's test) and the 99.5 per cent significance obtained by the t-test is a measure of the 'dirtiness' or loss of efficiency of the test. This difference may well be an unnecessary refinement since in most cases met in industry 95 per cent significance is an acceptable standard.

4.5.3 LORD'S TEST FOR THE VALIDITY OF A MEAN VALUE

If an 'expected value' is known for the mean of a set of values, Lord's test for the difference between two means can be adapted to give a measure of the validity of the actual mean of the set of values. The test requires calculation of the statistic

$$u = \frac{|\bar{x} - \mu|}{w}$$

in which $\bar{x}$ is the actual mean, μ is the expected mean and w is the range of values in the set.

Table 6 (Appendix) quotes the minimum values of u to indicate significant differences between the expected and actual means for sets of 2 to 10 values at 95, 97.5, 99, and 99.5 per cent levels of probability.

I.S. 1—8

Many occasions arise in industry where an 'expected value' is known; examples are the weight of product packed into a standard container, the standard yield of a process, the standard time for a repetitive job, the standard cost of a repetitive job. We do not accept a standard rate for accidents so that any comparison made with accidents will use 'last year's average' or maybe 'last month's average' as the expected value.

For example, a product is supposed to be machine-filled in 50 lb net bags, and the weights of 10 bags taken at random from a lot are

$$49\tfrac{3}{4}, \quad 50\tfrac{1}{4}, \quad 50\tfrac{1}{4}, \quad 50\tfrac{1}{2}, \quad 49\tfrac{3}{4},$$
$$50\tfrac{3}{4}, \quad 50, \quad 50\tfrac{1}{4}, \quad 50\tfrac{1}{2}, \quad 50\tfrac{1}{2}.$$

Then for this set $\bar{x} = 50{\cdot}25$; $\mu = 50$; $w = 50\tfrac{3}{4} - 49\tfrac{3}{4} = 1$, so that

$$u = \frac{50{\cdot}25 - 50}{1} = 0{\cdot}25.$$

The tabulated values for a set size of 10 values show 0·230 at 97·5 per cent probability and 0·288 at 99 per cent probability. The calculated value of 0·25 lies between these so that it may be said, with a 97·5 per cent probability of being correct, that the machine is running consistently overweight.

Or again, consider the seven-monthly yields quoted in Example 4.6, which are to be compared with the plant standard of 134·0. Then for this set of values

$$\bar{x} = 131{\cdot}614, \ \mu = 134{\cdot}0, \ n = 7, \text{ and } w = 135{\cdot}1 - 127{\cdot}4 = 7{\cdot}7 \text{ so that}$$

$$u = \frac{|131{\cdot}614 - 134|}{7{\cdot}7} = \frac{2{\cdot}386}{7{\cdot}7} = 0{\cdot}31.$$

The tabulated values for a set size of 7 values show 0·263 at 95 per cent probability and 0·333 at 97·5 per cent probability. The calculated value of 0·31 lies between these two (but very near the 97·5 per cent critical value) so it may be said, with a 95 per cent probability of being correct, that the plant is being worked at below standard yield.

4.5.4 TEST FOR THE DIFFERENCE BETWEEN TWO DISPERSIONS

The most frequent use found for this, so far, has been the comparison of the repeatabilities or reproducibilities of two test methods, as for instance when it is proposed to replace a long-standing method by a new method. However, this test can be used for comparison of the dispersions (or spreads) of any two sets of values assumed to have been drawn from the same population, and tests whether or not this assumption can be accepted.

The procedure to be followed is

1 Determine the range of each set of values, w_1 and w_2 (with $w_1 > w_2$).

2 Form the ratio $\dfrac{\text{larger range}}{\text{smaller range}}, R = \dfrac{w_1}{w_2}.$

3 Compare this calculated ratio with the critical values in Table 7 (Appendix) which gives the minimum values for sets of 2 to 10 values at 95 per cent probability of a real difference between the dispersions.

For example, from the data in the example of section 4.5.1 we have

for Set A: $n_1 = 10$ and $w_1 = 16$; for Set B: $n_2 = 8$ and $w_2 = 12$; so that

$$R = 16/12 = 1{\cdot}33.$$

The tabulated critical value for $n_1 = 10$ and $n_2 = 8$ is $2{\cdot}1$; the calculated value is less than this and it is more than 95 per cent probable that the dispersions of values in the two sets are not different.

If we consider two sets of values obtained by alternative analytical methods on two samples

Set C: 29·6, 29·7, 29·7, 29·9, 29·6, 29·7, range = 0·3
Set D: 29·6, 29·3, 29·4, 29·9, 29·1, 29·4, range = 0·8,

then $\qquad\qquad R = 0{\cdot}8/0{\cdot}3 = 2{\cdot}67.$

The tabulated value for $n_1 = n_2 = 6$ is $2{\cdot}3$; the calculated value is greater than this and it is more than 95 per cent probable that method D is less precise than method C.

Again, if we consider sieve test results obtained by two different types of equipment, we have

Set E: 98·0, 98·2, 98·2, 98·9, 98·7, 98·6, 98·4, range = 0·9
Set F: 95·9, 97·1, 96·3, 97·5, 98·3, 97·1, range = 2·4,

and $\qquad\qquad R = 2{\cdot}4/0{\cdot}9 = 2{\cdot}67.$

The tabulated value for $n_1 = 6$ and $n_2 = 7$ is $2{\cdot}0$; the calculated value is greater than this and it is more than 95 per cent probable that Equipment E will give more reproducible results than Equipment F. Confidence limits for a single result obtained with Equipment F will be much wider than those for Equipment E.

4.6 rank tests of significance

Usually the comparison of two treatments (which may be different methods of analysis, techniques of operation, formulations of blending, operating conditions, etc.) is made by either (1) running a number of replicate trials on each treatment, in which case individual results are not related. For example, the fourth trial on one treatment is not related to the fourth (or any other) trial on the other treatment, or (2) running a number of paired comparisons which leads to a series of differences between results of the two treatments.

These differences are derived consistently, and there may be both positive and negative differences in the same series.

Ranking methods enable comparisons to be made between two treatments very quickly and easily. All that is necessary is to arrange the experimental results in order of rank, and the next three sections describe those tests.

4.6.1 COMPARISON BETWEEN UNPAIRED REPLICATE TRIALS ON TWO TREATMENTS

This test consists of allocating rankings to all the replicate results, regardless of which treatment they belong to, and comparing the smaller rank total with tabulated values. For example, replicate analyses on two samples gave the following results:

Sample A: 68, 68, 59, 72, 64, 67, 70, 74
Sample B: 60, 67, 61, 62, 67, 63, 56, 58

Allocating rank numbers to these results in increasing order of magnitude, so that the value 56 is ranked 1, the value 58 is ranked 2, the value 59 is ranked 3, etc., and giving a mean rank value to any equal results gives the following tabulation:

Sample A:	68	68	59	72	64	67	70	74
ranks:	12·5	12·5	3	15	8	10	14	16

giving a rank total of 91;

Sample B:	60	67	61	62	67	63	56	58
ranks:	4	10	5	6	10	7	1	5

giving a rank total of 45.

In this tabulation there are three values of 67 to fill the ninth, tenth, and eleventh ranks, so each is given a rank of 10; there are two values of 68 to fill the twelfth and thirteenth ranks, so each is given a rank of 12·5.

If there were no real difference between the sets of values for Samples A and B then the rank totals expected from 8 replications would fluctuate around the expected total of 68, which of course is one-half the sum of the numbers 1 to 16. The values shown in Table 8 (Appendix) are calculated from the known probability of occurrence of each total.

Table 8 shows that the probability of obtaining a total of 45 from 8 replicates is between 0·01 and 0·02, and it may be concluded that there is better than 98 per cent probability that there is a real difference between these two sets of results. An analysis of variance on the analytical results gives a mean square ratio of 7·72, while the F-table quotes values of 4·60 at the 0·05 and 8·86 at the 0·01 level of probability for 1 and 14 degrees of freedom (see Chapter 5).

Table 8 may be used to compare sets of 5 to 20 values, but there must be the same number of values in each set. When the number of replicates of each treatment exceeds 20, rank totals corresponding to probabilities of 0·05, 0·02 and 0·01 may be calculated from the formulae

$$T_{0·05} = \bar{T} - 1·960 \sqrt{\frac{N\bar{T}}{6}};$$

$$T_{0·02} = \bar{T} - 2·326 \sqrt{\frac{N\bar{T}}{6}};$$

$$T_{0·01} = \bar{T} - 2·576 \sqrt{\frac{N\bar{T}}{6}};$$

in which N is the number of replicates of each of the two treatments and $\bar{T}$ is the expected rank total if there is no difference between the two treatments, i.e. $\bar{T} = 2N(2N + 1)/4$.

4.6.2 COMPARISON BETWEEN PAIRED REPLICATE TRIALS ON TWO TREATMENTS

When making a comparison between paired replicate trials we have only one series of values to deal with, the differences between the values obtained in each pair of trials. It follows that it is necessary only to deal with the sum of rank numbers of one sign, + *or* −, whichever is the less, since for any given set of differences the rank total is determined when the sum of either the positive or the negative ranks is specified.

Table 4.6.2 shows the results obtained from paired analyses of 12 lots of finished product by two analytical methods; each lot sample was examined by each method and it was required to determine whether or not one method was likely to give consistently different results from the other method. The occasion was the proposed introduction of a simpler and quicker method of analysis.

The 'differences' between results are derived consistently, then in compiling the 'rank of difference' column the rank values allocated are those of the numerical values of the differences, regardless of sign; then these rankings are given the signs of their corresponding differences in the previous column.

Here, too, differences are ranked in ascending order and a mean rank value is given to equal differences. In Table 4.6.2 we see that the two differences of 0·04 are to occupy the second and third places in the rankings, and so each is given a rank of 2·5; it so happens that the differences are of different signs so that we have one rank of −2·5 and one of +2·5.

If there were no real difference between the two methods, we would expect the analytical differences to be randomly signed and the rank total of differences of one sign would be expected to fluctuate around an expected total of

Table 4.6.2 Paired analytical results

Lot	Analysis by method 1	Analysis by method 2	Differences M.1 − M.2	Rank of differences	Lower rank total of same sign
1	98·80	98·84	−0·04	−2·5	−2·5
2	98·17	98·04	+0·13	+7·5	
3	97·32	97·39	−0·07	−5	−5
4	97·11	97·06	+0·05	+4	
5	96·92	96·78	+0·14	+9	
6	96·84	96·80	+0·04	+2·5	
7	96·63	96·44	+0·19	+12	
8	96·16	96·00	+0·16	+10	
9	96·06	96·03	+0·03	+1	
10	95·57	95·40	+0·17	+11	
11	95·26	95·17	+0·09	+6	
12	95·24	95·11	+0·13	+7·5	

Total −7·5

78, one-half the sum of the numbers 1 to 12. The values shown in Table 9 (Appendix) are calculated from the known probability of occurrence of each total.

Table 9 shows that the probability of obtaining a rank total, of one sign, as small as 7·5 from a set of 12 paired trials is about 0·01. Hence the conclusion is reached that it is about 99 per cent probable that there is a real difference between the two methods, and within the range of experimentation studied Method 1 would be expected to give higher results than Method 2.

Table 9 may be used to compare sets of 6 to 20 paired trials. If the number of trials exceeds 20, rank totals corresponding to probabilities of 0·05, 0·02 and 0·01 may be calculated from the formulae

$$T_{0·05} = \overline{T} - 1·960 \sqrt{\frac{2N\overline{T}}{6}};$$

$$T_{0·02} = \overline{T} - 2·326 \sqrt{\frac{2N\overline{T}}{6}};$$

$$T_{0·01} = \overline{T} - 2·576 \sqrt{\frac{2N\overline{T}}{6}};$$

in which N is the number of paired trials under consideration and $\overline{T}$ is the expected rank total if there is no difference between the two treatments, i.e. $\overline{T} = N(N + 1)/4$.

4.6.3 COMPARISON BETWEEN TWO SETS OF GROUPED DATA

Sometimes it is necessary to compare two treatments under several different sets of conditions. For example, two operating techniques may be compared under different conditions of temperature or concentration of reactants or some other variable; or two analytical test methods may be compared in different laboratories or between different analysts. In such cases it is required to determine whether the two treatments may be expected to lead to different results, and also whether or not this difference is consistent over the range of values of the other controlled variable. The information is derived by the simple procedure of ranking values in each block.

Table 4.6.3 shows the yields obtained in a manufacturing plant when two process modifications were tried, each run at three levels of reaction temperature. Experimentation consisted of five (unpaired) runs on each process modification (treatment) at each temperature level, values at each temperature level being aggregated as a 'block'. Rank values 1 to 10 are allocated to the yields in ascending order within each block, and as done previously mean ranks are allocated for equal experimental yields.

Table 4.6.3 Process modification experimentation

Level of temperature	Modification 1 Yield	Rank		Modification 2 Yield	Rank	
	64	5		88	9	
	72	3		88	9	
(1)	56	1		88	9	
	68	4		84	7	
	76	6	(19)	60	2	(36)
	72	$8\frac{1}{2}$		64	3	
	56	1		72	$8\frac{1}{2}$	
(2)	68	$5\frac{1}{2}$		72	$8\frac{1}{2}$	
	64	3		68	$5\frac{1}{2}$	
	64	3	(21)	72	$8\frac{1}{2}$	(34)
	60	$2\frac{1}{2}$		84	$8\frac{1}{2}$	
	68	4		88	10	
(3)	44	1		72	6	
	75	7		70	5	
	60	$2\frac{1}{2}$	(17)	84	$8\frac{1}{2}$	(38)
		Total: 57			Total: 108	

If there were no real difference between the yields obtained from the two process modifications we would expect each block to total $27\frac{1}{2}$, one-half of the sum of the numbers 1 to 10, and the grand total of ranks for each modification would be expected to be $82\frac{1}{2}$. Table 10 (Appendix) shows values calculated from the known probability of occurrence of each total for sets of 2 to 7 replicates in 2 to 7 groups.

The grand total of ranks for Modification 1 is 57, and that for Modification 2 is 108. From Table 10 we see that for 5 replicates in each of 3 groups a lower rank total of 61 would be expected with a probability of occurrence of 0·01 if the treatments were really the same. Hence it is concluded that there is better than 99 per cent probability that there is a real difference between the two treatments, and Modification 2 may be expected to give higher yields than Modification 1.

Table 10 shows the minimum values for 2 to 7 replicates in each of 2 to 7 groups, and of course there must be the same number of replicates in each group. For numbers of groups and replicates above 7 the rank totals corresponding to probabilities of 0·05, 0·02 and 0·01 may be calculated from the formulae

$$T_{0·05} = n\bar{T} - 1·960 \sqrt{\frac{nN\bar{T}}{6}};$$

$$T_{0·02} = n\bar{T} - 2·326 \sqrt{\frac{nN\bar{T}}{6}};$$

$$T_{0·01} = n\bar{T} - 2·576 \sqrt{\frac{nN\bar{T}}{6}};$$

in which n is the number of groups (blocks), N is the number of replicates per group, and $\bar{T}$ is the expected total for one group, i.e. $\bar{T} = 2N(2N + 1)/4$.

For example, the experimentation shown in Table 4.6.3 was made with 5 replicates in each of 3 groups, so that $n = 3$, $N = 5$,

and $\bar{T} = 10 \times 11/4 = 27·5$.

Then $$T_{0·01} = (3 \times 27·5) - 2·576 \sqrt{\frac{3 \times 5 \times 27·5}{6}} = 82·5 - 21·35 = 61$$

and we would expect a value of 61 to occur with a probability of 0·01 if the treatments were the same.

4.7 sign tests of significance

Most of the tests of significance already described in this chapter require reference to tabulated critical values. This is not an onerous task, perhaps it is unfortunate that the necessary tables are seldom available – especially in the works – when they are wanted. Duckworth & Wyatt have developed some very simple tests which create their own comparators and need no reference to tables.

4.7.1 TEST FOR THE VALUE OF A MEAN

The mean value of a set of values can be compared with an expected mean value by counting the number of values in the set which are greater than the expected mean value (labelling them +) and the number of values in the set which are less than the expected mean value (and labelling these −). The difference between these numbers is compared with the statistic $2\sqrt{n}$ (for 95 per cent probability) where n is the total number of values different from the expected mean.

For example, the standard cycle time for a reaction is 37 hours, but cycle times obtained during one week and the signs of their differences from 37 were

35	37	38	40	39	36	37	40	40	41	38	39	39
−		+	+	+	−		+	+	+	+	+	+

40	37	40	42	34	38
+		+	+	−	+

In this set of signs there are 13+ and 3−, giving a difference of 10. There are 16 values different from 37 in the set, so the comparator is $2\sqrt{16} = 8$.

The difference found, 10, is greater than 8, so it may be said with 95 per cent probability of being correct that this set of reaction times does not belong to a population of mean 37. It may be concluded that reaction control has slipped somewhat and consequently time cycles have become extended.

In this test, and the two which follow, the comparator

$1\cdot6\sqrt{n}$ may be used for 90 per cent probability of there being a real difference,

$2\sqrt{n}$ may be used for 95 per cent probability of there being a real difference,

$2\cdot6\sqrt{n}$ may be used for 99 per cent probability of there being a real difference,

$3\cdot3\sqrt{n}$ may be used for 99·9 per cent probability of there being a real difference,

in which the values 1·6, 2, 2·6, and 3·3 are first-place approximations to the value of t for infinite degrees of freedom and the appropriate probabilities; other comparators may be derived as required.

4.7.2 TEST FOR THE COMPARISON OF TWO MEANS

This test can be used only where there is the same number of values in each set. The values are paired in random order and the signs of consistent differences are noted and compared with the comparator based on the number of values in each set.

For example, randomized pairings of two sets of assay results on alternative raw materials are obtained by drawing values from two heaps, and the signs of differences are

Set A:	57,	100,	101,	107,	109,	107,	94,	73,	53,	68,	98
Set B:	89,	60,	82,	56,	69,	72,	57,	62,	96,	59,	88
Sign of A–B:	−	+	+	+	+	+	+	+	−	+	+

Here the comparator for 95 per cent probability is $2\sqrt{11} = 6\cdot6$. The row of signs contains 9+ and 2−, the difference between these being 7. As 7 is greater than 6·6 it may be concluded, with 95 per cent probability of being correct, that there is a real difference between the means of the two sets of values and raw material A may be expected to give higher assays than raw material B.

This test has been based on random pairing of results in Set A with results in Set B and this procedure may not always indicate a difference in mean levels where one really exists. In the above sets, for instance, had any one of the values 88, 82 or 89 changed place with the value of 59 in Set B, the score would have been 8+ and 3− giving a difference of 5. This would have led to the conclusion that there was no real difference between the means of the two sets of values. The test appears to leave too much to chance and it is doubtful whether this test may be put into general use.

One way out of the difficulty is to arrange the values in each set in order of magnitude and make the comparison on the ordered values. The assay results quoted above would be arranged as

Set A: 53, 57, 68, 73, 94, 98, 100, 101, 107, 107, 109
Set B: 56, 57, 59, 60, 62, 69, 72, 82, 88, 89, 96
Sign of A–B: −, , +, +, +, +, +, +, +, +, +

Now the row of signs contains 9+ and 1− (one pair of equal values gives no sign) giving a difference of 8. The comparator remains at 6·6 and we conclude with 95 per cent probability of being correct that there is a real difference between the two means and raw material A may be expected to give higher assays than raw material B (as before).

Many occasions arise in industrial work where there is no need to randomize. When dealing with variables such as the yields or time cycles obtained from two reactors, or the effects of two process modifications, a comparison may be made between the results in order as they are obtained. Consider the yields quoted in Table 4.6.3, which are quoted downwards in the order of experimentation. Then, we have

Mod. 1: 64, 72, 56, 68, 76, 72, 56, 68, 64, 64, 60, 68, 44, 75, 60
Mod. 2: 88, 88, 88, 84, 60, 64, 72, 72, 68, 72, 84, 88, 72, 70, 84
Sign M2–M1: + + + + − − + + + + + + + − +

Here the comparator for 95 per cent probability is $2\sqrt{15} = 7\cdot7$. The row of signs contains 12+ and 3−, giving a difference of 9. This is greater than the comparator and we conclude, with 95 per cent probability of being correct, that there is a real difference between the means of the sets of values and Modification 2 may be expected to give higher yields than Modification 1.

Where paired values are obtained, as in Table 4.6.2, the signs of consistent differences may be used for this test. The column of differences in Table 4.6.2 shows 10+ and 2−, giving a difference of 8. Here the comparator is $2\sqrt{12} = 6\cdot9$, and again we can conclude, with 95 per cent probability of being correct, that there is a real difference between the means of these sets of analytical results and Method 1 may be expected to give higher results than Method 2.

4.7.3 A SIGN TEST FOR RANDOMNESS

Although not strictly a test of significance this test fits better under sign tests than under distributions, and may be used together with a test of significance when the distribution of values is in question.

In any set of n values there are, of course, $(n - 1)$ pairs of consecutive values. Each pair may be such that both values lie on the same side of the median or the values lie on opposite sides of the median. Then if we let F be the frequency with which pairs of consecutive values lie on the same side of the median and label each such pair $+$, and let G be the frequency with which pairs of consecutive values are split by the median and label each such pair $-$, we have

$$F + G = n - 1$$

The null hypothesis that the values are a random sample from the same population may be written as

$$|F - G| \geq 2\sqrt{(n - 1)}$$

or

$$|n - 2G - 1| \geq 2\sqrt{(n - 1)}$$

and the comparator for this test is based on the $(n - 1)$ consecutive pairs using a t-value for the appropriate level of probability as before.

For example, given the set of values

24	27	26	28	31	35	33	37	36	37	34	32	32
	+	+	+	−	+	+	+	+	+	+	+	+

29	28	28	30	28	26	25
−	+	+	−	−	+	+

for which the median is $29\frac{1}{2}$, the signs of pairs of consecutive values are as marked.

Since there are 20 values in the set, $n = 20$ and the comparator for 95 per cent probability is $2\sqrt{19} = 8.7$. The count of minus signs is 4, so the value of $|n - 2G - 1| = |20 - 8 - 1| = 11$. This is greater than the comparator and it may be concluded that the values are not drawn randomly from the population.

If we apply this test to the assay results in Set B of section 4.7.2, which has 72 as the median of the 11 values in the set, we have

Set B:	89	60	82	56	69	72	57	62	96	59	88
		−	−	−	+		+	−	−	−	−

which is an awkward situation and we need to try two conditions, firstly assuming that the value of 72 is on the other side of the median from the value of 69, and secondly assuming it to be on the same side. In either case the comparator for 95 per cent probability is $2\sqrt{10} = 6.4$.

In the first case the minus count is 8, so that $|n - 2G - 1| = |11 - 16 - 1|$ $= 6$, and in the second the minus count is 6 giving $|n - 2G - 1|$ $= |11 - 12 - 1| = 2$. In each case the pairs count is less than the comparator and it may be concluded with 95 per cent probability of being correct that these values are drawn randomly from the population.

SUGGESTIONS FOR FURTHER READING

2 G. U. YULE and M. G. KENDALL, Chapter 20, 1958.
3 C. A. BENNETT and N. L. FRANKLIN, Chapters 4 and 5, 1954.
20 M. G. KENDALL, 1948.
21 M. H. QUENOUILLE, 1960.
24 E. S. PEARSON and J. WISHART, 1958.

CHAPTER FIVE

ANALYSIS OF

VARIANCE

WE HAVE seen in previous chapters that when we set out to obtain a measurement of the value of a quantitative variable, such as yield or assay or batch cycle times, etc., experimental error and possibly other sources of error interfere with the experimentation. These prevent determination of the absolute value that we would like to measure and lead to a series of values which may be more or less widely spread about the mean of the values according to the magnitude of the error. From the measurements made we have been able to deduce the expected value, confidence limits which we expect to contain the expected value with some stated degree of probability, and an estimate of the value and validity of the experimentation.

Many occasions arise in industry where it is necessary to undertake experimentation in which more than one variable may be expected to exert some effect on the result (or response) of the experimentation. In section 4.6.3 we dealt with a simple example of such experimentation in which two variables — process modifications and levels of temperature — were mentioned; the method described in that section permitted us to make a distinction between the process modifications but not between the levels of temperature. We could guess that level of temperature (1) is the best because it gives the highest total of 5 yields, but since there is considerable overlap of yield values between levels of temperature we cannot be certain on the evidence of a count.

However, we are able to estimate the separate effects of a number of variables by means of a technique called 'Analysis of Variance'. Analysis of variance (sometimes referred to as ANOVA) may be defined as 'a statistical technique for the analysis of measurements which depend on several kinds of effects operating simultaneously, which permits us to decide which effects are important and enables us to estimate these effects'. The measurements may be made on variables in an experimental field such as laboratory investigation or manufacturing operation, or in a non-experimental field such as astronomy. The variables involved may be either quantitative or qualitative in character, because if an effect exists then analysis of variance will estimate that effect between levels of the variable irrespective of any numerical values which might be attached to these levels.

Analysis of variance was introduced by R. A. Fisher, who developed the technique for the elucidation of problems in agriculture. It has developed from simple block designs to very complicated composite and rotatable designs which cannot be elucidated without the aid of an electronic computer. Many books have been written on analysis of variance but this chapter will be restricted to the designs which are used most frequently in industry. As with all the statistical procedures described in previous chapters, only very simple arithmetic is used in the calculations required by analysis of variance. The only difficulty likely to arise is the allocation of the appropriate number of degrees of freedom to the various effects in a complicated design; and even this may be resolved easily if the analysis of the design is tackled in a systematic manner.

5.1 nested designs

The 'design' is the plan of action that defines the experiment; it specifies the sampling frequency, the number of variables to be studied, and the levels of each variable that are to be used in the study.

Nested designs are the simplest designs available and permit resolution of any difference between two variables. The word 'nested' seems to have been derived from the layout of the design in which values are tabulated under levels of one variable much as 'eggs in nests'. A nested design is a perfectly symmetrical design which is used mainly in sampling and testing procedures; the most common example is the use of a nested design to distinguish between 'variation among lots' and 'variation among samples within lots' to determine the value of an analytical test. For this, the design consists of taking a number of random samples from each of several lots – the same number of samples from each lot of course. In order to provide reliable estimates of error there should be at least three samples from each lot, and there should be at least three lots. A favourite design in chemical industry is the 5 × 5 design in which 5 samples are taken from each of five lots; as far as possible the lots chosen for experimentation should cover the range of the characteristic under test.

5.1.1 5 × 5 DESIGN TO DETERMINE THE VALUE OF AN ANALYTICAL TEST

Table 5.1.1.1 shows the analytical results obtained from the analysis of five samples taken at random from each of five lots of product. The five results for each lot are written in any order and there is no correspondence between lots.

Table 5.1.1.1 Analytical results on a 5 × 5 design for assay

Q.4	Q.9	Q.13	Q.17	Q.23
94·75	93·68	93·42	92·75	94·68
94·00	93·59	93·31	92·55	94·75
94·44	93·17	92·68	92·11	94·51
94·54	93·97	92·87	92·96	94·65
94·00	93·94	93·15	92·21	95·35

From these values we have to calculate the sum of squares for lots and the sum of squares for samples within lots. The easiest way to obtain these is to obtain the sum of the values for each lot (giving $\sum x$) and the sum of the squares of the values for each lot ($\sum x^2$); then correcting these sums of squares for the lot means ($(\sum x)^2/N$) gives the sum of squares for each lot ($\sum (x - \bar{x})^2$). Totalling for all lots enables us to determine the overall sum of squares of the values, which must be corrected for the overall mean.

Before starting these calculations we can simplify the arithmetic by subtracting 90·00 from each value and forgetting (temporarily) the decimal points. For all 25 values there are 24 degrees of freedom and these are apportioned as follows: for the five lots there are 4 degrees of freedom belonging to the sum of squares among lots, and since there are 4 degrees of freedom for each set of five samples within a lot then there are $5 \times 4 = 20$ degrees of freedom for the sum of squares among samples within lots. The necessary calculations are shown in Table 5.1.1.2.

In general, if the nested design consists of k samples drawn at random from each of n lots the total number of degrees of freedom to be allocated will be $(nk - 1)$. The sum of squares among lots will require $(n - 1)$ degrees of freedom, and the sum of squares among samples within lots will require $n(k - 1)$ degrees of freedom.

Table 5.1.1.2 Calculation of sums of squares from values of Table 5.1.1.1

	Q.4	Q.9	Q.13	Q.17	Q.23	Totals
	475	368	342	275	468	
	400	359	331	255	475	
	444	317	268	211	451	
	454	397	287	296	465	
	400	394	315	221	535	
$\sum x =$	2,173	1,835	1,543	1,258	2,394	9,203
$\sum x^2 =$	948,877	677,639	479,943	321,628	1,150,500	3,578,587
$(\sum x)^2/5 =$	944,385·8	673,445	476,169·8	316,512·8	1,146,247·2	3,556,760·6
$\sum (x - \bar{x})^2 =$	4,491·2	4,194	3,773·2	5,115·2	4,252·8	21,826·4
D.F.	4	4	4	4	4	20

From Table 5.1.1.2 we now calculate

$$\text{the correction for the grand mean} = (9,203)^2/25$$
$$= 3,387,808 \cdot 36$$
$$\text{so the total sum of squares} = 3,578,587 - 3,387,808 \cdot 36$$
$$= 190,778 \cdot 6$$
$$\text{and the sum of squares among lots} = 3,556,760 \cdot 6 - 3,387,808 \cdot 36$$
$$= 168,952 \cdot 24$$

and the analysis of variance table is constructed to show

Source of variation	Sum of squares	D.F.	Mean square	F-Ratio
Among lots	168,952	4	42,328	38·7
Among samples within lots	21,826	20	1,091	1
Total	190,778	24		

The F-ratio is the ratio of the mean squares, and the mean square 'among samples within lots' is always put as the denominator in forming the ratio. This enables us to determine whether or not the mean square 'among lots' is significantly larger than the mean square 'among samples within lots' and so to decide whether or not the test under examination can be expected to distinguish between lots such as those we have sampled.

The F-table quotes a value of 4·43 for 4 and 20 degrees of freedom at the 1 per cent level of probability. The F-ratio calculated above is greater than this so that we can say, with 99 per cent probability of being correct, that there is a real difference between the variance (or the mean square) 'among lots' and the variance 'among samples within lots', and this analytical test may be expected to distinguish between such lots as those examined. The F-table quotes a value of 2·87 for 4 and 20 degrees of freedom at the 5 per cent level of probability, and if the calculated F-ratio had been less than this we would have concluded that the test could not be expected to distinguish between these lots, and experimentation would have been undertaken to improve the test or provide an alternative test.

But note that the distinction between lots is based on analysis of five samples from each lot, and this is not a feasible proposition for routine control work. It is necessary to obtain an estimate of the value of a single sample, and this may be obtained from the variance 'among samples within lots'.

From the analysis of variance table the standard error of the test is $\sqrt{1091}$ or $\pm 33·03$. Now reverting to the original units we have the standard error as 0·3303, and the precision of the test, which is sometimes called the 'repeatability of the test', as indicated by the 95 per cent confidence limits for a single determination is given by

$$\pm 1·96 \times 0·3303 = \pm 0·65$$

where the factor 1·96 is the value of Student's t at 0·05 probability and infinite degrees of freedom. This repeatability is valid only for a range of test results between 92·11 and 95·35, which is the range of the results available for the statistical analysis; the repeatability may or may not hold outside this range, but we do not know.

EXPECTATION OF THE MEAN SQUARE. In addition to permitting us to distinguish between lots and samples, where such distinction exists, the mean squares derived in the analysis of variance can be used to determine the standard deviation due to samples (as we have done above) and the standard deviation due to lots. These quantities are estimated by the mean square and their respective squares (the variances) are known as the expectations of the mean squares. If we write σ_0^2 for the variance between samples, then we expect the mean square among samples within lots to be the best available estimate of σ_0^2.

Consider the case dealing with n samples per lot from each of m lots. Then if $\bar{x}_1, \bar{x}_2, \ldots, \bar{x}_m$ are the means of the n samples in each lot and $\bar{x}$ is the overall mean, the variance between the lot means is

$$\sum_{i=1}^{m} (\bar{x}_i - \bar{x})/(m - 1).$$

But if we write σ_1^2 as the variance due to lots, then the variance of the mean of n samples from any one lot is $\sigma_1^2 + \sigma_0^2/n$ and we have

$$\sum_{i=1}^{m} (\bar{x}_i - \bar{x})/(m - 1).$$

is the best estimate of $\sigma_1^2 + \sigma_0^2/n$, or

$$n . \sum_{i=1}^{m} (\bar{x}_i - \bar{x})/(m - 1),$$

which is the mean square for lots, is the best estimate of $n\sigma_1^2 + \sigma_0^2$ and the analysis of variance table can be expanded to

Source of variation	Sum of squares	D.F.	Mean square	Expectation of the mean square
Among lots	168,952	4	42,328	$\sigma_0^2 + 5\sigma_1^2$
Among samples within lots	21,826	20	1,091	σ_0^2
Total	190,778	24		

As long as we find a significant difference between the two mean squares we can say 1,091 is the best estimate of σ_0^2, whence $\sigma_0 \to 0.3303$ (reverting to original units) and

$$\left(\frac{42,328 - 1,091}{5}\right) = 8,247.4$$

is the best estimate of σ_1^2, whence again reverting gives $\sigma_1 \to 0.9081$.

Confidence limits for these standard deviations can be obtained by using the multipliers given in *Biometrika Tables for Statisticians*, Volume 1, Table 35.

5.2 cross designs

Whereas the nested designs have correspondence in columns and not between columns (this means that the values in a column are related to each other but are not related to any value in any other column), the cross design has 1:1 correspondence in rows and columns. Cross designs are used to distinguish between the effects of two factors each of which is studied at several levels; experimental results are tabulated in rows and columns so that values in each row refer to experimentation at a particular level of one factor, and values in each column refer to experimentation at a particular level of the other factor. The cross design is symmetrical and experimentation must be made at all combinations of the two factors so that all columns and all rows in the results tabulation are complete; it is possible to estimate the value of a missing result, but this is not good practice.

In the nested design the variance of one component — samples within lots — provided an estimate of experimental error, but analysis of a cross design provides estimates of the variance due to each factor and an estimate of experimental error. The minimum requirement in a cross design is experimentation at two levels of each factor and this may be extended as desired; it is not necessary to work at the same number of levels of each factor.

5.2.1 4 × 3 DESIGN ON TEMPERATURE AND CONCENTRATION

Experimentation which it was hoped would lead to an increase in the yield of product per batch was carried out at various levels of reaction temperature and initial concentration of one of the reactants, charge weights and all other factors being kept constant. The results obtained were

Table 5.2.1.1 Batch yields

		Levels of temperature (increasing)				Totals
		1	2	3	4	
Levels	1	195	201	218	220	834
of	2	235	243	230	239	947
concentration	3	251	270	274	268	1,063
Totals		681	714	722	727	2,844

It is obvious from these figures that the process yield increases with increasing temperature and with increasing concentration. However, a statistical analysis permits us to determine just how much of an increase in yield may be expected from an increase in temperature or an increase in concentration. If the levels of the factors have been chosen at equal intervals then an overall estimate of yield increase, such as per 1°C., may be obtained over the range of experimentation. It is not necessary to use equidistant levels, but where levels are not equidistant estimates of unit increase over more than one interval may not be permissible.

The statistical analysis follows the standard method. The overall total provides us with a correction for the mean; the twelve experimental results, corrected for the mean, provide us with the total sum of squares; the three row totals, corrected for the mean, provide us with the sum of squares for levels of concentration; the four column totals, corrected for the mean, provide us with the sum of squares for levels of temperature; and the residual sum of squares (total−rows−columns) provides us with an estimate of experimental error which may be used as the comparator for significance.

Then, the correction for the mean $= (2{,}844)^2/12 = 674{,}028$

Total sum of squares $= (195)^2 + (235)^2 + \ldots + (239)^2 + (268)^2 - CM$
$$= 681{,}446 - 674{,}028 = 7{,}418.$$

Sum of squares [temperatures] $= \dfrac{(681)^2 + (714)^2 + (722)^2 + (727)^2}{3} - CM$

$$= 674{,}456{\cdot}7 - 674{,}028 = 428{\cdot}7$$

Note the divisor of 3, because each temperature total is obtained from 3 levels of concentration.

Sum of squares [concentrations] $= \dfrac{(834)^2 + (947)^2 + (1{,}063)^2}{4} - CM$

$$= 680{,}583{\cdot}5 - 674{,}028 = 6{,}555{\cdot}5$$

Here the divisor is 4, because each concentration total is obtained from 4 levels of temperature. In general, the divisor will be the number of levels of all the other variables involved in a row or column or block total. And finally, residual sum of squares $= 7{,}418 - 428{\cdot}7 - 6{,}555{\cdot}5 = 433{\cdot}8$ and the analysis of variance table is

Source of variation	Sum of squares	D.F.	Mean square	F-Ratio
Levels of temperature	428·7	3	142·9	1·976
Levels of concentration	6,555·5	2	3,277·75	45·335
Residual	433·8	6	72·3	1
Total	7,418·0	11		

The degrees of freedom are allocated as follows: the twelve experimental results provide 11 degrees of freedom overall; the four levels of temperature require 3 degrees of freedom; the three levels of concentration require 2 degrees of freedom; and so there are $11 - 3 - 2 = 6$ degrees of freedom for the residual.

From the *F*-table (Table 3) we find that a minimum value of 3·29 is required for 3 and 6 degrees of freedom at the 0·1 level of probability; the value indicated above is less than this so we conclude that there is no significant improvement in batch yields due to increasing temperature. Also, we find that a minimum value of 10·92 is required for 2 and 6 degrees of freedom at the 0·01 level of probability; the value calculated above is greater than this so we conclude with 99 per cent probability of being correct, that there is a real improvement due to increasing the concentration.

The residual mean square provides an estimate of the overall experimental error, and we have that the standard error is $\sqrt{72·3} = \pm 8·503$. If the levels of concentration were equidistant we could say that the average increase in yield per increase in concentration level is $(1,063 - 834)/8 = 29$, and the confidence limits for 95 per cent probability attached to this value are $29 \pm (1·96)(8·503)$ or 29 ± 17. Within the control limits of the experimentation yield increases would be expected to lie within this confidence range as concentration is moved from one level to the next.

EXPECTATION OF THE MEAN SQUARE: As in Section 5.1 the analysis of variance table can be expanded to show the expectations of the mean squares, and in this case we have

Source of variation	Sum of squares	D.F.	Mean square	Expectation of the mean square
Levels of temperature	428·7	3	142·9	$\sigma_0^2 + 3\sigma_2^0$
Levels of concentration	6,555·5	2	3,277·75	$\sigma_0^2 + 4\sigma_1^2$
Residual	433·8	6	72·3	σ_0^2
Total	7,418·0	11		

Each of the multipliers 3 and 4 fitted to σ_2^2 and σ_1^2 is of course the number of levels of the other variable. The mean square calculated for levels of temperature is calculated over 3 levels of concentration, and the mean square calculated for levels of concentration is calculated over 4 levels of temperature. Generally, the multiplier for the variance of any factor in an analysis of variance is given by

$$M_k = \frac{\text{Total number of observations}}{\text{Number of levels of the variable } k}.$$

In this example we have found that levels of temperature do not exert any measurable effect on batch yield; the variance due to temperature, σ_2^2, therefore may not be significantly different from zero, and no attempt is made to estimate σ_2.

The variance due to concentration, σ_1^2, may be estimated, and this is

$$\sigma_1^2 = \tfrac{1}{4}(3,277·75 - 72·3) = 801·36, \quad \text{whence} \quad \sigma_1 = 28·31.$$

Using tabulated values of multipliers for 2 degrees of freedom, the 95 per cent confidence limits of σ_1 are $0 \cdot 521 \times 28 \cdot 31$ and $6 \cdot 28 \times 28 \cdot 31$ or $14 \cdot 75$ to $177 \cdot 79$. These very wide confidence limits result from the very small number of degrees of freedom.

5.2.2 A 4 × 6 CROSS DESIGN FOR RAW MATERIALS AND REACTORS

The example of the previous section showed how a cross design may be used to estimate the effects of various levels of continuous variables. One very useful application of cross designs is their application to discrete variables and this example deals with a chemical plant in which the reaction led to the formation of an undesirable byproduct. The plant had four reactors and there were available six grades of one of the raw materials used in the reaction. It was necessary to determine which of the grades of raw material was likely to give the lowest formation of byproduct, and whether or not there was any real difference between the reactors. Experimental results obtained are shown in Table 5.2.2.

Table 5.2.2 Data from experimentation on 4 reactors × 6 raw materials

		Reactor 1	2	3	4
	a	8·9	9·6	8·0	9·4
Raw	b	10·9	10·2	9·6	10·0
Material	c	9·7	10·5	8·8	10·8
Grades	d	12·0	10·7	10·6	11·1
	e	9·5	10·0	8·0	9·9
	f	10·5	11·0	9·0	11·1

The values shown are the percentages of byproduct formed in the experimental runs.

The statistical method to be used is exactly the same as in section 5.2.1, but first we can arrange to simplify the arithmetic by forgetting the decimal points and using a datum of 100. That is we shall carry out the procedure on values which are differences between the experimental values and 100; we are, in fact, using the transformation $x = 10(X - 10)$ and we shall work on the transformed values x instead of the experimental values X. Then we have

	R.1	R.2	R.3	R.4	Totals
RMa	−11	−4	−20	−6	−41
RMb	9	2	14	0	7
RMc	−3	5	12	8	−2
RMd	20	7	6	11	44
RMe	−5	0	−20	−1	−26
RMf	5	10	−10	11	16
Totals	15	20	−60	23	−2

The correction for the mean $= (-2)^2/24 = 0\cdot17$

Total sum of squares $= (-11)^2 + (9)^2 + \ldots + (-1)^2 + (11)^2 - \text{CM}$
$$= 2{,}294 - 0\cdot17 = 2{,}293\cdot83$$

Sum of squares [reactors]
$$= \frac{(15)^2 + (20)^2 + (-60)^2 + (23)^2}{6} - \text{CM}$$

$$= 792\cdot33 - 0\cdot17 = 792\cdot16$$

Sum of squares [RM]
$$= \frac{(-41)^2 + (7)^2 + (-2)^2 + (44)^2 + (-26)^2 + (16)^2}{4} - \text{CM}$$

$$= 1{,}150\cdot5 - 0\cdot17 = 1{,}150\cdot33$$

and residual sum of squares

$$= 2{,}293\cdot83 - 792\cdot16 - 1{,}150\cdot33 = 351\cdot34.$$

The 24 experimental results provide 23 degrees of freedom; the four reactors require 3 degrees of freedom; the six raw material grades require 5 degrees of freedom; and so there are $23 - 3 - 5 = 15$ degrees of freedom for the residual.

The analysis of variance table is

Source of variation	Sum of squares	D.F.	Mean square	F-Ratio	Quantity estimated
Between reactors	792·16	3	264·05	11·29	$\sigma^2 + [R]$
Between materials	1,150·33	5	230·06	9·89	$\sigma^2 + [M]$
Residual	351·34	15	23·42	1	σ^2
Total	2,293·83	23			

The column 'Quantity Estimated' is inserted in the table because we are not content with knowing whether or not there is a real effect due to reactors or to raw materials; if possible we want to determine the best raw material to use and to indicate whether or not there is a difference between the reactors. The residual mean square is the best estimate of the experimental error; the reactors mean square then estimates the experimental error plus the variation due to reactors; and the materials mean square estimates the experimental error plus the variation due to raw materials.

Here we use the F-test to determine whether the null hypothesis 'that there is no real effect due to variation between raw materials or to variation between reactors' is tenable. The tabulated value of F for 5 and 15 degrees of freedom at the 0·01 level of probability is 4·56: the F-ratio calculated above is greater than this and we may conclude, with 99 per cent probability of being correct, that there is a real effect due to variation between the grades of raw material used in the experimentation. We can investigate this a little further.

It seems obvious from Table 5.2.2 and the transformed values that RMa is the best grade to use and RMd the worst grade as far as formation of the byproduct is concerned. From the transformed values we see that the mean values attributable to the raw material grades are

RMa:	$-10\cdot25$		RMa:	$-10\cdot25$
RMb:	$1\cdot75$	or, in order	RMe:	$-6\cdot5$
RMc:	$-0\cdot5$		RMc:	$-0\cdot5$
RMd:	$11\cdot0$		RMb:	$1\cdot75$
RMe:	$-6\cdot5$		RMf:	$4\cdot0$
RMf:	$4\cdot0$		RMd:	$11\cdot0$

Now it is necessary to calculate the value of a statistic $q\sqrt{(M/k)}$ in which

M is the residual mean square

k is the number of levels over which each raw material grade has been tested (4 reactors)

and q is 'Tukey's value' as obtained from *Biometrika Tables for Statisticians,* Vol. 1, Table 29 entitled 'Percentage Points of the studentized range'. q is dependent on the number of degrees of freedom of $M(f)$, the confidence level desired (α), and the number of levels k.

In this example we wish to make the decision with 95 per cent probability of being correct so we take $\alpha = 0\cdot05$; the number of degrees of freedom for the residual mean square is 15, and the number of levels for k is 4; the tabulated value of q is 4·60, whence the upper limit of the range expected to cover raw material grades is

$$4\cdot60\sqrt{(23\cdot42/4)} = 11\cdot13.$$

Using this value we can estimate, with 95 per cent probability of being correct, whether or not there is a real difference between raw material grades. We find that mean values showing differences greater than 11·13 indicate that $a < b; a < f; a < d; e < d; c < d$; but that it is not possible to distinguish between a, e, and c, or between b, f, and d. However, we can state that for minimization of byproduct formation we should not use raw material grades b, d, and f, and since grade a shows significantly less byproduct formation than grade b whereas grade e does not show significantly less byproduct formation than grade b (on the above test) there is some likelihood that grade a is the better of these two. If further experimentation to distinguish between grades a and e cannot be made, we accept grade a as the best available.

From the analysis of variance table the standard error of the experimentation is $\sigma = \sqrt{23\cdot42} = \pm4\cdot837$, and if we wish to use this value in any further work it is useful to know just how good this estimate of the experimental error really is. The accuracy of the residual mean square taken as an estimate of the experimental error variance, σ^2, may be expressed by confidence limits, and the $100(1 - 2\alpha)$ per cent confidence limits for σ^2 are L_U and L_L where these limits are derived from the relationship

$$\chi^2_{(1-\alpha)} \leqq \frac{\text{Residual sum of squares}}{\sigma^2} \leqq \chi^2_{(\alpha)}$$

or

$$\frac{\text{Residual sum of squares}}{\chi^2_{(\alpha)}} \leqq \sigma^2 \leqq \frac{\text{Residual sum of squares}}{\chi^2_{(1-\alpha)}}$$

Usually the 95 per cent confidence limits are satisfactory; these require a value of $\alpha = 0.025$. The error variance is associated with 15 degrees of freedom and from Table 2 we obtain the necessary values of χ^2 for 15 degrees of freedom and 0.975 and 0.025 probability. Then the confidence limits are

$$\frac{351.34}{27.5} \leqq \sigma^2 \leqq \frac{351.34}{6.26}$$

or

$$12.776 \leqq \sigma^2 \leqq 56.12$$

which gives

$$3.576 \leqq \sigma \leqq 7.491$$

Thus for our estimated value for the standard error of the experimentation of 4.837 we have an upper confidence limit $L_U = 7.491$ and a lower confidence limit of $L_L = 3.576$. The confidence range does not include zero and we may use the calculated value of 4.837 as the best available estimate.

Finally, we are required to assess the performance of the reactors. This may be done in a manner like that used to compare raw material grades, but here we use an alternative method. As before, we tabulate the mean byproduct percentage for each reactor from the transformed data; arranged in order these are

$$\begin{aligned} R_3&: -10 \\ R_1&: \quad 2.5 \\ R_2&: \quad 3.3 \\ R_4&: \quad 3.8 \end{aligned}$$

For any comparison, such as $R_1 - R_3$, the confidence limits for the difference are given by

$$(\bar{x}_1 - \bar{x}_3) \pm t_\alpha \cdot \sqrt{\frac{2M}{n}}$$

in which $\bar{x}_1$ and $\bar{x}_3$ are the mean values for reactors 1 and 3 respectively; M is the residual mean square; n is the number of levels over which each reactor has been tested (6 raw material grades); and t_α is the tabulated value of Student's t (Table 4) for the number of degrees of freedom associated with

M and probability α. For our example, for 95 per cent confidence limits, $\alpha = 0\cdot025$ and we have confidence limits given by

$$(2\cdot5 + 10) \pm 2\cdot131\sqrt{(2 \times 23\cdot42/6)}$$

i.e. $\qquad\qquad 12\cdot5 \pm 6$ or a range of $6\cdot5$ to $18\cdot5$.

This range does not include zero so that we can say, with 95 per cent probability of being correct, that there is a real difference between the performance of reactor 1 and reactor 3. A glance at the other means shows that we will not be able to separate the performances of reactors 1, 2, and 4, but reactor 3 has a real difference in performance from each of the others.

Thus to minimize formation of byproduct we have shown that the process should be run on raw material grade a with reactor performance as that of reactor 3, and investigation into the operation of the reactors showed that the agitator in reactor 3 revolved at a greater speed than the other agitators and reactor 3 had a larger cooling coil than the others; these two items permitted a faster rate of reaction in reactor 3.

5.3 mixed designs

Mixed designs are those constructed from both nested and cross designs. For example, a mixed design would be used to investigate the effects of four solvents and three process modifications when three batches are to be examined from each of three reaction kettles under each solvent and process modification. The design would be

	Modification 1 K1 K2 K3 B1,2,3 B1,2,3 B1,2,3	Modification 2 K1 K2 K3 B1,2,3 B1,2,3 B1,2,3	Modification 3 K1 K2 K3 B1,2,3 B1,2,3 B1,2,3
Solvent A B C D			

and this design requires $3 \times 3 \times 3 \times 4 = 108$ experimental batches.

Mixed designs may be made as complicated as desired, and sometimes such designs present a little difficulty in the allocation of degrees of freedom to the various effects and interactions. This should not be so, and if the analysis is carried out in a systematic manner no difficulties should arise. The design shown above requires 108 experimental batches and so provides $108 - 1 = 107$ degrees of freedom, which can be allocated as follows: for the three processes two degrees of freedom are required; within each process the three kettles require 2 degrees of freedom and so overall for the 3 processes there are $3 \times 2 = 6$ degrees of freedom for kettles; within each kettle the three batches require 2 degrees of freedom and so overall there are $9 \times 2 = 18$ degrees of freedom for batches; for the four solvents three degrees of freedom are required. Then for the residual sum of squares there are $107 - 2 - 6 - 18 - 3 = 78$ degrees of freedom.

The analysis may be made in stages to determine various effects as required, and this is demonstrated in the next example.

5.3.1 A MIXED DESIGN FOR ASSESSMENT OF A NEW INSTRUMENT

A new instrument had been obtained by one of the research laboratories and it was necessary to determine whether or not the instrument was sufficiently sensitive to detect the small variations in concentration that were entailed in the current investigation. It was decided to run the test at six levels of concentration in each of two solvents and each preparation was to be examined in duplicate on three successive days. Coded values for the results obtained are shown in Table 5.3.1.

Table 5.3.1 Coded experimental observations from instrument

	Solution A							Solution B							
	Day 1		Day 2		Day 3		Sub	Day 1		Day 2		Day 3		Sub	
Levels	R.1	R.2	R.1	R.2	R.1	R.2	totals	R.1	R.2	R.1	R.2	R.1	R.2	totals	Totals
1	0	0	0	0	0	0	0	0	0	0	−1	0	0	−1	−1
2	30	31	22	21	21	21	146	21	21	20	19	21	21	123	269
3	48	47	43	42	42	43	265	42	41	39	39	38	38	237	502
4	67	69	66	66	65	64	397	61	59	59	57	57	57	350	747
5	85	86	84	82	84	86	507	78	77	77	77	76	75	460	967
6	103	101	105	105	101	102	617	97	98	99	96	96	93	579	1,196
Sub totals	333	334	320	316	313	316	1,932	299	296	294	287	288	284	1,748	3,680
Totals	667		636		629			595		581		572			

We can carry out the statistical analysis of these results in one stage, but it is more useful to do the work in steps. For a single-stage exercise the degrees of freedom are allocated as follows: Each replication within a day has 1 degree of freedom $(2 - 1 = 1)$ so that there are 6 degrees of freedom for replication; each day within a solution has 2 degrees of freedom, so that there are $2 \times 2 = 4$ degrees of freedom for day; the two solutions require 1 degree of freedom; and the 6 levels of experimentation require 5 degrees of freedom. Overall there are $72 - 1 = 71$ degrees of freedom available, so $71 - 6 - 4 - 1 - 5 = 55$ degrees of freedom are allocated to the residual sum of squares. As a first step, however, we can analyse the results within and between levels, using the totals for levels and the individual observations, to give

Correction for the mean $= (3,680)^2/72 = 188,088 \cdot 8$

Total sum of squares

$$= 0^2 + (30)^2 + (48)^2 + \ldots + (57)^2 + (75)^2 + (93)^2 - CM$$
$$= 271,506 - 188,088 \cdot 8 = 83,417 \cdot 1$$

(with 71 degrees of freedom)

Sum of squares between levels

$$= \frac{(-1)^2 + \ldots + (1,196)^2}{12} - CM$$

$$= 270,656 \cdot 6 - 188,088 \cdot 8 = 82,567 \cdot 7$$

(with 5 degrees of freedom)

so that the sum of squares within levels $= 83,417 \cdot 1 - 82,567 \cdot 7 = 849 \cdot 3$ (with $71 - 5 = 66$ degrees of freedom) and the preliminary analysis of variance table is

Source of variation	Sum of squares	D.F.	Mean square	F-Ratio
Between levels	82,567·7	5	16,513·5	1,280
Within levels	849·3	66	12·9	1
Total	83,417·1	71		

For 5 and 66 degrees of freedom the F-table quotes a value of $3 \cdot 31$ at the $0 \cdot 01$ level of probability. There can be no doubt, therefore, that the photometer may be expected to distinguish satisfactorily between the levels of concentration used in this experimentation.

Next, it is possible to subdivide the sum of squares 'within levels'; no division of the sum of squares 'between levels' can be made as no other factor is inter-related with 'levels'. As the experimentation is basically between 12 replications at each of 6 levels, then an analysis between replications and levels will permit estimation of the sum of squares for the residual, which we will take to represent the experimental error.

And we have, sum of squares for replicates

$$= \frac{(333)^2 + (334)^2 + \ldots + (284)^2}{6} - CM$$

$$= 188,658 - 188,088 \cdot 8 = 569 \cdot 1$$

(with 11 d.f.)

which gives sum of squares for residual = 849·3̇ − 569·1̇ = 280·2̇ (with 66 − 11 = 55 degrees of freedom), permitting an expansion of the analysis of variance table to

Source of variation	Sum of squares	D.F.	Mean square	F-Ratio
Between levels	82,567·7̇	5	16,513·5	
Between replicates	569·1̇	11	51·7	10
Residual	280·2̇	55	5·1	1
Total	83,417·1̇	71		

For 11 and 55 degrees of freedom the F-table quotes a value of (about) 2·6 at the 0·01 level of probability (arithmetic interpolation is good enough here). The variance between replicates, therefore, is highly significant, and the analysis of variance may be continued in order that we may account in more detail for this variance.

Sum of squares for days

$$= \frac{(667)^2 + (636)^2 + \ldots + (572)^2}{12} - CM$$

$$= 188,649·6̇ - 188,088·8̇ = 560·7̇ \text{ (with 5 degrees of freedom)}$$

whence the sum of squares for replication (replicates within days)

$$= 569·1̇ - 560·7̇ = 8·3̇ \text{ (with } 11 - 5 = 6 \text{ degrees of freedom).}$$

Also, we have that the sum of squares for solvents

$$= \frac{(1,932)^2 + (1,748)^2}{36} - CM$$

$$= 188·559·1̇ - 188,088·8̇ = 470·2̇ \text{ (with 1 degree of freedom)}$$

leaving a sum of squares for days within solvents = 560·7̇ − 470·2̇ = 90·5̇ (with 5 − 1 = 4 degrees of freedom).

Thus the actual effect due to replication is very small. Most of the variance attributed to replicates in the table above has been shown to be due to a variance between solvents; as we would expect from the progressive reductions in daily totals, which occurs with both solvents, there is a fairly large variance due to the effect of days and this must be due to some deterioration of the various preparations with the passage of time.

The full analysis of variance table is

Source of variation	Sum of squares	D.F.	Mean square	F-Ratio			
Between levels of concentration	82,567·7	5	16,513·5				1,280
Between solutions	470·2	1	470·2			80·6	
Between days (within solutions)	90·5	4	22·6		4·78		1
Replication	8·3	6	1·4	<1		1	
Residual (experimental error)	280·2	55	5·1	1	1		
Total	83,417·1	71					

The mean square for replication is compared with the residual and we see that there is no detectable effect due to replication in the experimentation. Combining the sums of squares for replication and residual gives 288·5 for 61 degrees of freedom, which gives a 'total error' mean square of 4·73.

Comparing the mean square 'between days' with this 'total error' mean square gives an F-ratio of 4·78; the tabulated value for 4 and 61 degrees of freedom is 3·65 at the 0·01 level of probability. There is a real effect due to days, and most likely this is due to some degree of decomposition or other chemical reaction which proceeds very slowly but which has been noticed in the experimentation.

Next we combine the sums of squares 'between days' and 'total error' to give a sum of squares 'within solutions' of 379·1 with 65 degrees of freedom, and this gives a 'within solutions' mean square of 5·83. Comparing the mean square 'between solutions' with this 'within solutions' mean square gives an F-ratio of 80·6; the tabulated value for 1 and 65 degrees of freedom is 7·04 at the 0·01 level of probability. There is a real effect due to solutions, and it is very likely that Solvent A is more efficient in extracting the chemical concerned than Solvent B; Solvent A would be used in all further work.

Finally we have, as found previously, better than a 99·9 per cent probability that the instrument may be expected to distinguish between the levels of concentration.

Analysis of variance of a mixed design is not difficult, but step-by-step analysis may help unravel any complications that may be encountered.

5.4 randomized block designs

Randomized block designs are used for experimentation in which there are one or more 'nuisance' variations. These include: firstly, such variations as the batch-to-batch variations introduced when experimentation attempts to compare various treatments applied to a variety of raw materials; secondly, processes and especially those using a catalyst frequently show the existence of a time trend which must be included in any experimental data; thirdly, many control or measuring instruments tend to drift with time and allowance must be made for this. The procedure is to divide the trend into blocks and then conduct experiments at random within each block. For instance, if a process were affected by a time trend such as AB (Figure 5.4) then an experiment performed on a simple cross design would include the whole time trend AB. However, if the time trend is divided into four blocks, as shown, and the set of treatments is carried out at random in each block, analysis of results

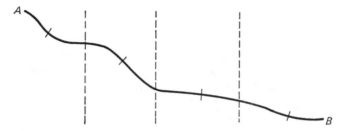

Fig. 5.4. REPRESENTATION OF A TIME TREND

eliminates variation between block mean levels. This restricts the variation to smaller variations within blocks and greatly reduces the experimental error.

The straightforward cross design is, of course, the simplest form of a randomized block design in which there is only one entry in each block. The analysis is similar to that of a cross design, sums of squares are obtained for blocks and treatments and residual, and each of the blocks mean square and treatments mean square is compared with the residual mean square to determine whether or not the effect is significant. The fundamental assumption made in using a randomized block is that the effects of blocks and treatments are independent and additive.

5.4.1 A RANDOMIZED BLOCK DESIGN TO ESTIMATE THE EFFECT OF SOLVENT RECOVERY

Many chemical reactions take place in solution, and where one of the reactants is also a good solvent for the other reactants it is customary to run the reaction in the presence of a large excess of the solvent-reactant. At the end of the reaction the excess solvent-reactant has to be recovered for re-use, and very often is found to be contaminated with some impurity formed in the reaction. If this impurity content increases on repeated recovery, it may inhibit the reaction and it is necessary to cleanse the solvent by some means or another. One way in which an estimate may be made of whether or not the solvent needs cleansing is to check the reaction batch time-cycles, and this example deals with one such case. The experimental results are shown in

Table 5.4.1 in which the five reactors are labelled A, B, C, D and E, and runs are blocked so that Block 1 deals with runs made with fresh solvent, Block 2 deals with runs made with some fresh and some recovered solvent, while Block 3 deals with runs made with some fresh solvent and some solvent which has been through the process twice. Batches were started in the various reactors in random order, and Table 5.4.1 shows this randomization.

Table 5.4.1 Random block design for effect of solvent impurities
Order of Starting Batches

	1	2	3	4	5
Block 1	(E) 18·4	(C) 18·0	(B)18·4	(A)18·2	(D) 18·0
Block 2	(D)18·4	(A)18·6	(E) 19·0	(B) 19·0	(C) 18·6
Block 3	(B) 19·5	(D) 18·9	(C)19·6	(E) 20·0	(A)19·3

Now rearranging these values and transforming them to simplify the arithmetic (subtract 18·0, the lowest value, from all values and forget the decimal points temporarily) we have the experimental time-cycles for reactors within blocks:

	Reactor					
	A	B	C	D	E	Totals
Block 1	2	4	0	0	4	10
Block 2	6	10	6	4	10	36
Block 3	13	15	16	9	20	73
Totals	21	29	22	13	34	119

It is obvious that time cycles have increased with additional use of recovered solvent and we need to determine whether or not this increase is significant and if it affects all the reactors in the same way.

The analysis of variance is straightforward:

Correction for the mean

$$= (119)^2/15 = 944 \cdot 07$$

Total sum of squares

$$= 2^2 + 6^2 + \ldots + 10^2 + 20^2 - CM$$
$$= 1,455 - 944 = 511$$
$$\text{(for } 15 - 1 = 14 \text{ degrees of freedom)}$$

Blocks sum of squares

$$= \frac{(10)^2 + (36)^2 + (73)^2}{5} - CM$$

$$= 1,345 - 944 = 401$$
$$\text{(for } 3 - 1 = 2 \text{ degrees of freedom)}$$

Reactors sum of squares

$$= \frac{(21)^2 + (29)^2 + (22)^2 + (13)^2 + (34)^2}{3} - CM$$

$$= 1,030 - 944 = 86$$

(for $5 - 1 = 4$ degrees of freedom)

and the residual sum of squares is $511 - 401 - 86 = 24$ (for $14 - 2 - 4 = 8$ degrees of freedom).

The analysis of variance table is (with the decimal points replaced)

Source of variation	Sum of squares	D.F.	Mean square	F-Ratio
Blocks	4·01	2	2·005	66·8
Reactors	0·86	4	0·215	7·16
Residual	0·24	8	0·03	1
Total	5·11	14		

Each of the mean squares for blocks and reactors is compared with the residual mean square to obtain the F-ratio. From the F-table we find that a value of 8·65 is significant for 2 and 8 degrees of freedom at the 0·01 level of probability, and a value of 7·01 is significant for 4 and 8 degrees of freedom also at the 0·01 level of probability. Therefore there is a real effect due to blocks — reuse of recovered solvent — and there is a real difference between reactors. We can examine these effects further:

Average values obtained in the experimentation are

Block 1: 18·2;   and   Reactor A: 18·7
Block 2: 18·72;   Reactor B: 18·96
Block 3: 19·46;   Reactor C: 18·73
                         Reactor D: 18·43
                         Reactor E: 19·13

Confidence limits for the average values of reactors are obtained as follows:

The residual mean square is a measure of the experimental error variance, σ^2, and the variance of the average for one reactor is $\sigma^2/3$ which in this case $= 0·03/3 = 0·01$ from which the standard error is $\sqrt{0·01} = 0·1$.

The residual has 8 degrees of freedom, and from Table 4 we find that the value of t for 8 degrees of freedom and 0·05 probability is 2·306. The 95 per cent confidence limits for each reactor are given by its average value $\pm 2·306 \times 0·1$. Arranging the average values in ascending order shows

| | | 95% Confidence limits | |
Reactor	Average value	Lower	Upper
D	18·43	18·2	18·66
A	18·7	18·47	18·93
C	18·73	18·5	18·96
B	18·96	18·73	19·19
E	19·13	18·9	19·36

There is considerable overlap between some of these limits, such as those for A and C, but we can say, with 95 per cent probability of being correct, that reactor D operates in such a way that the average time cycle is shorter than those of reactors B and E. There is not much of an overlap between the limits for D and C, and for further investigational work we could include reactor C with reactors B and E.

If the analysis of variance table is expanded to include the expectation of the mean square, we have

Source of variation	Sum of squares	D.F.	Mean square	Expectation of the M.S.
Blocks	4·01	2	2·005	$\sigma_0^2 + \sigma_2^2$
Reactors	0·86	4	0·215	$\sigma_0^2 + \sigma_1^2$
Residual	0·24	8	0·03	σ_0^2
Total	5·11	14		

in which σ_1^2 and σ_2^2 are measures of the variation due to reactors and blocks respectively, and these are analogous to variances of which σ_1 and σ_2 would be their respective standard deviations.

From this we find that $\sigma_1^2 = 0·185$, whence $\sigma_1 = 0·43$. The five reactors do not constitute a random sample but the batches worked in them do, and σ_1 is a measure of the variation likely to be imposed on the batch cycle times when batches in all reactors are considered. Similarly, $\sigma_2^2 = 1·975$, whence $\sigma_2 = 1·405$ and this is a measure of the variation imposed on batch cycle times by reuse of solvent. In each case the standard deviation is estimated from a small number of values and should be considered only as an approximate estimate.

5.5 latin squares

A latin square is a block design concerned with three sources of variation, which are identified as rows, columns, and treatments. Levels of one variable are arranged in the rows, levels of the second variable are arranged in the columns, and levels of the third variable are arranged in the treatments and the overall arrangement of the latin square requires these to be equal, so that

Number of rows = Number of columns = Number of treatments.

Usually the treatments are represented by letters within the square and the balance of design must be maintained with each treatment appearing once and only once in every row and in every column. Any linear trend is eliminated by the use of a latin square and there is no limit to the number of treatments (and rows and columns) that can be included in a latin square. The one important requirement for use of a latin square is that there must be no interaction between any of the treatments or between any of rows, columns and treatments; that is, all the effects must be independent. Such a square could be used to investigate an analytical test using 4 lots of a product, 4 analysts and 4 sets of apparatus, and the full design would be

	Analysts			
	1	2	3	4
Lots 1	A	B	C	D
2	C	D	A	B
3	D	C	B	A
4	B	A	D	C

in which the letters A, B, C, D represent the 4 sets of apparatus, the rows give the lot values, and the columns give the analyst values. Note that the 16 experiments required by the design are made in random order; note also that the design remains a latin square after any interchange of rows or of columns.

If such an investigation were to be made using a block design, $4 \times 4 \times 4 = 64$ experiments would be necessary. It is seen immediately that use of a latin square reduces the work involved in an investigation by a factor equal to the number of levels of each variable, and gives almost an equally precise estimate of the effects as long as the design is fully orthogonal. That is, a latin square may be used when the rows, columns, and treatments affect the results independently of one another so that in practice the interactions, if not negligible, are small compared with the effects that are to be estimated.

The analysis of variance is carried out in the usual manner, using row totals, column totals and treatment totals to calculate the sums of squares. The number of degrees of freedom attached to each variable is, of course, one less than the number of levels of each of the variables. Thus in an $n \times n$ latin square there are $(n - 1)$ degrees of freedom for each of rows, columns, and treatments, leaving $n^2 - 1 - 3(n - 1) = (n - 1)(n - 2)$ degrees of freedom for the residual sum of squares. We see from this that a 2×2 latin square has one degree of freedom for each variable and has no residual sum of squares.

5.5.1 LATIN SQUARE DESIGN FOR ANALYSTS AND TEST APPARATUS

The experimental design used and results obtained are given in Table 5.5.1 in which the rows refer to the 8 sets of apparatus used, the columns refer to the 8 samples of product examined, and the treatments refer to the 8 analysts who took part in the investigation. A sample of product was taken from each of 8 lots of recent manufacture, each sample being examined in each set of apparatus. The 8 analysts were the eight people normally employed in the laboratory which tested this product, any one of whom could be expected to run a test at any time. As all eight analysts could not work on this investigation at the same time, experiments were randomized within the design and were performed over the course of several days. The product was known to be unaffected by storage of this short duration.

Table 5.5.1 8 × 8 Latin square experiment

		1	2	3	4	Lots 5	6	7	8	Totals
Sets of apparatus	1	D(21)	H(19)	C(15)	B(12)	E(13)	A(22)	G(17)	F(19)	138
	2	F(14)	E(11)	G(17)	A(19)	H(21)	B(20)	C(13)	D(19)	134
	3	B(15)	C(22)	H(18)	D(18)	G(20)	F(14)	E(10)	A(20)	137
	4	A(13)	G(13)	E(11)	F(14)	C(13)	D(20)	H(19)	B(12)	115
	5	C(17)	B(14)	D(20)	H(18)	A(15)	E(11)	F(14)	G(18)	127
	6	E(13)	F(19)	A(12)	G(18)	D(14)	C(16)	B(11)	H(13)	116
	7	G(20)	A(14)	F(20)	E(11)	B(19)	H(12)	D(20)	C(19)	135
	8	H(17)	D(13)	B(11)	C(17)	F(13)	G(19)	A(20)	E(12)	122
Totals		130	125	124	127	128	134	124	132	1,024

Note that the arithmetic can be reduced by subtracting the lowest value (10) from all values tabulated. We have not bothered to do this in this example.

The totals for analysts are

$$A: 135; \quad C: 132; \quad E: 92; \quad G: 142;$$
$$B: 114; \quad D: 145; \quad F: 127; \quad H: 137;$$

and the analysis of variance proceeds in the usual manner.

The correction for the mean is $(1{,}024)^2/64 = 16{,}384$.

Total sum of squares

$$= (21)^2 + (19)^2 + (15)^2 + \ldots + (20)^2 + (12)^2 - CM$$
$$= 17{,}134 - 16{,}384 = 750.$$

$$\text{Sum of squares for rows} = \frac{(138)^2 + \ldots + (122)^2}{8} - CM$$

$$= 16{,}461 - 16{,}384 = 77.$$

$$\text{Sum of squares for columns} = \frac{(130)^2 + \ldots + (132)^2}{8} - CM$$

$$= 16{,}391 \cdot 75 - 16{,}384 = 7 \cdot 75$$

$$\text{Sum of squares for treatments} = \frac{(135)^2 + \ldots + (137)^2}{8} - \text{CM}$$

$$= 16{,}648{\cdot}5 - 16{,}384 = 264{\cdot}5$$

and the residual sum of squares $= 750 - (264{\cdot}5 + 7{\cdot}75 + 77) = 400{\cdot}75$.

The full analysis of variance table is

Source of variation	Sum of squares	D.F.	Mean square	F-Ratio	Expectation of mean square
Apparatus (rows)	77	7	11	1·152	$\sigma_0^2 + 8\sigma_3^2$
Lots (columns)	7·75	7	1·107	<1	$\sigma_0^2 + 8\sigma_2^2$
Analysts (treatments)	264·5	7	37·8	3·961	$\sigma_0^2 + 8\sigma_1^2$
Residual (exp. error)	400·75	42	9·542	1	σ_0^2
Total	750·00	63			

The experimental error variance can be represented by σ_0^2, and if they exist the other variances can be represented by σ_1^2 for variance due to analysts, σ_2^2 for the variance due to lots, and σ_3^2 for the variance due to sets of apparatus. However, for 7 and 42 degrees of freedom the F-table quotes values of 1·87 at the 0·10 level of probability and 3·11 at the 0·01 level of probability. Thus there is a highly significant effect due to analysts, but no significant effect due to lots or to sets of apparatus; σ_2^2 and σ_3^2 therefore may not exist and we are concerned only with σ_1^2.

The residual variance is 9·542 so that the expected variance due to experimental error when one analyst performs one test on one lot sample is $9{\cdot}542/8 = 1{\cdot}193$, and the standard error is $\sqrt{1{\cdot}193} = 1{\cdot}39$ based on 42 degrees of freedom. The tabulated value of t for 42 degrees of freedom and a 5 per cent level of significance is 2·02, so that the 95 per cent confidence limits applicable to the mean value obtained by each analyst is $2{\cdot}02 \times 1{\cdot}39 = 2{\cdot}8$. Then the mean and confidence limits for each analyst are

Analyst	Total	Mean	Confidence limits	Analyst	Total	Mean	Confidence limits
A	135	16·9	14·1 − 19·7	E	92	11·5	8·7 − 14·3
B	114	14·2	11·4 − 17·0	F	127	15·9	13·1 − 18·7
C	132	16·5	13·7 − 19·3	G	142	17·8	15·0 − 20·6
D	145	18·1	15·3 − 20·9	H	137	17·1	14·3 − 19·9

Most of these confidence ranges overlap so that we cannot distinguish between the analysts. We can say, however, that analyst E is likely to report lower values for this test than analysts D, G and H. Since there is very little overlap between the confidence ranges for analysts A and E, probably we could include analyst A in the higher value group.

Finally, we can estimate the precision of the test by examining all the variances that must be included in the test. From the expectation column of the analysis of variance table we see that

$$\sigma_0^2 = \text{experimental error variance} = 9\cdot542$$
$$\sigma_1^2 = \text{analyst variance} = 3\cdot532$$
$$\sigma_3^2 = \text{apparatus variance} = 0\cdot182$$
$$\text{Total test variance} = 13\cdot256$$

The reproducibility of the test as given by the 95 per cent confidence limits for a single test is $1\cdot96\sqrt{13\cdot256}$, i.e. $\pm7\cdot13$, and this is extremely high and warrants further investigation.

5.5.2 GRAECO-LATIN SQUARES

Cases arise in which 4 independent effects are to be estimated in a minimum of experimentation and this may be achieved by superposition of two latin squares to form a graeco-latin square. For example two 4×4 latin squares may be combined to form one 4×4 graeco-latin square as follows

L. square A					L. square P					G.L. square AP			
A	B	C	D		P	Q	R	S		AP	BQ	CR	DS
B	A	D	C		R	S	P	Q	→	BR	AS	DP	CQ
C	D	A	B		S	R	Q	P		CS	DR	AQ	BP
D	C	B	A		Q	P	S	R		DQ	CP	BS	AR

In the graeco-latin square each letter of Set A and each letter of Set P occur once and only once in each row and in each column; additionally, each letter of Set A occurs once and only once with each letter of Set P. The square is fully orthogonal and it is possible to estimate the effects separately.

The analysis of variance proceeds as a simple extension of that for the latin square. Sums of squares are obtained for the total, for rows, for columns, for treatments A and for treatments P and the residual sum of squares obtained by difference. Since the total number of degrees of freedom is limited, and is equal to $m^2 - 1$ for an $m \times m$ graeco-latin square, while each variable requires $(m - 1)$ degrees of freedom, then it should be noted that a 3×3 graeco-latin square has no degrees of freedom for the residual so that no test of significance can be made.

Following Euler's original work on graeco-latin squares it had been considered impossible to construct an $m \times m$ graeco-latin square where $m = 4k - 2$, k being any integer; graeco-latin squares may be constructed of course when m is an odd number. However, Parker, Bose and Shrikhande (*Scientific American*, Nov. 1959) used a computer to construct graeco-latin squares where $m = 10, 14, 18, 22$, etc.; that for $m = 6$ still has not been constructed.

The square AP shown above is not the only graceo-latin square that can be constructed from two latin squares and we note that

for a 4 × 4 graeco-latin square there are 3 orthogonal squares
5 × 5 graeco-latin square there are 4 orthogonal squares
6 × 6 graeco-latin square there are NO orthogonal squares
7 × 7 graeco-latin square there are 6 orthogonal squares, etc.

5.5.3 HYPER-GRAECO-LATIN SQUARES

These are a further extension of graeco-latin squares in which three latin squares are combined to permit the estimation of five independent effects with little experimentation.

Square A	*Square P*	*Square W*	*Square APW*
A B C D	P Q R S	W X Y Z	APW BQX CRY DSZ
B A D C	R S P Q	Z Y X W →	BRZ ASY DPX CQW
C D A B	S R Q P	X W Z Y	CSX DRW AQZ BPY
D C B A	Q P S R	Y Z W X	DQY CPZ BSW ARX

The square remains fully orthogonal and all five effects may be estimated provided that they are independent. It is important to remember to allow a reasonable number of degrees of freedom for the residual (as a measure of experimental error against which significance tests may be made) in all squares, and sometimes it may be necessary to introduce replication to cover this. For an $m \times m$ square note that

with 1 set of letters there are $(m^2 - 1) - 3(m - 1) = (m - 1)(m - 2)$
d.f. for the residual;
with 2 sets of letters there are $(m^2 - 1) - 4(m - 1) = (m - 1)(m - 3)$
d.f. for the residual;
and with 3 sets of letters there are $(m^2 - 1) - 5(m - 1) = (m - 1)(m - 4)$
d.f. for the residual.

In general, an $m \times m$ square cannot be used for more than $(m - 2)$ sets of letters if an estimate of error variance is required unless replication is introduced.

EXAMPLE OF USE OF HYPER-GRAECO-LATIN SQUARE: Batches in a manufacturing department were examined for impurity content and it was thought that occasional low-value results could be due to something more than random error. An experiment was designed on the five factors: grades of raw material; analysts; sets of testing apparatus; reactors; and days of the week. The design used and the results obtained are as shown

		Reactors						Reactors			
	1	2	3	4	5	1	2	3	4	5
Days M	CLR	AMS	DNT	BJP	EKQ	2·2	3·9	4·1	4·1	4·6
T	AJT	KDP	BLQ	EMR	CNS	4·1	4·2	4·0	3·1	4·1
W	ENP	CJQ	AKR	DLS	BMT	4·8	4·0	2·3	4·0	4·2
Th	BKS	ELT	CMP	ANQ	DJR	3·9	4·8	4·4	3·9	2·2
F	DMQ	BNR	EJS	CKT	ALP	3·9	2·4	4·7	4·2	4·2

in which the letters A, B, C, D, E represent 5 analysts;
J, K, L, M, N represent 5 sets of testing apparatus; and
P, Q, R, S, T represent 5 grades of raw material.

Taking totals we have

Days	Reactors	Analysts	Sets of apparatus	Grades
M = 18·9	1 = 18·9	A = 18·4	J = 19·1	P = 21·7
T = 19·5	2 = 19·3	B = 18·6	K = 19·2	Q = 20·4
W = 19·3	3 = 19·5	C = 18·9	L = 19·2	R = 12·2
Th = 19·2	4 = 19·3	D = 18·4	M = 19·5	S = 20·6
F = 19·4	5 = 19·3	E = 22·0	N = 19·3	T = 21·4
96·3	96·3	96·3	96·3	96·3

It is immediately obvious that discrepancies in results are likely to be due to Analyst E, who tends to report higher values than his colleagues, or to the use of raw material Grade R which results in just over half the impurity content given by the other four grades.

The analysis of variance is straightforward. Each factor has 4 degrees of freedom leaving 4 for the residual sum of squares which we accept as due to error. Then

Correction for the mean $= (96·3)^2/25 = 370·9476$.

Sum of squares [days]
$$= \frac{(18·9)^2 + (19·5)^2 + (19·3)^2 + (19·2)^2 + (19·4)^2}{5} - 370·9476 = 0·0424.$$

Sum of squares [reactors]
$$= \frac{(18·9)^2 + (19·3)^2 + (19·5)^2 + (19·3)^2 + (19·3)^2}{5} - 370·9476 = 0·0384.$$

Sum of squares [analysts]
$$= \frac{(18·4)^2 + (18·6)^2 + (18·9)^2 + (18·4)^2 + (22·0)^2}{5} - 370·9476 = 1·9104.$$

Sum of squares [apparatus]

$$= \frac{(19\cdot1)^2 + (19\cdot2)^2 + (19\cdot2)^2 + (19\cdot5)^2 + (19\cdot3)^2}{5} - 370\cdot9476 = 0\cdot0185.$$

Sum of squares [grades]

$$= \frac{(21\cdot7)^2 + (20\cdot4)^2 + (12\cdot2)^2 + (20\cdot6)^2 + (21\cdot4)^2}{5} - 370\cdot9476 = 12\cdot6944.$$

The total sum of squares is $(2\cdot2)^2 + (4\cdot1)^2 + \ldots + (2\cdot2)^2 + (4\cdot2)^2 - 370\cdot9476 = 14\cdot7224$, and the sum of squares [error] $= 14\cdot7224 - (0\cdot0424 + 0\cdot0384 + 1\cdot9104 + 0\cdot0185 + 12\cdot6944) = 0\cdot0183$, and the analysis of variance table is as follows

Source of variation	Sum of squares	D.F.	Mean square	F-Ratio	Difference
Days	0·0424	4	0·0106	2·317	No significant difference
Reactors	0·0384	4	0·0096	2·098	
Sets of apparatus	0·0185	4	0·004625	1·011	
Analysts	1·9104	4	0·4776	104·4	Significant at 99% level of probability
Grades of raw materials	12·6944	4	3·1686	692·59	
Error	0·0183	4	0·004575	1	
Total	14·7224	24			

For 4 and 4 degrees of freedom the F-table quotes values of 4·11, 6·39, and 15·98 at the 10, 5, and 1 per cent levels of probability respectively. We conclude, therefore, that days, reactors, and sets of apparatus have no effect on the reported batch impurity contents, but that there are very significant effects due to variations induced by analysts and by grades of raw material.

5.6 factorial designs

A factorial design is one which covers experimentation in which one or more trials of the process are carried out at each of the possible combinations of all the levels of all the factors (variables concerned). A cross design is the simplest example of a factorial design, and may be regarded as an $m \times n$ factorial; that is, a factorial design which investigates operation at m levels of one factor and n levels of the other. The scope of the design may be increased by increasing the number of levels of each factor, or by increasing the number of variables, such as $m \times n \times p \times q \times r$, or by replication.

The following definitions are in common use:

Factor: any feature of the experimental conditions which may be assigned at will from one trial to another, for example temperature, pressure, space velocity, different items of equipment, different operators, different days or shifts, different batches of material, etc. There are two classes of factors
> 1 those that can be varied deliberately and whose effect can be calculated, and
> 2 those that cannot be controlled and which lead to an estimate of residual variance or experimental error.
> Quantitative factors are numerical and have values which can be arranged in order of magnitude while Qualitative factors do not have such values.

Levels: the various values of the factors which are to be examined in the experimentation.

Treatment: the set of levels of all factors employed in any given trial. This is also called a *treatment combination.*

Response: the numerical result of a trial based on any given treatment is called the response of that treatment. The response may be expressed as percentage yield, absolute yield, purity, assay, cost, etc.

Effect of a factor is the change in response produced by a change in the level of a factor. The overall average effect is called the main effect of the factor. Where the effect of one factor depends on the level of another factor the two factors are said to interact, and the effect is called an *interaction.*

A factorial design is the most efficient method that can be used to obtain the required information with the required degree of precision and with the minimum of effort when

1 there are no interactions, so that the factorial design gives the maximum efficiency in the estimation of the effects;
2 interactions exist, their nature being unknown, so that a factorial design is necessary to avoid misleading conclusions;
3 the effect of a factor is estimated at several levels of other factors—as it is in every factorial design—so that the conclusions hold over a wide range of conditions.

5.6.1 2^n FACTORIAL DESIGNS

The 2^n factorial designs are special types of design which can be analysed very easily. In the 2^n factorial design every one of the n variables is assessed at only 2 levels, and the value of 2^n is, of course, the number of trials included in the design. This design is particularly useful when dealing with a large number of variables which may interact; if more complicated designs are warranted, a 3^n factorial or a general $m \times n \times p \times q \ldots$ factorial may be used but the need for these is not frequent.

We can illustrate the procedure demanded in a 2^n factorial by means of a 2^3 design, that is, an experiment in which the trials are to be carried out at 2 levels of each of three factors. Each factor is represented by a capital letter, A, B and C, and since each factor is to be assessed at only two levels then the lower level of each factor can be represented by (1) and the higher level of each factor by the letter a, b or c as the case may be. Thus we use the nomenclature

(1) for the lower level and (a) for the higher level of Factor A,
(1) for the lower level and (b) for the higher level of Factor B, and
(1) for the lower level and (c) for the higher level of Factor C.

In the case of a 2^3 factorial the experimental space may be shown graphically as in Figure 5.6.1, and it is possible to insert values for the level of each

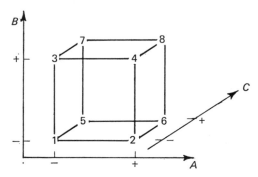

Fig. 5.6.1. EXPERIMENTAL SPACE FOR A 2^3-FACTORIAL

factor and to work with these values. Such a representation cannot be made for a design on four or more factors, but the experimental design for any 2^n factorial can be represented by a plus-minus array, which for a 2^3 factorial is

Run No.	A	B	C
1	−	−	−
2	+	−	−
3	−	+	−
4	+	+	−
5	−	−	+
6	+	−	+
7	−	+	+
8	+	+	+

in which a minus, $-$, stands for the lower level of a factor and a plus, $+$, for the higher level. Correspondence between the plus-minus array, the graphical model and the (1), (a), (b), (c) nomenclature is obvious. The plus-minus array may be extended to any number of factors; the array is arranged in an orderly manner and representation of additional factors is obvious. Using either the plus-minus array or the abc nomenclature an algebraic representation of the eight experimental points can be derived, and this is

(1); a; b; ab; c; ac; bc; abc

in which (1) indicates all factors at their lower levels and each letter indicates the higher level (the 'plus') of a factor.

Usually, in the analysis of a 2^n factorial we are more concerned with the effects than with the mean squares and the following calculations may be made to determine the effects

1. The effect of a factor is the mean value of results at the higher level of the factor—the mean value of results at the lower level of the factor.
2. Interaction is half the difference between the effect of a factor at the higher level of a second factor and the effect of the factor at the lower level of the second factor.

Thus, in a 2^3 factorial between A, B and C we have

the average with A at upper level is $\frac{1}{4}(a + ab + ac + abc)$ [the four runs with $+$ under A in the array] and the average with A at lower level is $\frac{1}{4}((1) + b + c + bc)$ [the four runs with $-$ under A in the array].

The main effect of A, therefore, is $\frac{1}{4}[a + ab + ac + abc - (1) - b - c - bc]$ and if these symbols are treated as algebraic symbols, the expression reduces to

$$A \rightarrow \frac{1}{4}[(a - 1) + (ab - b) + (ac - c) + (abc - bc)]$$
$$\rightarrow \frac{1}{4}[(a - 1).(b + 1).(c + 1)]$$

But it must be remembered at all times that expressions such as this are purely symbolic and cannot be used as such; the expression must be expanded before numerical results can be substituted.

Similarly, we find that $B \rightarrow \frac{1}{4}[(a + 1).(b - 1).(c + 1)]$
and $C \rightarrow \frac{1}{4}[(a + 1).(b + 1).(c - 1)]$

and this provides a simple method of defining any main effect, however many factors may be employed.

We find that Interaction AB

$$= \frac{1}{2}[\frac{1}{2}(abc + ab) - \frac{1}{2}(bc + b) - \frac{1}{2}\{(ac + a) - (c + 1)\}]$$
whence $AB \rightarrow \frac{1}{4}[(a - 1).(b - 1).(c + 1)]$
and similarly we find that $AC \rightarrow \frac{1}{4}[(a - 1).(b + 1).(c - 1)]$
and $BC \rightarrow \frac{1}{4}[(a + 1).(b - 1).(c - 1)]$

The Interaction ABC is defined as half the difference between the interaction AB when C is at its higher level and when C is at its lower level and the algebraic representation is

$$ABC = \tfrac{1}{2}[\tfrac{1}{2}(abc - bc - ac + c) - \tfrac{1}{2}(ab - b - a + 1)]$$
$$\text{whence } ABC \rightarrow \tfrac{1}{4}[(a - 1).(h - 1).(c - 1)]$$

so that any interaction may be determined readily by expansion of the appropriate algebraic identity.

In the general case of the 2^n factorial, the effects and interactions are given by

$$D \rightarrow 1/2^{n-1}.(a + 1).(b + 1).....(d - 1).....(n + 1)$$
$$DL \rightarrow 1/2^{n-1}.(a + 1).(b + 1).....(d - 1).....(l - 1).....(n + 1)$$
$$ABC.....N$$
$$\rightarrow 1/2^{n-1}.(a - 1).(b - 1).....(d - 1).....(l - 1).....(n - 1).$$

5.6.2 GENERAL ANALYSIS OF 2^n FACTORIAL DESIGNS

The procedure to be followed may be detailed as

1 Calculate for each treatment combination the sum of the replicate observations.
2 Arrange these sums in the standard order as shown in the plus-minus array and derive columns of sums and differences by taking the observations in pairs. Derive as many columns as there are variables in the experiment. The values listed in each column are to be the sums of each pair of values in the previous column, tabulated in order, followed by the differences of each pair of values in the previous column, again in order.
3 Note that the effects and mean squares calculated must be divided by the number of replicates.
4 Each main effect, A, B, C, etc., has 1 degree of freedom, giving a total of n d.f. for main effects.
   Each 2-factor interaction, AB, AC, BC, etc., has 1 degree of freedom, giving a total of $\tfrac{1}{2}.n.(n - 1)$ d.f. for 2-factor interactions.
   Each 3-factor interaction, ABC, ABD, BCD, etc., has 1 degree of freedom, giving a total of $\tfrac{1}{6}.n.(n - 1)(n - 2)$ d.f. for 3-factor interactions.
   and generally, each r-factor interaction, ABC...R, etc., has 1 degree of freedom, giving a total of ^nC_r d.f. for r-factor interactions.
   The sum over all treatments has $(2^n - 1)$ degrees of freedom.
   The total sum of squares has $(m.2^n - 1)$ degrees of freedom, where m is the number of replicates at each point.
   The residual sum of squares, taken to be a measure of experimental error, therefore has $2^n(m - 1)$ degrees of freedom.

5 A standard order is defined for listing the treatment combinations and this may be derived from the plus-minus array; it is

(1), a, b, ab, c, ac, bc, abc, d, ad, bd, abd, cd, acd, bcd, abcd, etc.

and this can be extended to any number of factors. The following symbolic expressions hold for a 2^3 factorial

$$A \to \tfrac{1}{4}(a - 1).(b + 1).(c + 1)$$
$$B \to \tfrac{1}{4}(a + 1).(b - 1).(c + 1)$$
$$AB \to \tfrac{1}{4}(a - 1).(b - 1).(c + 1)$$
$$C \to \tfrac{1}{4}(a + 1).(b + 1).(c - 1)$$
$$AC \to \tfrac{1}{4}(a - 1).(b + 1).(c - 1)$$
$$BC \to \tfrac{1}{4}(a + 1).(b - 1).(c - 1)$$
$$ABC \to \tfrac{1}{4}(a - 1).(b - 1).(c - 1)$$

and this method of representation may be extended to any number of factors for any 2^n factorial design.

Corresponding to these symbolic representations is the array

Treatment combination	Total	A	B	AB	C	AC	BC	ABC
(1)	+	−	−	+	−	+	+	−
a	+	+	−	−	−	−	+	+
b	+	−	+	−	−	+	−	+
ab	+	+	+	+	−	−	−	−
c	+	−	−	+	+	−	−	+
ac	+	+	−	−	+	+	−	−
bc	+	−	+	−	+	−	+	−
abc	+	+	+	+	+	+	+	+

in which the signs refer to the signs in the expanded equations for the effects, for example

$$AB \to \tfrac{1}{4}(a - 1).(b - 1).(c + 1)$$
$$= \tfrac{1}{4}(1 - a - b + ab + c - ac - bc + abc).$$

The signs in the factor columns may be multiplied algebraically to give the respective interaction signs, and this array is developed from the plus-minus array given previously. For example, the signs in the AB column are the algebraic products of the corresponding signs in Columns A and B.

This array gives the complete specification for all treatment effects in a 2^3 factorial design. Note that the sum of the signs in any of the main effects columns, or in any column obtained by multiplying the signs in two or more other columns, is always zero, so that all variable factors are orthogonal to each other. Thus all the effects may be estimated from the experimental results. The array table may be used directly to operate on the 8 experimental results obtained in the 2^3 design, with the appropriate signs, to give the effects of the factors.

5.6.3 EXAMPLE: 2^3 FACTORIAL DESIGN

Experimental results, arranged in the standard order, are

$$18 \cdot 5; \ 28 \cdot 5; \ 33 \cdot 5; \ 42 \cdot 5; \ 3 \cdot 0; \ 14 \cdot 0; \ 17 \cdot 0; \ 34 \cdot 0;$$

and whereas these results may be analysed as a block design, by calculating sums of squares for each factor, Yates' method of addition and subtraction of pairs of values is much simpler. We have

Treatment	Response	Col. I	Col. II	Col. III	Effect		Mean square
(1)	18·5	47	123	191			
a	28·5	76	68	47	A →	11·75	276·125
b	33·5	17	19	63	B →	15·75	496·125
ab	42·5	51	28	5	AB →	1·25	3·125
c	3·0	10	29	−55	C →	−13·75	378·125
ac	14·0	9	34	9	AC →	2·25	10·125
bc	17·0	11	−1	5	BC →	1·25	3·125
abc	34·0	17	6	7	ABC →	1·75	6·125
							1,172·875

Col. I, Col. II, and Col. III are formed by adding pairs of values from the preceding column and by subtracting the values in these pairs from each other and in each case the first value is subtracted from the second value of each pair. For example, the values of Col. I are obtained from the column of responses as follows

$$
\begin{array}{ll}
18 \cdot 5 + 28 \cdot 5 = 47 & \quad 28 \cdot 5 - 18 \cdot 5 = 10 \\
33 \cdot 5 + 42 \cdot 5 = 76 & \quad 42 \cdot 5 - 33 \cdot 5 = 9 \\
3 \cdot 0 + 14 \cdot 0 = 17 & \quad 14 \cdot 0 - 3 \cdot 0 = 11 \\
17 \cdot 0 + 34 \cdot 0 = 51 & \quad 34 \cdot 0 - 17 \cdot 0 = 17
\end{array}
$$

followed by

Col. II is derived in this manner from Col. I, and Col. III from Col. II. In any analysis there must be as many columns as there are factors in the experimentation.

The effect of each factor and interaction is obtained by dividing the corresponding value in the final column by 2^{n-1}, so here the divisor is $2^2 = 4$. Since each treatment has only 1 degree of freedom the sum of squares equals the mean square for each treatment and the mean square is given by (Value in final column)$^2/2^n$; the mean squares may be added to give the total sum of squares, and as a check on the eight responses we find that the total sum of squares is

$$5{,}733 - (191)^2/8 = 5{,}733 - 4{,}560{\cdot}125 = 1{,}172{\cdot}875.$$

In this experimentation there is nothing available for a residual sum of squares. The 7 treatments have used the available 7 degrees of freedom and to obtain a residual every run would need to be replicated. However, the mean squares show that those for the treatments ab, ac, bc, and abc are very small and are not significantly different from each other. If no previous estimate of experimental error is available, we can combine these four mean squares to give a residual sum of squares of 22·5 with 4 d.f.

Then the analysis of variance table will be

Source of variation	Sum of squares	D.F.	Mean square	F-Ratio	Significance value
Factor A	276·125	1	276·125	49·09	
Factor B	496·125	1	496·125	88·2	21·20 at 0·01
Factor C	378·125	1	378·125	67·2	probability
Residual (= exptl error)	22·5	4	5·625	1	

Total 1,172·875 7

and we see that all three factors exert a highly significant effect on the process. From the calculated effects in the Yates table we have that

increasing the level of A to its higher value may be expected to increase the yield by 11·75;

increasing the level of B to its higher value may be expected to increase the yield by 15·75;

and increasing the level of C to its higher value may be expected to decrease the yield by 13·75.

Further experimentation would be undertaken at still higher levels of Factors A and B, but in lower levels of Factor C.

Sometimes it is desired not to group the interaction effects to provide an estimate of error, and the standard error may not be known from previous experimentation. In such cases it is possible to obtain an estimate of error from the responses of the high and low levels of a factor if that factor seems not to be of significant effect in the experimentation. For example consider the following experimental data and Yates analysis:

Treatment	Response	Col. I	Col. II	Col. III	Effect		Mean square
(1)	3·6	7·8	10·3	21·7			
a	4·2	2·5	11·4	1·9	A →	0·475	0·45125
b	1·0	7·9	1·1	−9·7	B →	−2·425	11·76125
ab	1·5	3·5	0·8	−0·7	AB →	−0·175	0·06125
c	3·3	0·6	−5·3	1·1	C →	0·275	0·15125
ac	4·6	0·5	−4·4	−0·3	AC →	−0·075	0·01125
bc	1·7	0·7	−0·1	0·9	BC →	0·225	0·10125
abc	1·8	0·1	−0·6	−0·5	ABC →	−0·125	0·03125

The effect of Factor A is much less than that of Factor B and the mean squares show that there is a likelihood that A may be found to be not significant. Then responses at the levels of A are

$$
\begin{aligned}
&\text{a} - (1) \quad \text{which give the differences} \quad 4·2 - 3·6 = 0·6 \\
&\text{ab} - \text{b} \qquad\qquad\qquad\qquad\qquad\qquad 1·5 - 1·0 = 0·5 \\
&\text{ac} - \text{c} \qquad\qquad\qquad\qquad\qquad\qquad 4·6 - 3·3 = 1·3 \\
&\text{abc} - \text{bc} \qquad\qquad\qquad\qquad\qquad\; 1·8 - 1·7 = 0·1 \\
&\qquad\qquad\qquad\qquad\qquad \text{Total} = 2·5 \quad \text{Mean } 0·625
\end{aligned}
$$

The estimated variance of the difference, for three degrees of freedom, is

$$\tfrac{1}{3}[(0·6)^2 + (0·5)^2 + (1·3)^2 + (0·1)^2 - (2·5)^2/4] = 0·1869,$$

from which the variance of the mean difference is $0·1869/4 = 0·046725$, and the standard error of this is $\sqrt{0·046725} = 0·216$.

Now applying the t-test we have $\dfrac{\text{Mean difference}}{\text{Standard error}} = \dfrac{0·625}{0·216} = 2·893$

which fails to reach significance at the 5 per cent level and the estimated value of 0·216 may be used to determine significance within the factorial.

Had we combined the interactions in this factorial the residual sum of squares would have been 0·205, giving a mean square of 0·05125 and an estimated standard error of 0·226, which is reasonable agreement with the value estimated from the levels of A. But when combining sums of squares for interactions to provide an estimate of error it is important to remember how large may be the differences in mean squares based on small numbers of degrees of freedom due to chance alone. The hypothesis that the mean squares calculated are in fact estimates of the same variance, which then may be grouped to form an estimate of error can be tested by Bartlett's Rule, which may be stated as follows:

Suppose there are k mean squares, $V_1, V_2, \ldots, V_i, \ldots, V_k$, based on $Q_1, Q_2, \ldots Q_i \ldots Q_k$ degrees of freedom respectively, and that Q is the total degrees of freedom so that the average variance is

$$V = \frac{\sum Q_i V_i}{Q}$$

Then the criterion measuring the divergence in the V's is

$$M = Q \ln V - \Sigma Q_i . \ln V_i.$$

and significance points for M, where each estimate has 1 degree of freedom are given in Table 5.6.3.

Table 5.6.3 Significance points for Bartlett's rule

Value of K	2	3	4	5	6	7	8	9	10
5% Point	5·1	7·7	10·0	12·0	14·1	15·9	17·9	19·6	21·3
1% Point	8·3	11·5	14·0	16·5	18·9	21·0	23·1	25·2	27·2

For example, suppose the interaction mean squares have been determined as follows

$$\begin{aligned}
\text{ABC} &\to \text{M.S.} = 885 \quad \text{from which log MS} = 2·9469 \\
\text{ABD} &\to \qquad\quad 410 \qquad\qquad\qquad\qquad\quad 2·6128 \\
\text{ACD} &\to \qquad\qquad 2 \qquad\qquad\qquad\qquad\; 0·3010 \quad \text{Each } Q_i = 1 \\
\text{BCD} &\to \qquad\quad 613 \qquad\qquad\qquad\qquad\quad 2·7875 \qquad \text{and } Q = 5 \\
\text{ABCD} &\to \qquad\quad 14 \qquad\qquad\qquad\qquad\quad 1·1461
\end{aligned}$$

$$\Sigma Q_i \log V_i = 9·7943$$

Then
$$\Sigma Q_i \ln V_i = 22·5522.$$

And we have $V = 1,924/5 = 384·8$, whence $\ln V \doteq 5·9526$ and $Q \ln V = 5(5·9526) = 29·7632$ so that $M = Q \ln V - \Sigma Q_i \ln V_i = 29·7632 - 22·5522 = 7·2110$.

But from the M-table, Table 5.6.3, a value of 12·0 is required to indicate heterogeneity at the 5 per cent level of significance and this has not been achieved. Thus the mean squares for interactions may be combined to give a residual sum of squares with 5 degrees of freedom.

However, if the numbers of degrees of freedom in the estimates to be compared are not the same, no exact significance points are available and the following approximation is used; this is sufficiently accurate for small numbers of degrees of freedom. The procedure to be followed is to calculate

1. $A = \dfrac{1}{3(k-1)} - \Sigma \left(\dfrac{1}{Q_i} - \dfrac{1}{Q} \right).$

Note that where the d.f. are the same for all the mean squares then $A = (k+1)/3Q$.

2. $f_1 = (k-1).$ 3. $f_2 = (k+1)/A^2.$

4. $b = \dfrac{f_2}{1 - A + 2/f_2}$

I.S. 1—11

and apply the F-test with f_1 and f_2 degrees of freedom to the ratio

$$\frac{f_2 . M}{f_1(b - M)}.$$

For the 5-interaction example used above, in which $k = 5$ and all $Q_t - 1$ we have

1. $A = 6/(3 \times 5) = 0.4$.
2. $f_1 = k - 1 = 4$.   3. $f_2 = 6/(0.4)^2 = 37.5$.

4. $b = \dfrac{37.5}{1 - 0.4 + 2/37.5} = 57.4$

from which $b - M = 57.4 - 7.21$ (value of M calculated above was 7.211) $= 50.19$ and the F-value is $\dfrac{37.5 \times 7.21}{4 \times 50.19} = 1.35$, which is not significant.

5.7 other designs for analysis of variance

In this chapter we have dealt with some of the more commonly used experimental designs. There are many other designs available for use, among which are

1 BALANCED INCOMPLETE BLOCK DESIGNS: which are used when it is not practicable to examine all the treatments together under comparable conditions, or where it may not be possible to classify the materials in precisely the number of categories required, or the available materials of uniform quality may be sufficient only for a limited number of trials. Where there are more treatments to be examined than can be compared at one time a balanced incomplete randomized block design may be used to provide information in less than the full number of combinations required by a complete balanced design; where the number of treatments exceeds the number that can be examined in every block, a control must be run in every block or balanced complete designs must be used. An IRBD is balanced when every pair of treatments occurs together in a block the same number of times, such as

Run	Treatment			
1	A	B	C	D
2	A	B	C	E
3	A	B	D	E
4	A	C	D	E
5	B	C	D	E

where there is one less testing position than treatment in each block.

2 SYMMETRICAL BALANCED INCOMPLETE BLOCK DESIGNS are those which are arranged so that every pair of blocks has the same number of treatments in common. The necessary and sufficient condition is that the number of blocks equals the number of treatments.

3 YOUDEN SQUARES are symmetrical balanced incomplete block designs in which each treatment occurs once and once only in each position in the block. A Youden square is a latin square from which one or more rows (or columns) are missing; but note that a latin square with one or more rows (or columns) removed is not of necessity a Youden square. The Youden square type is

Block	Treatment			
	A	*B*	*C*	*D*
1	α	β	γ	—
2	γ	—	β	α
3	β	α	—	γ
4	—	γ	α	β

When the number of treatments per block is restricted to 4, Youden squares may be designed to compare 5 treatments in 5 runs, 7 treatments in 7 runs, or 13 treatments in 13 runs; intermediate squares do not exist. These squares eliminate the variation between runs and between positions to achieve maximum precision.

4 NON-BALANCED INCOMPLETE BLOCKS AND LATTICE SQUARES: these designs are used when the number of treatments to be compared is large, so that a completely balanced design would be unwieldy. For the lattice square the number of treatments must be a perfect square as shown

	A						*B*			
Run	*Treatment*					*Run*	*Treatment*			
1	1	2	3	4		1	1	5	9	13
2	5	6	7	8		2	2	6	10	14
3	9	10	11	12		3	3	7	11	15
4	13	14	15	16		4	4	8	12	16

With one square only, treatments within any one row may be compared directly with one another, but comparison of any two treatments occurring in different rows will have a lower degree of precision because of the variation between runs. The second square increases the number of treatments that may be compared directly within runs, and together the two squares enable all pairs of treatments to be compared.

5 CHAIN BLOCK DESIGNS: where physical measurements can be made with high precision and the experimental material may be considered relatively homogeneous, there is no need to put great reliance on replication in order to achieve good results. Excellent estimates may be obtained from one measurement, or from two or three at most. The chain block design proposed to meet this position is very flexible and the number of replications required is very small; for any set of quantities to be compared, some are measured twice and the others once.

6 CONFOUNDING IN FACTORIAL DESIGNS: The 2^n factorial design uses all the degrees of freedom available to cover the various effects; all variables must be controlled to minimize error, and uniform conditions must be maintained over the whole design. However, when three or more factors are to be investigated simultaneously the appropriate factorial design may be larger than can be carried out under uniform conditions, such as one homogeneous batch of raw material, or on one plant unit in a reasonably short time.

The most efficient way of dealing with a situation such as this is to divide the experimental data into smaller blocks in a particular manner so that the main effects of the factors and their more important interactions are investigated under uniform conditions. The heterogeneity introduced in consequence of the size of the experiment is allowed to affect only those interactions which are likely to be unimportant.

The process by which unimportant comparisons are deliberately confused for the purpose of assessing the more important comparisons with greater precision is called *confounding*. Confounding is required in factorial experiments in which the number of observations which can be performed under strictly comparable conditions is less than the number required for the whole design. It is seen immediately that confounded factorial designs serve the same purpose for full factorial designs that balanced or semi-balanced incomplete blocks serve towards random blocks.

7 FRACTIONAL FACTORIAL DESIGNS: a complete factorial design, in which all possible combinations of all the levels of the different factors are investigated, will involve a large number of trials when the number of factors is 5 or more. Such experimentation can lose value because too much interaction causes wastage of information. However, it is possible to investigate the main effects of the factors and their more important interactions in a fraction of the number of trials required for the complete factorial experiment. In effect, a fractional factorial design is equivalent to one block in a system of confounding.

8 FACTORIAL DESIGNS WITH FACTORS AT MORE THAN TWO LEVELS: in which we find four types of factorial design which cover most situations likely to be met in industrial experimentation. These are

(*a*) a multi-factorial experiment with all factors qualitative (i.e. discontinuous levels);

(*b*) a two-factor experiment with both factors quantitative (i.e. denoted by points on a numerical scale);

(*c*) a two-factor experiment with one factor quantitative and one factor qualitative;

(*d*) experiments with several factors, qualitative or quantitative, all at three levels.

In this section we have only mentioned the various designs which can be used, and we hope that the reader's appetite has been whetted. There are several books available which deal in detail with the various techniques of analysis of variance, some of which are mentioned below.

SUGGESTIONS FOR FURTHER READING

3 C. A. BENNETT and N. L. FRANKLIN, Chapters 7 and 8, 1954.
4 O. L. DAVIES (ed.), Oliver & Boyd, London, 1956.
9 K. A. BROWNLEE, Wiley, New York, 1960.
10 H. SCHEFFÉ, Wiley, New York, 1959.
12 B. C. BROOKES and W. F. L. DICK, Heinemann, London, 1963.

CHAPTER SIX

CORRELATION

THE TERM *correlation* is used in dealing with two (or more) variables when any variation in one variable is accompanied by (or associated with) a variation in another variable. There are several kinds of correlation but in this chapter we shall consider only the simple correlations.

6.1 linear relationship between two variables

The term *linear relationship* is used where the relationship between two variables may be expressed as a straight line; where the relationship may be expressed as a curve it is referred to as a *curvilinear relationship*, and the two terms are restricted to these definitions.

A linear relationship between two variables, x and y, is of the form $y = a + bx$ in which a and b are constants whose values may be estimated from the known variations in x and y. Two kinds of relationship are defined: functional relationship and regression relationship, but the equation expressing the relationship is calculated in the same way whether the relationship be functional or regression.

6.1.1 FUNCTIONAL RELATIONSHIP

A functional relationship is a unique relationship between two variables and may be represented by a straight line about which experimental observations will vary only with random experimental error. The more precisely the one variable is measured, the more precise will be the estimate of the other variable. The functional relationship is expressed by the equation $y = a + bx$ which is built of y on x, and then may be used to deduce values of x from measurements of y. This functional equation is unique, and none other can satisfy the measurements.

This is the most common linear relationship and is widely used in chemical industry. For example, calibration curves for a variety of instruments;

yield–temperature relationships; specific gravity–assay relationships, as shown in Figure 6.1.1; melting point–assay lines; etc.

6.1.2 REGRESSION RELATIONSHIP

The regression relationship between two variables is not unique in the sense that, apart from experimental error, a particular value of one variable always corresponds to the same value of the other variable. Experimental observa-

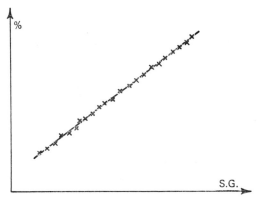

Fig. 6.1.1. FUNCTIONAL RELATIONSHIP BETWEEN ASSAY AND S.G.

tions may vary with experimental error plus a variation between samples, and often the variation between samples is greater than the experimental error.

As an example, consider the possible relationship between the height and weight of the population of adult males. We would find short men who were very fat and so were very heavy, and we would find tall men who were very thin and so might be very light. We would find a distribution of heights for any given weight and a distribution of weights for any given height. So that although there will be errors of measurement of weight and height, most of the variation will be due to variation between individuals and there will be no unique relationship between true height and true weight. However, the average observed height for a given weight will increase with increasing weight, and the average observed weight for a given height will increase with increasing height. Thus in this case the relationship between height and weight can be expressed only by two regression lines: that of height on weight, and that of weight on height.

There are, therefore, two lines indicating the mean value of one variable for given values of the other variable and these are known as the regression lines. For the two variables, x and y, the two regression lines are defined as

1 the regression line of y on x is the locus of mean values of y for any given x; and

2 the regression line of x on y is the locus of mean values of x for any given y;

and generally these two lines are different, as may be seen from Figure 6.1.2, which shows the scatter-diagram of experimental points and the construction of the two regression lines. If there were a functional relationship between the two variables the functional line would be midway between the two regression lines. The two regression lines may be regarded as lines of equal probability.

In every case of linear regression it is necessary to determine whether it is desired to predict y from x, in which case a regression of y on x is required; or to predict x from y, in which case a regression of x on y is necessary. The

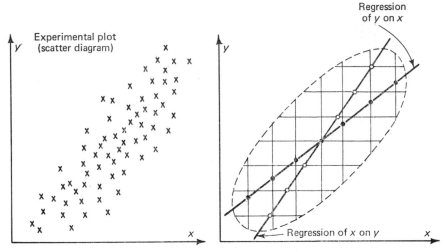

Fig. 6.1.2. CONSTRUCTION OF THE REGRESSION LINES

regression line of y on x should not be used to estimate values of x from measurements of y. If the experimental error is in the y-direction the relationship is estimated as a regression of y on x; if the experimental error is in the x-direction then the relationship is estimated as a regression of x on y. Where both variables are subject to experimental error then a special method of estimating the relationship is used (see Section 6.1.11). The relationship to be used determines the nomenclature adopted, as for example in the regression of y on x represented by the equation $y = a + bx$ in which

a is the value of the intercept on the y-axis; b is the slope of the line; x is a value of the *independent* variable and y is the corresponding value of the *dependent* variable.

The terms *dependent* and *independent* are mathematical terms implying that y may be expressed in terms of x, but that x may not be expressed in terms of y.

The usual procedure for calculation of the regression line is by the method of least squares, but before making this calculation it is often well worth while examining the data by a simple procedure which tells us whether a relationship is likely to exist and this can be done by means of Tukey's quadrant sum test or the quadrant count test, and these tests are discussed next.

6.1.3 THE QUADRANT SUM TEST

This is a very simple method, developed by Tukey, of determining whether or not a significant relationship is likely to exist between the values reported for two variables. The procedure is as follows

1 First plot a scatter diagram for ALL the available pairs of values of the two variables, x and y. The independent variable — the one that can be controlled the more easily and has the less experimental error — is assigned to be the x-variable and is measured on the horizontal axis. The other variable, movements of which are associated with movements of x, becomes the y-variable and is measured on the vertical axis.

2 On the scatter diagram draw the vertical x-median line such that half the points are to the left and the other half to the right of this line. Draw the horizontal y-median line such that half the points are above and the other half below this line.

   Note that if an odd number of pairs of values is being considered obviously there will be an odd number of points plotted on the scatter diagram, therefore there will be at least one point on the x-median and at least one point on the y-median. There may be several points on either median whether the number of points plotted be even or odd. Sometimes duplicate pairs of values will be reported and these must both be recorded on the scatter diagram; the usual method is to plot a 'dot' the first time a pair of values is met and to draw an 'arm' to the dot next time that pair of values occurs.

3 If, with a large number of plotted points, several points lie on a median and these points lie at the extremes of the scatter diagram it is very unlikely that there is a linear relationship between the variables and the exercise may be stopped at this point. If there are several points on a median, within the main body of the other points, they may be neglected.

   If there is one point on the x-median and one point on the y-median these two points must be coalesced into a point having the x-value of the point on the y-median and the y-value of the point on the x-median. If the 'odd point' happens to lie at the intersection of the two medians it may be neglected.

4 The two medians divide the chart into four quadrants. The upper right and lower left quadrants are labelled + (positive, since a line extending between these two quadrants will have a positive slope); the upper left and lower right quadrants are labelled − (negative, since a line

extending between these two quadrants will have a negative slope). The edges of the diagram are labelled Top, Bottom, Left, and Right (or N, S, W, and E if preferred).

5 Starting from the extreme right of the scatter diagram, and moving towards the x-median, count all the points on one side of the y-median before a point is reached on the opposite side of the y-median, and stop counting when this opposite side point is reached. If there are several points reached at this time, some on each side of the y-median, the group is estimated as

$$\frac{\text{Number favourable for inclusion in the quadrant sum being counted}}{1 + \text{number unfavourable for inclusion}}$$

and this estimate is added to the count. Note the number of points counted and designate + or − according to the sign of the quadrant in which they occurred.

6 Make a second count starting from the extreme left of the scatter diagram, moving to the right towards the x-median. Make a third count starting from the bottom of the scatter diagram and moving upwards towards the y-median until the first point on the other side of the x-median is reached.

Make a fourth count starting from the top of the scatter diagram and moving downwards towards the y-median.

Note that each count is entirely independent and no point is to be excluded from any count because it may have been included in a previous count.

7 The quadrant sum is the total of the four counts, and the probability that an association exists between the variables is obtained from the table

Quadrant sum (+ or −)	Probability that a real relationship exists per cent
9	90
10	93
11	95
12	97
13	98
14	99

The probability is affected to a small extent by the size of the sample but usually this is not significant. If the quadrant sum shows that the probability of a relationship is less than 90 per cent (and 95 per cent is to be preferred) then ordinarily there is no justification for any further work to locate and determine the equation of the regression line.

EXAMPLE: Figure 6.1.3 shows the scatter diagram of 37 experimental points with the *x*-median and *y*-median drawn. There is one point (shown as ✕) on each of these medians, the points (5·14, 5108) and (5·24, 5102); these points are coalesced to the point (5·24, 5108; also shown by ✕) and this point replaces the two points on the medians for quadrant counting.

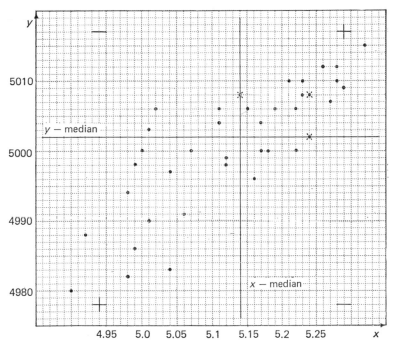

Fig. 6.1.3. SCATTER DIAGRAM FOR QUADRANT SUM TEST FOR ASSOCIATION

Now start counting from the top, counting towards the *y*-median. The first points met are in the + quadrant and there are 10 points counted before any points in the −quadrant are reached. At this level there are 3 points in the + quadrant and 2 points in the −quadrant and this group is evaluated as $3/(1 + 2) = 1$ for inclusion in the quadrant count, giving a total count of +11. Continuing from the other edges of the diagram, we have the quadrant sum composed of

$$
\begin{aligned}
\text{Count from Top} \ &= +11 \\
\text{Bottom} &= +8 \\
\text{Left} \ &= +7\tfrac{1}{2} \\
\text{Right} \ &= +9\tfrac{1}{2} \quad \text{Total} = +36
\end{aligned}
$$

which is a very high value and there can be no doubt that a linear regression may be calculated for these data.

Note that a linear relationship can be deduced for many patterns of data points, including parts of a circle. In general, if the middle section of the data points lies on one side of the regression line (or an estimated regression line drawn by eye) while the end sections of data points both lie on the other side of the line, then a curve will be a better fit to the data than the straight line. Even in these cases the straight line may be a useful first approximation.

6.1.4 DRAWING THE LINEAR REGRESSION LINE

When the quadrant sum test has indicated that a linear relationship may be expected between two variables, it may be required to draw the regression line and calculate the equation. The same scatter diagram may be used for this purpose but here, for clarity, the data points are plotted again in Figure 6.1.4 with the single point replacing the two points on the medians.

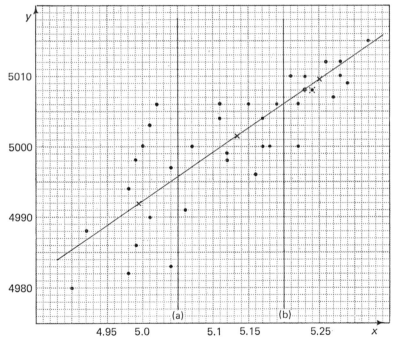

Fig. 6.1.4. LOCATION OF THE REGRESSION LINE

The plotted points are divided by vertical lines (a) and (b) into three numerically equal sections – any excess points are left in the centre section – and the median points of the two outer sections are determined. These median points are joined by a straight line, as shown in Figure 6.1.4. Next the overall median is determined and if the three medians do not lie on a straight line a perpendicular is drawn from the overall median to the line joining the two outer medians.

If the three medians lie on a straight line, this line is the required regression line. If they do not, the regression line is drawn parallel to the outer median line at a point one-third the way up the perpendicular from the outer median line. In Figure 6.1.4 the overall median lies on, or very close to the outer median line and this is accepted as the regression line.

The equation of the regression line may be calculated from the co-ordinates of any two points on the line. For example, from the points (4·95, 4989) and (5·3, 5013) the slope of the line $y = a + bx$ is given by

$$b = \frac{5013 - 4989}{5·3 - 4·95} = \frac{24}{0·35} = 68·6.$$

and the constant, a, is given by $a = 4989 - (68·6 \times 4·95) = 4649$, so that the equation of the regression line is $y = 4649 - 68·6x$.

6.1.5 THE QUADRANT COUNT TEST

On occasions it may seem that the points plotted in a scatter diagram would indicate a linear relationship if only one or two points could be omitted, since these points obviously cause the quadrant sum test to fail. It is not permissible to omit any points, but in such cases as these the quadrant count test may be used.

In this test the points which lie in ANY ONE quadrant are counted, choosing the quadrant which contains the larger OR the smaller number of points and the count is compared with the critical values shown in Table 6.1.1. If the smaller count is equal to or less than the appropriate value in the 'lower' column of the table, or if the larger count is equal to or greater than the appropriate value in the 'upper' column of the table, then there is likely to be a linear relationship with the quoted probability. Both counts may be tried and a significant relationship may be indicated by a successful match of either count.

Figure 6.1.5 shows the scatter diagram of the 37 original points of Figure 6.1.3 with three additional points (marked as x). The quadrant sum test for these 40 points is

$$2 + 2\tfrac{1}{2} + 2 + 1 = 7\tfrac{1}{2}$$

which indicates that there is no significant relationship between the variables, and this is because of the three additional points.

The quadrant count gives 14 for the larger count, or 6 for the smaller count, and comparison with Table 6.1.1 for 40 points shows that either count indicates 95 per cent probability that a linear relationship exists between the two variables. Table 6.1.1 quotes 5 per cent and 1 per cent significance levels for sets of points between 8 and 400, and the quadrant count test has been found to be most useful where a large number of data points is involved.

6.1.6 GENERAL INDICATION OF A LINEAR RELATIONSHIP

Occasionally we are faced with a situation in which numerical values of one variable are associated with vague 'approximates' or relationships of a second

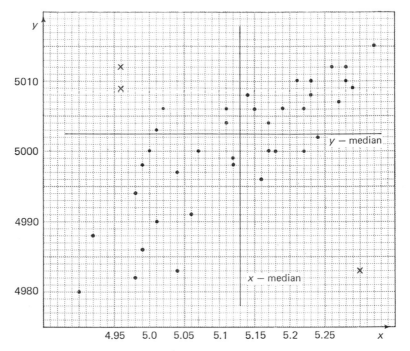

Fig. 6.1.5. SCATTER PLOT FOR QUADRANT COUNT TEST

variable, and it is desired to know whether or not the values indicate a relationship between the two variables. An example of such a situation is where the impurity content of a product, which may be determined analytically and expressed numerically, is believed to be associated with the darkness of the product, which may be estimated by visual inspection.

In such cases the procedure to be adopted is to arrange the numerical values in order of increasing estimates of the vague variable and divide the numerical values into three groups. If there are any excess values these are placed in the middle group. Now determine the average value of each group; if there is a difference of the same sign between the average of Group 1 and the average of Group 2 as there is between the average of Group 2 and the average of Group 3, then some relationship may exist. So transfer the innermost value of each of the outer groups to the inner group and calculate the new averages. If these averages show similar differences to those of the original groups, it is very likely that a linear relationship exists between the two variables.

For example, if we consider the 37 points plotted in Figure 6.1.3, arrange the values of y according to ascending order of x and divide them into three groups, we have

Table 6.1.1 Significance levels for the number of points falling in one quadrant

Number of points	Lower 5%	Lower 1%	Upper 5%	Upper 1%	Number of points	Lower 5%	Lower 1%	Upper 5%	Upper 1%
8–9	0	—	4	—	74–75	13	12	24	25
10–11	0	0	5	5	76–77	14	12	24	26
12–13	0	0	6	6	78–79	14	13	25	26
14–15	1	0	6	7	80–81	15	13	25	27
16–17	1	0	7	8	82–83	15	14	26	27
18–19	1	1	8	8	84–85	16	14	26	28
20–21	2	1	8	9	86–87	16	15	27	28
22–23	2	2	9	9	88–89	16	15	28	29
24–25	3	2	9	10	90–91	17	15	28	30
26–27	3	2	10	11	92–93	17	16	29	30
28–29	3	3	11	11	94–95	18	16	29	31
30–31	4	3	11	12	96–97	18	17	30	31
32–33	4	3	12	13	98–99	19	17	30	32
34–35	5	4	12	13	100–101	19	18	31	32
36–37	5	4	13	14	110–111	21	20	34	35
38–39	6	5	13	14	120–121	24	22	36	38
40–41	6	5	14	15	130–131	26	24	39	41
42–43	6	5	15	16	140–141	28	26	42	44
44–45	7	6	15	16	150–151	31	29	44	46
46–47	7	6	16	17	160–161	33	31	47	49
48–49	8	7	16	17	170–171	35	33	50	52
50–51	8	7	17	18	180–181	37	35	53	55
52–53	8	7	18	19	200–201	42	40	58	60
54–55	9	8	18	19	220–221	47	44	63	66
56–57	9	8	19	20	240–241	51	49	69	71
58–59	10	9	19	20	260–261	56	54	74	76
60–61	10	9	20	21	280–281	61	58	79	82
62–63	11	9	20	22	300–301	66	63	84	87
64–65	11	10	21	22	320–321	70	67	90	93
66–67	12	10	21	23	340–341	75	72	95	98
68–69	12	11	22	23	360–361	80	77	100	103
70–71	12	11	23	24	380–381	84	81	106	109
72–73	13	12	23	24	400–401	89	86	111	114

Reproduced from *Rapid Statistical Calculations* by M. H. Quenouille, Charles Griffin & Co. Ltd., by permission of author and publisher.

	1.		2.	3.
	4980		4991	5010
	4988		5000	5006
	4982		5004	5000
	4994		5006	5008
	4986		4998	5010
	4998		4999	5002
	5000		5008	5012
	4990		5006	5007
	5003		4996	5010
	5006		4998	5012
	4983		5002	5009
	4997		4998	5015
			5006	
Total:	59,907		65,012	60,101
Average:	4,992		5,001	5,008

The difference Average 3 — Average 2 is $+7$ and the difference Average 2 — Average 1 is $+9$, which is promising. The last two points in column 1 had the same value of the x-variable so we transfer both of these points and the top point of column 3 to column 2 and recalculate. This gives

	1.	2.	3.
Total:	49,927	80,012	55,091
Average:	4,993	5,001	5,008

and the difference Average 3 — Average 2 is $+7$, and the difference Average 2 — Average 1 is $+8$ and we conclude that it is very likely that a linear relationship exists between the two variables.

6.1.7 CALCULATION OF THE LINEAR REGRESSION EQUATION

The equations for the functional line and the regression line are calculated in the same way. The method of least squares is used, and this minimizes the sum of squares of the deviations of the observed values from the regression line. But remember that when calculating any regression equation the factor y is to be applied to the variable which is the more likely to contain the greater experimental error.

Then, given two series of values for these variables, measured in pairs,

$$(x_1, y_1), (x_2, y_2), \ldots, (x_n, y_n)$$

the equation of the regression line of y on x is

$$(y - \bar{y}) = b(x - \bar{x}) \quad \text{or} \quad y = \bar{y} + b(x - \bar{x})$$

which is the equation of a line passing through $(\bar{x}, \bar{y})$, the mid-point of the experimental area, and having slope b; b is called the regression coefficient and of course may be positive or negative. By the method of least squares it follows that

$$b = \frac{\sum (x - \bar{x})(y - \bar{y})}{\sum (x - \bar{x})^2} = \frac{\sum xy - (\sum x)(\sum y)/n}{\sum x^2 - (\sum x)^2/n}$$

which permits easy calculation of the equation of the regression line. An equation can be calculated for any number of points (two or more) unless the points lie at the vertices of a regular geometrical figure.

Having estimated the value of b it is necessary to determine whether or not the value is real, that is, that b is significantly different from zero, and this can be done either by calculating the confidence limits for b or by carrying out an F-test on the regression.

Firstly, to calculate the confidence limits for b

The sum of squares due to the regression is $\dfrac{[\sum (x - \bar{x})(y - \bar{y})]^2}{\sum (x - \bar{x})^2}$

The total sum of squares is given by $\sum (y - \bar{y})^2$

So that the sum of squares about the regression is

$$\sum (y - \bar{y})^2 - \frac{[\sum (x - \bar{x})(y - \bar{y})]^2}{\sum (x - \bar{x})^2},$$

and this has $(n - 2)$ degrees of freedom (we can say that we have lost 1 d.f. for each of the two means). Then the regression mean square, s^2, is given by

$$s^2 = \frac{\sum (y - \bar{y})^2 - [\sum (x - \bar{x})(y - \bar{y})]^2/[\sum (x - \bar{x})^2]}{n - 2}$$

and the error variance of b is given by

$$V(b) = \frac{s^2}{\sum (x - \bar{x})^2}$$

so that the 95 per cent confidence limits for b are given by $b \pm t\sqrt{[V(b)]}$ in which t is the tabulated t-value for 0·05 probability and $(n - 2)$ degrees of freedom. If these confidence limits do not include zero, then b is real and the regression line exists. If these confidence limits include zero, then we have no reason to say that b must have any value other than zero, b is not real and the regression line may not exist.

Next we can establish the 95 per cent confidence limits for the regression as $\pm t_1 s$ in which t_1 is the tabulated t-value for 0·05 probability and infinite degrees of freedom and the final regression equation is in the form

$$y = \bar{y} + b(x - \bar{x})[\pm t_1 s]$$

and the value $\bar{y} - b\bar{x}$ can be condensed to give the value of a, the equation assuming the form

$$y = a + bx[\pm t_1 s]$$

Alternatively, we can form the analysis of variance table and test for the existence of a real relationship by the F-test between the mean squares:

Source of variation	Sum of squares	D.F.	Mean square	F-Ratio
Due to the regression	$b.\sum (x - \bar{x})(y - \bar{y})$	1	$b.\sum (x - \bar{x})(y - \bar{y})$	F
About the regression	$\sum (y - \bar{y})^2 - b.\sum (x - \bar{x})(y - \bar{y})$	$n - 2$	s^2	1
Total	$\sum (y - \bar{y})^2$	$n - 1$		

and the calculated value of F is compared with the tabulated value for 1 and $(n - 2)$ d.f. in the usual way.

For example consider the data of the scatter diagram in Figure 6.1.3, where we have the pairs of values

x	y	x	y	x	y	x	y
4·90	4980	5·02	5006	5·14	5008	5·22	5000
4·92	4988	5·04	4983	5·15	5006	5·23	5008
4·98	4982	5·04	4997	5·16	4996	5·23	5010
4·98	4994	5·06	4991	5·17	4998	5·24	5002
4·99	4986	5·07	5000	5·17	5002	5·26	5012
4·99	4994	5·11	5004	5·18	4998	5·27	5007
5·00	5000	5·11	5006	5·19	5006	5·28	5010
5·01	4990	5·12	4998	5·21	5010	5·28	5012
5·01	5003	5·12	4999	5·22	5006	5·29	5009
						5·32	5015

For these values the sums of squares and crossproducts are calculated and found to be

$$\sum (x - \bar{x})^2 = 0\cdot4728; \; \sum (y - \bar{y})^2 = 2{,}886; \; \sum (x - \bar{x})(y - \bar{y}) = 29\cdot53;$$
$$\text{and } n = 37.$$

Then, if the equation of the regression line is written as $y = \bar{y} + b(x - \bar{x})$, the regression coefficient, b, is given by

$$b = \frac{\sum (x - \bar{x})(y - \bar{y})}{\sum (x - \bar{x})^2} = \frac{29\cdot53}{0\cdot4728} = 62\cdot46$$

(compared with the value of 68·6 we estimated in Secton 6.1.4)

The sum of squares due to the regression $= \dfrac{[\sum (x - \bar{x})(y - \bar{y})]^2}{\sum (x - \bar{x})^2} = 1{,}844\cdot44$

so that the sum of squares about the regression is $2{,}886 - 1{,}844\cdot44 = 1{,}041\cdot56$, and an analysis of variance shows that

Source of variation	Sum of squares	D.F.	Mean square	F-Ratio
Due to the regression	1,844·44	1	1,844·44	61·98
About the regression	1,041·56	35	29·76	1
Total	2,886·00	36		

For 1 and 35 degrees of freedom the F-table quotes a value of about 7·4 at the 0·01 level of probability; the calculated value is greater than this and so we can say, with 99 per cent probability of being correct, that there is a real difference between the two mean squares. The mean square 'About the regression' is adequately small and we expect the regression line to be real and the calculated equation to be valid.

Otherwise, we can continue determining confidence limits for b:

The sum of squares about the regression is based on $(n - 2)$ degrees of freedom and the regression mean square is $1{,}041 \cdot 56/35 = 29 \cdot 76 (= s^2)$. The variance of the regression coefficient is given by

$$V(b) = \frac{s^2}{\sum (x - \bar{x})^2} = \frac{29 \cdot 76}{0 \cdot 4728} = 62 \cdot 94$$

and the standard error of this is $\sqrt{62 \cdot 94} = 7 \cdot 93$.

The tabulated t-value for $0 \cdot 05$ probability and 35 degrees of freedom is $2 \cdot 03$, and the 95 per cent confidence limits for b are $62 \cdot 46 \pm (2 \cdot 03)(7 \cdot 93)$ or $46 \cdot 36$ to $78 \cdot 56$. Since these confidence limits do not include zero we can expect b to be real and the calculated regression equation to be valid.

The mean values calculated from the data are $\bar{x} = 5 \cdot 13$ and $\bar{y} = 5{,}000 \cdot 5$, so that the calculated regression equation is $y = 5{,}000 \cdot 5 + 62 \cdot 46(x - 5 \cdot 13)$ or $y = 4{,}680 \cdot 1 + 62 \cdot 46x$ and the confidence limits of this are $\pm 1 \cdot 96s = 1 \cdot 96 \sqrt{29 \cdot 76} = \pm 10 \cdot 69$, and the regression equation is reported as $y = 4{,}680 \cdot 1 + 62 \cdot 46x [\pm 10 \cdot 69]$.

We can extend our analysis by one further step and determine confidence limits for mean values of y from any given values of x. The *variance of the regression estimate*, that is the variance of the mean value of y for any given value of x, say x_a, is given by

$$V(\bar{y}_a) = s^2 \left[\frac{1}{n} + \frac{(x_a - \bar{x})^2}{\sum (x - \bar{x})^2} \right]$$

which for our example becomes $V(\bar{y}_a) = 29 \cdot 76 \left[\dfrac{1}{37} + \dfrac{(x_a - 5 \cdot 13)^2}{0 \cdot 4728} \right]$

$$= 0 \cdot 804 + 62 \cdot 94(x_a - 5 \cdot 13)^2,$$

the standard error is the square root of this quantity, and the 95 per cent confidence limits are given by $\pm t \sqrt{[V(\bar{y}_a)]}$ where t is the tabulated t-value for $0 \cdot 05$ probability and $(n - 2)$ degrees of freedom. The confidence limits can be calculated for a selection of values x_a and the limits plotted as two curves, one on each side of the regression line; the two curves are closest together at the point $\bar{x}$.

When calculating a linear regression the following rules of behaviour must be followed at all times

1 The data under consideration must include the entire range of values of the independent variable for which information is required.

2 Measurement of the data must not be so inaccurate that it obliterates any possible correlation.

3 No data shall be discarded without good reason, and a better fit is not a good reason.

4 Correlation indicates association between the variables and not causation. Causation must be proved otherwise.

6.1.8 THE CORRELATION COEFFICIENT

In the preceding sections of this chapter we have given linear relationship a fairly full statistical treatment. While it is nice, and proper, to be able to follow these procedures, it is not always necessary to do so, and use of the correlation coefficient provides one way of determining the significance of a linear relationship without a t-test or an F-test, though in fact there is very little difference in the arithmetic required.

The correlation coefficient is defined as the covariance of x and y divided by the product of the standard deviations of x and y.

$$r = \frac{\text{cov}(x, y)}{s_x \cdot s_y} = \frac{\sum (x - \bar{x})(y - \bar{y})}{\sqrt{[\sum (x - \bar{x})^2 \cdot \sum (y - \bar{y})^2]}}.$$

Values of r which are minima to indicate 'just significant' relationships are given in Table 6.1.2. Comparison of the calculated value of r with the tabulated value for the appropriate probability and degrees of freedom may be used instead of the analysis of variance procedure described in Section 6.1.7. Identical results are obtained.

Usually the calculated correlation coefficient is compared with the 0·05 probability value, indicating a 95 per cent probability of acceptance, to determine whether or not a significant relationship exists between the two variables.

The regression equation of y on x may be written as

$$\frac{y - \bar{y}}{s_y} = r \cdot \frac{x - \bar{x}}{s_x}$$

that is the correlation coefficient is numerically the same as the regression coefficient when the variates are expressed in standardized measure. Similarly, the regression equation of x on y is

$$\frac{x - \bar{x}}{s_x} = r \cdot \frac{y - \bar{y}}{s_y}.$$

The sum of squares due to the regression of y on x is

$$\frac{[\sum (x - \bar{x})(y - \bar{y})]^2}{\sum (x - \bar{x})^2} = r^2 \cdot \sum (y - \bar{y})^2,$$

Table 6.1.2 The correlation coefficient

Minimum values of 'r' to indicate a 'just significant' relationship

D.F. = n − 2	Probability 0·10	0·05	0·02	0·01	0·001
1	0·988	0·997	1·000	1·000	1·000
2	0·900	0·950	0·980	0·990	0·999
3	0·805	0·878	0·934	0·959	0·991
4	0·729	0·811	0·882	0·917	0·974
5	0·669	0·754	0·833	0·874	0·951
6	0·621	0·707	0·789	0·834	0·925
7	0·582	0·666	0·750	0·798	0·898
8	0·549	0·632	0·715	0·763	0·872
9	0·521	0·602	0·685	0·735	0·847
10	0·497	0·576	0·658	0·708	0·823
11	0·476	0·553	0·634	0·683	0·801
12	0·457	0·532	0·612	0·661	0·780
13	0·441	0·514	0·592	0·641	0·760
14	0·426	0·497	0·574	0·623	0·742
15	0·412	0·482	0·558	0·605	0·725
16	0·400	0·468	0·542	0·590	0·708
17	0·389	0·455	0·528	0·575	0·693
18	0·378	0·444	0·515	0·561	0·679
19	0·369	0·433	0·503	0·549	0·665
20	0·360	0·423	0·492	0·537	0·652
25	0·323	0·381	0·445	0·487	0·597
30	0·296	0·349	0·409	0·449	0·554
35	0·275	0·325	0·381	0·418	0·519
40	0·257	0·304	0·358	0·393	0·490
45	0·243	0·287	0·338	0·372	0·465
50	0·231	0·273	0·322	0·354	0·443
60	0·211	0·250	0·295	0·325	0·408
70	0·195	0·232	0·274	0·302	0·380
80	0·183	0·217	0·256	0·283	0·357
90	0·173	0·205	0·242	0·267	0·337
100	0·164	0·195	0·230	0·254	0·321

This table is taken from Table 3 of Fisher and Yates, *Statistical Tables for Biological, Agricultural and Medical Research,* published by Oliver and Boyd Limited, Edinburgh, and by permission of the authors and publishers.

that is, r^2 represents the proportion of the total sum of squares in one variable accounted for by the other variable. The sum of squares about the regression of y on x is $(1 - r^2) \sum (y - \bar{y})^2$, and therefore the ratio

$$\frac{\text{Mean square due to the regression}}{\text{Mean square about the regression}} = \frac{(n - 2).r^2}{1 - r^2}.$$

The equation for the measure of the spread of the points in a scatter diagram about the regression line is

$$f(y, x) = (1 - r^2)^{\frac{1}{2}} . \left[\frac{\sum (y - \bar{y})^2}{n - 2} \right]^{\frac{1}{2}}$$

and the confidence limits are given by $\pm t.f(y, x)$ where t is the tabulated t-value for the required probability and infinite degrees of freedom.

For the example data in Section 6.1.7 we have

$$r = \frac{\sum (x - \bar{x})(y - \bar{y})}{\sqrt{[\sum (x - \bar{x})^2 . \sum (y - \bar{y})^2]}} = \frac{29 \cdot 53}{\sqrt{(0 \cdot 4728 \times 2{,}886)}} = \frac{29 \cdot 53}{36 \cdot 93} = 0 \cdot 8$$

Table 6.1.2 shows that for 35 degrees of freedom and 0·05 probability the 'just significant' value is 0·325; the calculated value of r is greater than this so there is more than 95 per cent probability that a real linear relationship exists between the two variables.

The equation of the regression line of y on x (substituting values quoted in Section 6.1.7) is

$$\frac{y - 5{,}000 \cdot 5}{\sqrt{2886}} = \frac{0 \cdot 8(x - 5 \cdot 13)}{\sqrt{0 \cdot 6876}}$$

which reduces to $y = 4{,}680 + 62 \cdot 46x$ as before.

The measure of the spread of the points about the regression line is given by

$$f(y, x) = \sqrt{\frac{(1 - 0 \cdot 64) \cdot 2886}{35}} = \sqrt{29 \cdot 68}$$

which is almost exactly the value obtained in Section 6.1.7; the difference is due to rounding errors.

6.1.9 COMPARISON OF TWO CALCULATED LINEAR REGRESSIONS

Where two independent samples of n_1 and n_2 pairs of observations, which provide estimates of regression b_1 and b_2 respectively, are derived from the same population (or are thought to have been derived from this population) a t-test may be applied to determine whether or not one linear regression fits both sets of observations.

The estimate of the assumed common array variance of the y's is obtained from the pooled sums of squares of the residuals from the two fitted regression lines; the degrees of freedom of this estimate, s^2, now number $(n_1 + n_2 - 4)$. If a regression coefficient, b, may be applied to both samples, then the value

$$t = \frac{b_1 - b_2}{s\sqrt{[1/ \sum\limits_{i=1}^{n_1} (x_i - \bar{x}_1)^2 + 1/ \sum\limits_{j=1}^{n_2} (x_j - \bar{x}_2)^2]}}$$

will follow Student's distribution, and a calculated value of t may be compared with the tabulated value of t for $(n_1 + n_2 - 4)$ degrees of freedom and the required probability.

As an example consider the case where it is suspected that a change in the process has resulted in increased corrosion in the reaction vessel. The measurements made are the thickness of the reactor wall and the duration of service.

A satisfactory linear regression of thickness on time was obtained for each period reviewed. The data are

1 for the period immediately before the process change:

$$\sum (x_1 - \bar{x}_1)^2 = 10,285; \sum (y_1 - \bar{y}_1)^2 = 0\cdot1261; \sum (x_1 - \bar{x}_1)(y_1 - \bar{y}_1)$$
$$= -22\cdot16; n_1 = 23$$

from which $b_1 = -0\cdot00681$ and sum of squares about the regression $= 0\cdot0785$ for 21 d.f.

2 for the period immediately following the process change:

$$\sum (x_2 - \bar{x}_2)^2 = 2,763\cdot7; \sum (y_2 - \bar{y}_2)^2 = 0\cdot2655; \sum (x_2 - \bar{x}_2)(y_2 - \bar{y}_2)$$
$$= -18\cdot82; n_2 = 15$$

from which $b_2 = -0\cdot00781$ and sum of squares about the regression $= 0\cdot1373$ for 13 d.f.

From these values of b_1 and b_2 it seems that the data are not from the same population and corrosion after the process change is about three times its value before the change was made. To confirm this we calculate

the overall variance for both regressions is s^2, where

$$s^2 = (0\cdot0785 + 0\cdot1373)/(21 + 13) = 0\cdot2158/34 = 0\cdot006347,$$

whence the overall standard error is $s = 0\cdot07966$, and the value of t is given by

$$t = \frac{0\cdot00681 - 0\cdot00215}{0\cdot07966 \times \sqrt{(1/10,285 + 1/2,763\cdot7)}} = \frac{0\cdot00466}{0\cdot0017} = 2\cdot741$$

The tabulated t-value for $0\cdot01$ probability and 34 degrees of freedom is $2\cdot73$. The calculated value is greater than this so that it is 99 per cent probable that a real difference exists between b_1 and b_2 and we may accept that there has been a real increase in corrosion since the process change was made.

Note that an alternative to this procedure would be to translate the two samples of n_1 and n_2 pairs of observations into two samples of n_1 and n_2 ratios, taking the ratio y_i/x_i of each pair of observations, and then apply a t-test to the two sets of ratios to determine whether or not they belong to the same population.

6.1.10 GOODNESS OF FIT

Use of a calculated regression equation assumes that the regression line really fits the data. But if a significant lack of fit is present, predictions obtained from the regression equation will be biased and may be seriously in error. A check on the representational accuracy of the model may be included as a routine part of the analysis if arrangements can be made beforehand to make duplicate runs on some or all of the experimental points.

If we let N be the number of experimental points in a single replicate of the experimental design;

R be the number of these points run in duplicate, so that $1 \leqq R \leqq N$;

y_{i1} and y_{i2} be the observed values for the i-th duplicated point; and

$SS[A]$ be the residual sum of squares from the regression analysis, with Q d.f. (in a linear regression this will be the sum of squares about the regression).

The sum of squares for duplicates is given by

$$SS[D] = \left[\sum_{i=1}^{R} (y_{i1} - y_{i2})^2 \right] \Big/ 2$$

and this has R degrees of freedom, and the difference between these sums of squares gives the sum of squares for lack of fit, $SS[LF]$, that is,

$$SS[LF] = SS[A] - SS[D] \text{ with } (Q - R) \text{ degrees of freedom.}$$

The F-ratio is given by

$$F = \frac{\text{Mean square } [LF]}{\text{Mean square } [D]} \text{ for } (Q - R) \text{ and } R \text{ degrees of freedom}$$

which can be tested for significance by comparison with tabulated values.

If the calculated value of F is greater than the tabulated value at any desired probability level, then the calculated equation is inadequate and there is a significant lack of fit. Inclusion of further terms may be necessary in a polynomial, or a non-linear model may provide a better fit than an assumed linear model.

It has been suggested that as long as the calculated value of F is less than *three* times the tabulated value, probably the calculated regression equation is usable. Significant lack of fit up to this extent may not render results of the regression analysis completely invalid.

The experimental data given in Section 6.1.7 consists of 37 pairs of values of which there are ten duplicated values of x. All 37 pairs of values were used to calculate the regression equation in Section 6.1.7, but if we now assume that the ten duplications were made to assess the goodness of fit—and we assume the second entry of each x-value to be the duplicate—calculation of the regression equation is made from the coded data (datum for $x = 4.90$; datum for $y = 4,980$)

x	y	x	y	x	y	x	y	x	y
0	0	0·12	26	0·24	28	0·29	26	0·36	32
0·02	8	0·14	3	0·25	26	0·31	30	0·37	27
0·08	2	0·16	11	0·26	16	0·32	26	0·38	30
0·09	6	0·17	20	0·27	18	0·33	28	0·39	29
0·10	20	0·21	24	0·28	18	0·34	22	0·42	35
0·11	10	0·22	18						

For these data we have

$$\sum (x - \bar{x})^2 = 0{\cdot}3670; \; \sum (y - \bar{y})^2 = 2{,}553; \; \sum (x - \bar{x})(y - \bar{y}) = 25{\cdot}37;$$

$$n = 27.$$

The calculated value of b is 69·128 and the regression equation is $y = 4{,}645{\cdot}4 + 69{\cdot}13x$. The sum of squares due to the regression is 1753·78, and the sum of squares about the regression, $SS[R]$ is 799·22 with 25 degrees of freedom. Then the regression mean square is $799{\cdot}22/25 = 31{\cdot}9688$ and the variance of b is $31{\cdot}9688/0{\cdot}3670 = 87{\cdot}1084$. The standard error of this is 9·333, so that the confidence limits of b are $69{\cdot}128 \pm (2{\cdot}06)(9{\cdot}333)$. These limits do not include zero and so we accept the regression equation as valid, but we have the data available to test the goodness of fit of this equation.

The sum of squares for duplicates, $SS[D]$ is given by

$$SS[D] = \frac{12^2 + 8^2 + 13^2 + 14^2 + 2^2 + 1^2 + 4^2 + 6^2 + 2^2 + 2^2}{2} = 328$$

so that the sum of squares for lack of fit, $SS[LF]$, is $799{\cdot}22 - 328 = 471{\cdot}22$ for $25 - 10 = 15$ d.f.

The F-test for lack of fit is made from the mean squares and is

$$F = \frac{MS[LF]}{MS[D]} = \frac{471{\cdot}22/15}{328/10} = \frac{31{\cdot}4}{32{\cdot}8} \text{ which is less than } 1.$$

We have no reason to suppose, therefore, that the calculated regression line is not an adequate fit to the data.

6.1.11 FITTING A STRAIGHT LINE WHEN BOTH VARIABLES ARE SUBJECT TO ERROR

It is necessary to distinguish between the linear regression equation of a variable y on a second variable x and a linear functional relationship between two variables x and y which are masked by errors. The former equation is still available for prediction even if the variable x is subject to error, but is not necessarily appropriate for a functional relationship when one exists. It is possible to set up maximum likelihood equations for the second problem, but they do not lead to a unique solution without further assumptions, such as an assumption about the relative magnitude of the errors in x and y.

In the common case where the observations have equal weight — or where it is not possible to distinguish the weightings so that they must be assumed to be equal — it is useful to consider the following elementary method

1 For the location of the fitted straight line use as one point the mean co-ordinates $(\bar{x}, \bar{y})$ just as in the least squares method, where $\bar{x}$ and $\bar{y}$ are the mean values of the n values of x and y under consideration.

2 For the slope of the line, first divide the n plotted points into 3 groups, the equal numbers k in the two extreme groups being chosen to be as near $n/3$ as possible; the three groups are to be non-overlapping when considered in the x-direction. The join of the mean co-ordinates $(x_1, \bar{y}_1)$ and $(\bar{x}_3, \bar{y}_3)$ for the two extreme groups is taken as the slope of the required line.

Thus the fitted straight line passes through $(\bar{x}, \bar{y})$ and has slope $(\bar{y}_3 - \bar{y}_1)/(\bar{x}_3 - \bar{x}_1)$, and its equation may be written as

$$y - \bar{y} = \frac{\bar{y}_3 - \bar{y}_1}{\bar{x}_3 - \bar{x}_1}(x - \bar{x});$$

the value $(\bar{y}_3 - \bar{y}_1)/(\bar{x}_3 - \bar{x}_1)$ becomes the regression coefficient and it is necessary to determine the confidence limits of this coefficient. If we represent this regression coefficient by b, and if we let β represent the true regression coefficient (if it exists) we can form the t-statistic for the difference between these values as

$$t = \frac{(\bar{x}_3 - \bar{x}_1)(b - \beta)\sqrt{(k/2)}}{s(\beta)}$$

where $s(\beta)$ is the standard error of β. Although the denominator in this expression depends on β, this t-variate may be used to determine a confidence interval for β. Thus for a value t corresponding to any chosen probability value and $(n - 3)$ degrees of freedom we have the confidence interval determined from an equation for β derived from this t-statistic, since

$$(\bar{x}_3 - \bar{x}_1)^2(b - \beta)^2 k/2 = t^2 . s^2(\beta)$$

The variance of β has $(n - 3)$ degrees of freedom — we have lost one degree of freedom for each of the group means — and this equation may be rewritten as

$$(\bar{x}_3 - \bar{x}_1)^2(b - \beta)^2 k = 2t^2(s_y^2 - 2\beta s_{xy} + \beta^2 s_x^2)/(n - 3)$$

in which
$$s_x^2 = \sum_1 (x_{1i} - \bar{x}_1)^2 + \sum_2 (x_{2i} - \bar{x}_2)^2 + \sum_3 (x_{3i} - \bar{x}_3)^2$$
$$s_y^2 = \sum_1 (y_{1i} - \bar{y}_1)^2 + \sum_2 (y_{2i} - \bar{y}_2)^2 + \sum_3 (y_{3i} - \bar{y}_3)^2$$

and
$$s_{xy} = \sum_1 (x_{1i} - \bar{x}_1)(y_{1i} - \bar{y}_1) + \sum_2 (x_{2i} - \bar{x}_2)(y_{2i} - \bar{y}_2)$$
$$+ \sum_3 (x_{3i} - \bar{x}_3)(y_{3i} - \bar{y}_3).$$

For example, consider the 27 pairs of values given in Section 6.1.10. These may be arranged in three groups of 9, so that $n = 27$ and $k = 9$, in ascending order of the x-variable to give

Group 1		Group 2		Group 3	
x	y	x	y	x	y
4·90	4980	5·07	5000	5·21	5010
4·92	4988	5·11	5004	5·22	5006
4·98	4982	5·12	4998	5·23	5008
4·99	4986	5·14	5008	5·24	5002
5·00	5000	5·15	5006	5·26	5012
5·01	4990	5·16	4996	5·27	5007
5·02	5006	5·17	4998	5·28	5010
5·04	4983	5·18	4998	5·29	5009
5·06	4991	5·19	5006	5·32	5015
Means 4·99	4990			5·26	5009

overall means: $\bar{x} = 5\cdot13$; $\bar{y} = 5000$.

Then the slope of the regression line may be given by

$$b = \frac{5009 - 4990}{5\cdot26 - 4\cdot99} = \frac{19}{0\cdot27} = 70\cdot37$$

and the equation of the line is $y - 5000 = 70\cdot37(x - 5\cdot13)$ or $y = 4639 + 70\cdot37x$ and we shall investigate the confidence limits for the regression coefficient. We find that

$$s_x{}^2 = 0\cdot0219 + 0\cdot0116 + 0\cdot0104 = 0\cdot0439,$$
$$s_y{}^2 = 588\cdot2 + 158\cdot2 + 109\cdot6 = 856.$$

and
$$s_{xy} = 1\cdot424 + 0\cdot013 + 0\cdot596 = 2\cdot033$$

and the equation to derive the confidence limits of β is

$$(5\cdot26 - 4\cdot99)^2(70\cdot37 - \beta)^2 \cdot \tfrac{9}{2} = t^2(856 - 4\cdot066\beta + 0\cdot0439\beta^2)/24$$

The tabulated t-value for 0·05 probability and 24 degrees of freedom is 2·064, and the equation reduces to

$$9(0\cdot27)^2(70\cdot37 - \beta)^2 = 2(2\cdot064)^2(856 - 4\cdot066\beta + 0\cdot0439\beta^2)/24.$$

This equation reduces to $0\cdot9762\beta^2 - 138\cdot54\beta + 4483\cdot766 = 0$ and the solutions of this are $\beta = 70\cdot96 \pm 21\cdot03$.

We should use this value of $\beta = 70\cdot96$ in the regression equation, and note that the confidence limits, at $\pm21\cdot03$, are wider than the $\pm16\cdot1$ calculated in Section 6.1.7 because now we have assumed that values of x as well as values of y are subject to error; formerly we assumed that errors in x did not exist or were negligible.

6.1.12 RANK CORRELATION

In Section 6.1.6 we discussed briefly the situation in which numerical values of one variable are associated with vague approximate values or rankings of a second variable, and we were able to estimate whether or not a linear relationship was likely to exist between the two variables. Now we shall deal with the case where no numerical values are attached to the available data points for either variable; instead we have a series of rankings for each variable which show no more than whether the value of a variable at any given data point is better or worse than the value of that variable at any other data point.

For example, 12 samples of a product might be examined on two characteristics such as taste and colour, and it is required to determine if there is any relationship between these two characteristics from the data, quoted here in the order of testing, with samples ranked 1 to 12 for each characteristic according to preference, 1 being the best and 12 being the worst in each case

Sample:	1	2	3	4	5	6	7	8	9	10	11	12
Ranks for taste:	8	3	11	1	2	9	10	12	4	7	5	6 (x)
Ranks for colour:	10	1	12	3	6	8	7	11	4	9	2	5 (y)

The procedure to adopt in these cases is to determine the difference, d, between each pair of associated rankings, taking the differences consistently so that for the i-th pair of x and y values $d_i = x_i - y_i$. Where there are n pairs of associated values the rank correlation coefficient, ρ, is given by

$$\rho = 1 - \frac{6\Sigma d^2}{n(n^2 - 1)},$$

(and this is Spearman's rank correlation coefficient). This relationship may be deduced very simply from the relationship for the correlation coefficient.

We see that when the rankings in each pair are equal, every $d_i = 0$ and so the value of the rank correlation coefficient is 1. When the rankings are exactly reversed there is the greatest possible disagreement between the rankings, $\Sigma d^2 = n(n^2 - 1)/3$ and the value of the rank correlation coefficient is -1. For any two sets of rankings chosen at random the expected value of the rank correlation coefficient is zero, and for indication of an acceptable relationship of >0.5 should be obtained.

'Student' showed that the standard deviation of this rank correlation coefficient is given by

$$\sigma_\rho = \frac{1}{\sqrt{(n - 1)}}$$

but the distribution is not normal, especially for small samples and this value cannot be used as a standard error. For values of n greater than 8 a t-value can be calculated from the relationship

$$t = \frac{\rho\sqrt{(n - 2)}}{\sqrt{(1 - \rho^2)}}$$

and this can be tested against tabulated t-values for $(n - 2)$ degrees of freedom.

For example, consider the series of rankings quoted above for taste (x) and colour (y). The differences ($x - y$) in every case are

$$-2, 2, -1, -2, -4, 1, 3, 1, 0, -2, 3, 1$$

and these add up to zero, as they should. Then we have $n = 12$, and $\sum d^2 = 54$, so that

$$\rho = 1 - \frac{6 \times 54}{12(143)} = 1 - 0.19 = 0.81$$

This is quite a high value and we accept that there is an association between the two characteristics such that a good colour product is associated with a pleasing (or at any rate, acceptable) taste.

A t-test for this value of the coefficient gives

$$t = \frac{0.81\sqrt{10}}{\sqrt{(1 - 0.6561)}} = 4.19$$

which, on comparison with tabulated values of t for 10 degrees of freedom we find to be significant at the 0·002 level of probability. This is very a high level of significance and we can be assured that there is a real association between the two variables. If we re-arrange the rankings according to the order of ranks for taste we can see that this association seems to be likely merely by inspection

Ranks for taste:	1	2	3	4	5	6	7	8	9	10	11	12
Ranks for colour:	3	6	1	4	2	5	9	10	8	7	12	11.

6.1.13 TRANSFORMATIONS TO LINEARITY

Many occasions arise when an equation has been calculated and found to be acceptable as the best fit to the experimental data and is non-linear in form, that is, it may be drawn as a curve of some sort. Or the experimental data, when plotted, indicate that whatever may be the relationship, if it can be calculated, it will not be a straight line. Prediction from and comparison with the calculated equation are made much easier if some transformation of either or both variables can be made to convert the curvilinear into a linear form. It may be found that a transformation performs more than one function; it may make a skewed distribution more nearly normal, and it may make the standard deviation (or variance) independent of the mean. Some of the more common transformations used to achieve these ends are mentioned below.

1 *Equation* $y = a + bx$: This is the required form of equation to which other non-linear forms are to be transformed. When y is plotted against x on arithmetic graph paper (written as plot y vs. x; y on the vertical axis, x on the horizontal axis) a is the intercept on the y-axis and b is the slope of the line.

2 *Equation $y = a/x$*: Use the transform $X = 1/x$ and plot the equation $y = aX$. That is, plot y vs. X on arithmetic graph paper. The line passes through the origin and has slope a. This is a pretty severe transformation and may be found useful when dealing with rate data; the transform converts, for example, pounds per hour into hours per pound.

3 *Equation $y = a/(b + x)$*: Use the transform $Y = 1/y$ and plot the equation $Y = A + Bx$, where $A = b/a$ and $B = 1/a$. That is, plot Y vs. x on arithmetic graph paper.

4 *Equation $y = ax/(b + x)$*: Use the transform $Y = 1/y$, $X = 1/x$ and plot the equation $Y = A + BX$, where $A = b/a$ and $B = 1/a$. That is, plot Y vs. X on arithmetic graph paper.

5 *Equation $y = ax^b$*: Use the transform $Y = \log y$, $X = \log x$ and plot the equation $Y = A + bX$ where $A = \log a$. That is, plot Y vs. X on log-log graph paper.

6 *Equation $y = ab^x$*: Use the transform $Y = \log y$ and plot the equation $Y = A + Bx$ where $A = \log a$ and $B = \log b$. That is, plot Y vs. x on log-arithmetic graph paper.

7 *Equation $y = ax^{bx}$*: Use the transform $Y = \log y$, $X = x \log x$ and plot the equation $Y = A + bX$ where $A = \log 1$. That is, plot Y vs. X on log-arithmetic graph paper.

8 *Equation $y = ae^{bx}$*: Use the transform $Y = \ln y$ and plot the equation $Y = A + bx$, where $A = \ln a$. That is, plot Y vs. x on log-arithmetic graph paper.

9 *Equation $y = ae^{b/x}$*: Use the transform $Y = \ln y$, $X = 1/x$, and plot the equation $Y = A + bX$ where $A = \ln a$. That is, plot Y vs. X on log-arithmetic graph paper.

10 *Equation $y = a + bx + cx^2$*: This cannot be transformed easily into linear form; to a great extent any possible transformation depends on the values of a, b, and c. If the equation can be rewritten as $y = (a + bx)^c$ then use the transform $Y = \log y$, $X = \log (a + bx)$ and plot the equation $Y = cX$. That is, plot Y vs. X on log-log graph paper.

Note that in cases where y represents a proportion or percentage, the transformation $Y = \sin^{-1} \sqrt{y}$ gives a transform to linearity when Y is plotted against x. This arcsin transformation assumes that the extremes zero and 100 per cent are feasible.

With more complicated relationships such as the Gompertz growth curve, $y = ka^{x^b}$, the transform $Y = \log (\log y/k)$, $X = \log x$, gives a transform to linearity when Y is plotted against X.

6.2 curvilinear relationship between two variables

Curvilinear regression is a procedure whereby polynomials of form

$$y = a_0 + a_1 x + a_2 x^2 + \ldots$$

may be fitted to a given set of data so that the best estimates of a_0, a_1, a_2, etc., are obtained. Here again the method of least squares is used, so that the deviations of the observations from the curve are minimized.

It is not possible to elucidate high-order polynomials without the aid of an electronic computer, but simple cases may be solved by transforming the equation above to one of the form

$$y = B_0 + B_1 P_1 + B_2 P_2 + \ldots$$

in which the B's are constants to be fitted to the data and the P's are orthogonal polynomials in x such that P_i is of degree i, that is

$$P_i = c_{0i} + c_{1i}x + c_{2i}x^2 + \ldots + c_{ii}x^i$$

and in this equation the c's are constants calculated from the experimental data and which depend only on the values of x.

Note that with orthogonal polynomials $\sum_n P_i P_j = 0$ for all $i \neq j$, and this relationship is most useful in cases where the x-values are at *regular and equally-spaced intervals*, 0–1–2–3–4–etc., with one value of y corresponding to each value of x. Values in geometric series, such as 0·01–0·1–1·0–10·0 etc. would be transformed to equally spaced intervals by using logarithms of these values.

6.2.1 METHOD OF DETERMINATION OF A CURVILINEAR RELATIONSHIP

The method falls conveniently into five steps, as follows

1 DERIVATION OF THE ORTHOGONAL COEFFICIENTS, ϕ: For the use of orthogonal coefficients the x-values must be equally spaced. The ϕ-coefficients are tabulated in *Biometrika Tables for Statisticians*, Volume 1, Table 47, but may be calculated from the following formulae

$$\phi_0 = 1$$
$$\phi_1 = \lambda_1(x - \bar{x})$$
$$\phi_2 = \lambda_2\{(x - \bar{x})^2 - (n^2 - 1)/12\}.$$
$$\phi_3 = \lambda_3\{(x - \bar{x})^3 - (3n^2 - 7)(x - \bar{x})/20\}.$$
$$\phi_4 = \lambda_4\{(x - \bar{x})^4 - (3n^2 - 13)(x - \bar{x})^2/14 + 3(n^2 - 9)(n^2 - 1)\}.$$
$$\phi_5 = \lambda_5\{(x - \bar{x})^5 - 5(n^2 - 7)(x - \bar{x})^3/18$$
$$+ (15n^4 - 230n^2 + 407)(x - \bar{x})/1008\}.$$
$$\phi_6 = \lambda_6\{(x - \bar{x})^6 - 5(3n^2 - 31)(x - \bar{x})^4/44$$
$$+ (5n^4 - 110n^2 + 329)(x - \bar{x})^2/176 - 5(n^2 - 1)(n^2 - 9)(n^2 - 25)/$$
$$14,784\}$$

in which

ϕ_i are the orthogonal coefficients to be used for estimation of the i-th regression coefficient,

n is the number of observations in the experiment (the number of equally-spaced values of x, usually, as there will be one value of y for each value of x),

$\bar{x}$ is the average of the values of x used in the experimentation, and

x takes the values 1 to n in turn, so that there are n coefficients in each ϕ-column,

and λ_i is a scale factor; there is one value of λ for each ϕ-column and these are shown in Table 6.2.1.

Table 6.2.1 Values of the scale factor λ for orthogonal coefficients

n	ϕ_1	ϕ_2	ϕ_3	ϕ_4	ϕ_5	ϕ_6
3	1	3				
4	2	1	10/3			
5	1	1	5/6	35/12		
6	2	3/2	5/3	7/12	21/10	
7	1	1	1/6	7/12	7/20	77/60
8	2	1	2/3	7/12	7/10	11/60
9	1	3	5/6	7/12	3/20	11/60
10	2	1/2	5/3	5/12	1/10	11/240
11	1	1	5/6	1/12	1/40	11/120
12	2	3	2/3	7/24	3/20	11/360
13	1	1	1/6	7/12	7/120	11/360
14	2	1/2	5/3	7/12	7/30	77/720
15	1	3	5/6	35/12	21/20	11/180
16	2	1	10/3	7/12	1/10	1/60
17	1	1	1/6	1/12	1/20	1/60
18	2	3/2	1/3	1/12	3/10	11/240
19	1	1	5/6	7/12	1/40	11/120
20	2	1	10/3	35/24	7/20	11/120
21	1	3	5/6	7/12	21/40	77/360
22	2	1/2	1/3	7/12	7/30	11/720

Note that $\phi_0 = 1$ for all n.

2 ESTIMATION OF THE CONSTANTS, B: The standard formula is

$$B_i \rightarrow b_i = \left(\frac{\lambda}{T}\right)_i \sum_{j=1}^{n} \phi_i y_j$$

which is read as 'the best estimate of B_i is given by b_i, which is calculated as ...'. The values of T, λ, and ϕ are tabulated (BTS Table 47) for various values of n. As mentioned previously, λ is a scale factor, and T is the total of the squares of the values of ϕ in each column. Thus values of ϕ_1 are used to calculate the constant b_1, values of ϕ_2 for b_2, values of ϕ_3 for b_3, etc., and since $\phi_0 = 1$ for all n, b_0 is estimated by $\bar{y}$.

3 CALCULATION OF THE POLYNOMIALS: The polynomials, P, are calculated individually, by means of the formula

$$P_{r+1} = P_r P_1 - \frac{r^2(n^2 - r^2)}{4(4r^2 - 1)} \cdot P_{r-1}$$

in which n is the number of observations made and $r = 0, 1, 2, 3$, etc. in turn.

The first two values of P are

$$P_0 = 1$$
$$P_1 = (x - \bar{x}) \text{ in every case,}$$

and the other polynomials, P_2, P_3, etc. are calculated from these using the equation for P_{r+1} given above.

4 ANALYSIS OF VARIANCE OF THE POLYNOMIALS: When the polynomials have been calculated it is necessary to determine the contribution of each to the sum of squares for the regression, and thereby find out how many terms are essential to the regression equation. Since the polynomials are orthogonal, all are independent; the sums of squares may be estimated separately and are additive.

The residual sum of squares is reduced by each term added into the equation, as for example with one term we have

the total sum of squares is $\sum (y - \bar{y})^2$, and
the residual after one term is $\sum [y - \bar{y} - b(x - \bar{x})]^2$.

So with the orthogonal polynomials, $\sum (y - b_0 P_0)^2$ is reduced after one term to $\sum (y - b_0 P_0 - b_1 P_1)^2$ and so on, and the effect of adding extra terms is determined easily.

The formula to determine these effects is that the reduction in the residual sum of squares due to the inclusion of the term $b_i P_i$ is a quantity given by $[\sum \phi_i y]^2 / T_i$, so that

the sum of squares due to $b_0 P_0$ is $(\sum y)^2 / n$;
the sum of squares due to $b_1 P_1$ is $(\sum \phi_1 y)^2 / T_1$;
the sum of squares due to $b_2 P_2$ is $(\sum \phi_2 y)^2 / T_2$; etc.

The analysis of variance table may be constructed from all the $b_i P_i$ terms, naming them linear, quadratic, cubic, quartic, quintic, etc. In the analysis of variance table the residual mean square gives an estimate of experimental error so that a decision may be made whether the polynomial gives an adequate fit, and how many terms are required for this adequate fit.

5 CALCULATION OF CONFIDENCE LIMITS: Confidence limits for the coefficients are obtained from the formula

$$V(b_i) = \left(\frac{\lambda^2}{T}\right)_i \sigma_0^2$$

and the $100(1 - 2\alpha)$ per cent confidence limits are $b_i \pm t_\alpha \sqrt{[V(b_i)]}$.

Confidence limits for the response, y, are obtained from the variance given by

$$V(y) = V(b_0) + P_1^2 . V(b_1) + P_2^2 . V(b_2) + \ldots$$

in which $P_1 = (x - \bar{x})$ etc. as in paragraph 3. A numerical value of x is substituted to give a numerical value of y, and the tabulated t-value for the appropriate probability and degrees of freedom is applied to give the confidence limits.

6 EXAMPLE CALCULATION. Analysis of samples taken from a reactor at hourly intervals shows the following percentage conversions, and it is required to determine the best fit equation relating percentage conversion with time.

Time in hours (x):	0	1	2	3	4	5	6	7	8	9	10
% Conversion (y):	0	2	4	14	20	28	40	44	54	57	53

The experimental data are shown in Figure 6.2.1. The data for orthogonal polynomials for $n = 11$, taken from BTS, Table 47, with the experimental y-values and ϕy calculations are

x	y	ϕ_0	ϕ_1	ϕ_2	ϕ_3	$\phi_1 y$	$\phi_2 y$	$\phi_3 y$
0	0	1	-5	15	-30	0	0	0
1	2	1	-4	6	6	-8	12	12
2	4	1	-3	-1	22	-12	-4	88
3	14	1	-2	-6	23	-28	-84	322
4	20	1	-1	-9	14	-20	-180	280
5	28	1	0	-10	0	0	-280	0
6	40	1	1	-9	-14	40	-360	-560
7	44	1	2	-6	-23	88	-264	-1012
8	54	1	3	-1	-22	162	-54	-1188
9	57	1	4	6	-6	228	342	-342
10	53	1	5	15	30	265	795	1590
		T:	110	858	4,290	Totals 715	-77	-810
		λ:	1	1	$\frac{5}{6}$			

The plotted data points in Figure 6.2.1 indicate that a third-degree equation should provide an adequate fit and we shall work on that assumption so that calculations are made using ϕ-values only up to ϕ_3.

The estimates of the regression coefficients are

$$b_0 = \frac{\Sigma y}{n} = \frac{316}{11} = 28 \cdot 73.$$

$$b_1 = \left(\frac{\lambda}{T}\right)_1 \Sigma \phi_1 y = \frac{1}{110} \times 715 = 6 \cdot 5.$$

$$b_2 = \left(\frac{\lambda}{T}\right)_2 \Sigma \phi_2 y = \frac{1}{858} \times -77 = -0 \cdot 09.$$

$$b_3 = \left(\frac{\lambda}{T}\right)_3 \Sigma \phi_3 y = \frac{5}{6 \times 4290} \times -810 = -0 \cdot 19.$$

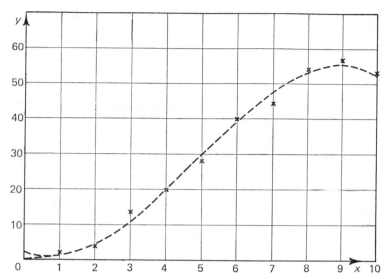

Fig. 6.2.1. EXAMPLE OF CURVILINEAR REGRESSION

Now we can test the significance of the estimates of the coefficients

The total sum of squares is $\quad \Sigma(y - \bar{y})^2 = 13{,}910 - 9{,}077{\cdot}8$
$$= 4{,}832{\cdot}2$$

The sum of squares for $b_1 P_1$ is $(\Sigma\phi_1 y)^2/T_1 = (715)^2/110 = 4{,}647{\cdot}5$
leaving a residual sum of squares $= 184{\cdot}7$

The sum of squares for $b_2 P_2$ is $(\Sigma\phi_2 y)^2/T_2 = (77)^2/858 = 6{\cdot}9$
leaving a residual sum of squares $= 177{\cdot}8$

The sum of squares for $b_3 P_3$ is $(\Sigma\phi_3 y)^2/T_3 = (810)^2/4{,}290 = 152{\cdot}9$
leaving a residual sum of squares $= 24{\cdot}9$

and as this residual sum of squares has 7 degrees of freedom, the residual mean square seems to be acceptably small, and not much is to be gained by introducing higher terms into the regression. The analysis of variance is

Source of variation	Sum of squares	D.F.	Mean square	F-Ratio
Linear term $b_1 P_1$	4,647·5	1	4,647·5	1,305
Quadratic term $b_2 P_2$	6·9	1	6·9	1·9
Cubic term $b_3 P_3$	152·9	1	152·9	43
Residual	24·9	7	3·56	1
Total	4,832·2	10		

For 1 and 7 degrees of freedom the F-table quotes values of 3·59 and 12·25 at the 0·1 and 0·01 levels of probability respectively. The linear and cubic terms, therefore, are highly significant, and the quadratic term is not significant. However, since the cubic term is to be included in the regression, we shall include the quadratic term as well.

Using the relationship for the polynomials $P_{r+1} = P_r P_1 - r^2(n^2 - r^2)P_{r-1}/4(4r^2 - 1)$, we have

$$P_0 = 1.$$
$$P_1 = (x - \bar{x}) = (x - 5).$$

$$P_2 = (x - 5)(x - 5) - \frac{1(121 - 1)}{4(4 - 1)} = x_2 - 10x + 15.$$

$$P_3 = (x^2 - 10x + 15)(x - 5) - \frac{4(121 - 4)}{4(16 - 1)}(x - 5)$$
$$= x^3 - 15x^2 + 57.2x - 36.$$

The regression equation $y = b_0 + b_1 P_1 + b_2 P_2 + b_3 P_3$ may be written now as

$$y = 28.73 + 6.5(x - 5) - 0.09(x^2 - 10x + 15)$$
$$- 0.19(x^3 - 15x^2 + 57.2x - 36)$$

which reduces to $y = 1.72 - 3.468x + 2.76x^2 - 0.19x^3$,

and we can compare the experimental values of y, from which this equation was derived, with values for $\hat{y}$ calculated from the equation

$x =$	0	1	2	3	4	5	6	7	8	9	10
$y =$	0	2	4	14	20	28	40	44	54	57	53
$\hat{y} =$	1.72	0.82	4.3	11.0	19.85	29.63	39.23	47.51	53.34	55.56	53.04

These values are plotted in Figure 6.2.1 and the curve is drawn. We note that since a third-degree equation was postulated for the curvilinear regression, the curve has two turning points within the limits of the experimentation. It is an obvious fact that values of y cannot increase for values of x decreasing below $x = 1$, and so the curve is 'adjusted' so that it connects to the point (0, 0).

Finally, we can calculate the confidence limits of the regression coefficients. Using the relationship given in paragraph 5 and noting that the residual (or error) variance, σ_0^2, is calculated in the analysis of variance table to be 3·56, we have

$$V(b_1) = (\lambda^2/T)_1.\sigma_0^2 = (1/110) \times 3.56 = 0.03236$$

so that the standard error of b_1 is $\sqrt{0.03236} = \pm 0.18$. The tabulated value of t for 0·05 probability and 7 degrees of freedom is 2·365, and so the 95 per cent confidence limits for b_1 are $6.5 \pm (2.365 \times 0.18)$. These limits do not include zero and we may accept the calculated value of b_1 as valid.

Similarly, $V(b_2) = (\lambda^2/T)_2.\sigma_0^2 = (1/858) \times 3.56 = 0.004149$

so that the standard error of b_2 is $\sqrt{0.004149} = \pm 0.0644$, and the 95 per cent confidence limits for b_2 are $-0.09 \pm (2.365 \times 0.0644)$. These confidence limits include zero, and we have no reason to believe that b_2 may have any value other than zero; we deduced from the analysis of variance that b_2 was a doubtful starter but we decided to include the quadratic term because the cubic term was significant. Now we can check on the confidence limits of b_3.

$$V(b_3) = (\lambda^2/T)_3 \cdot \sigma_0^2 = \frac{25 \times 3.56}{36 \times 4,290} = 0.0005763$$

so that the standard error of b_3 is $\sqrt{0.0005763} = \pm 0.024$, and the 95 per cent confidence limits for b_3 are $-0.19 \pm (2.365 \times 0.024)$. These confidence limits do not include zero and we may accept the calculated value of b_3 as valid. On balance, therefore, we retain all three coefficients and accept the regression equation to be $y = 1.72 - 3.468x + 2.76x^2 - 0.19x^3$.

Note that if replicate values of y are obtained in the experimentation the same number of replicate values, r, must be obtained at each value of x. This number r must be included in every calculation made; for example, the expression for b becomes

$$b_i = \left(\frac{\lambda}{rT}\right)_i \sum_{j=1}^{n} \phi_i y_j$$

and r appears as a divisor in calculations for the sums of squares. In these cases the total of the r values of y obtained at each value of x is used as the experimental y for the calculations.

In many instances in chemical industry a third-degree equation has proved an adequate fit to the experimental data and it has become customary, where a given set of data obviously is not a straight line relationship, to start with polynomials up to the cubic and then calculate the analysis of variance table. This shows how adequately the cubic equation fits the data and indicates whether or not further terms are advisable.

6.2.2 METHOD OF APPROXIMATING TO A CURVILINEAR REGRESSION BETWEEN TWO VARIABLES

Calculation of a curvilinear regression by the method of least squares and the use of orthogonal polynomials demands that data be obtained at regular and equally-spaced intervals of the x-variable. Often it is not possible to arrange experimentation so that values of one variable are observed at equidistant values – or values which may be transformed somehow or another into equidistant values – of the other variable. Sometimes values of both variables are obtained by experimentation or by analysis of a reaction mixture so that levels of the x-variable cannot be predetermined.

In such cases it is not possible to carry out the regular statistical procedure to calculate the equation of the curvilinear regression line, and it is possible only to provide an approximate fit to the data. The goodness of fit of this approximate fit will depend on the judgment of the fitter; the following procedure, which uses only simple arithmetic, may assist any judgment to be made.

1 First all the data points are plotted on a scatter diagram which has values of x on the horizontal axis (this is to be the independent variable) and values of y, the dependent variable, on the vertical axis. From the plot an estimate is made of the general shape of the curve which seems most likely to fit most of the points; 'most' of the points because there always seem to be a small number of plotted points which will not agree with any sort of a curve. Bearing in mind that a curve such as

$$y = a_0 + a_1x + a_2x^2 \qquad \text{has 1 turning point,}$$
$$y = a_0 + a_1x + a_2x^2 + a_3x^3 \text{ has 2 turning points, etc.,}$$

and in general a curve has one less turning point than the highest power of x in the equation, so that the degree of the desired equation can be determined.

2 There will be one more coefficient a_i in the equation than there are terms in x, and it is necessary to select from the data, or to impose on the data, a number of points equal to the number of coefficients in the equation. Selection can be made by selecting points which are very near the imagined curve; imposed points are derived from the most likely experimental points.

3 The values of each selected point, as read from the scatter diagram, are substituted in the agreed equation to give an equal number of linear equations in the coefficients a_i which may be solved by the usual methods.

Thus, for a cubic equation, which will have two turning points, there will be four coefficients a and four points must be chosen from the scatter diagram. If these four points are represented by the pairs (x_1, y_1), (x_2, y_2), (x_3, y_3) and (x_4, y_4) then substitution of these values in the general cubic equation will give four equations in the four coefficients

$$y_1 = a_0 + a_1x_1 + a_2x_1^2 + a_3x_1^3 \qquad (1)$$
$$y_2 = a_0 + a_1x_2 + a_2x_2^2 + a_3x_2^3 \qquad (2)$$
$$y_3 = a_0 + a_1x_3 + a_2x_3^2 + a_3x_3^3 \qquad (3)$$
$$y_4 = a_0 + a_1x_4 + a_2x_4^2 + a_3x_4^3 \qquad (4)$$

which may be solved for a_0, a_1, a_2 and a_3.

For example, Figure 6.2.2 shows the scatter plot obtained from 24 experimental runs in each of which the percentages of products A and B formed in a reaction were determined. The general impression from the data points is that of a curve, and if it is thought that the best fit equation should be of form

$$y = a_0 + a_1x + a_2x^2 + a_3x^3$$

then four points are required to determine the coefficients in this equation. We know that at time zero, before the reaction has started, neither A nor

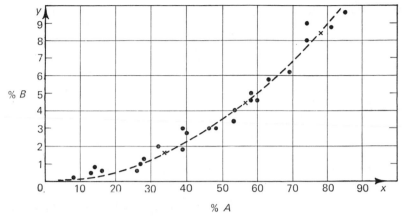

Fig. 6.2.2. APPROXIMATE CURVILINEAR REGRESSION

B is present in the reaction mix and so the point $(0, 0)$ must be chosen. This means, of course, that $a_0 = 0$.

Next a point near the other end of the supposed curve must be selected, and for this the four points at $x = 74$ (2 points), 81 and 85 are considered. The last point $(85, 9\cdot6)$ may indeed lie on the true regression line but should not be chosen as there is no point beyond it, in the current experimentation, which can confirm it. The point $(74, 9\cdot0)$ seems to be wrong as it is out of alignment with the other three points. Both the points $(74, 8\cdot0)$ and $(81, 8\cdot8)$ seem about right and so we select the mid-point between these two, $(77\cdot5, 8\cdot4)$ as one of our points.

By similar arguments two points between these extremes are chosen, and we select the points $(56\cdot5, 4\cdot5)$ as midway between the points $(53, 4\cdot0)$ and $(60, 5\cdot0)$ and $(33\cdot5, 1\cdot6)$ as midway between the points $(28, 1\cdot3)$ and $(39, 1\cdot8)$. The four selected points are shown on the scatter diagram by $\times$; they are fairly well distributed over the experimental area. These four points on substitution in the general cubic equation give

$$a_0 = 0 \tag{1}$$

and hence

$$8\cdot4 = 77\cdot5a_1 + (77\cdot5)^2 a_2 + (77\cdot5)^3 a_3 \tag{2}$$
$$4\cdot5 = 56\cdot5a_1 + (56\cdot5)^2 a_2 + (56\cdot5)^3 a_3 \tag{3}$$
$$1\cdot6 = 33\cdot5a_1 + (33\cdot5)^2 a_2 + (33\cdot5)^3 a_3 \tag{4}$$

and the last three equations may be written more conveniently as

$$0\cdot108{,}387 = a_1 + 77\cdot5a_2 + 6{,}006\cdot25a_3 \tag{2}$$
$$0\cdot079{,}646 = a_1 + 56\cdot5a_2 + 3{,}192\cdot25a_3 \tag{3}$$
$$0\cdot047{,}761 = a_1 + 33\cdot5a_2 + 1{,}122\cdot25a_3 \tag{4}$$

from which $(2) - (3)$ and $(2) - (4)$ give

$$0\cdot028{,}741 = 21a_2 + 2{,}814a_3 \quad \text{or} \quad 0\cdot001{,}369 = a_2 + 134a_3, \text{ and}$$
$$0\cdot060{,}626 = 44a_2 + 4{,}884a_3 \quad \text{or} \quad 0\cdot001{,}378 = a_2 + 111a_3.$$

and it follows immediately that

$$a_3 = -0.000,000,4$$
$$a_2 = +0.001,322$$
and
$$a_1 = +0.003,913$$

and the curvilinear regression calculated from the coordinates of the four imposed points is

$$y = 0.003,913x + 0.001,322x^2 - 0.000,000\ 4x^3.$$

In this case the coefficient of x^3 is so small that the probability that the cubic term can be neglected must be considered. The value of the cubic term can be determined by substituting two or three values of x, in turn, in this equation when the contribution of the cubic term to the value of y is made clear. If this contribution is not measurable under the conditions of the experiment then the cubic term may be omitted from the equation. For instance, the scatter plot shows that a value of x greater than 90 is very unlikely, so with a value $x = 90$ the contribution to y of the cubic term is $-0.000,000,4 \times (90)^3$ $= -0.2916$, which is a measurable quantity, so that the cubic term must be retained in the equation, certainly for higher values of x. We see that at $x = 10$, the contribution of the cubic term is -0.0004 which is not measurable, and we may decide to include the cubic term when $x > 50$ but to neglect it at lower values.

Convenient values of x are substituted in the equation to provide a sufficient number of points to permit the curve to be drawn as in Figure 6.2.2. This curve shows how, under standard conditions of reaction, the amount of $B(y)$ formed in the reaction varies as the amount of $A(x)$ is formed; it does not indicate that the amount of B formed depends on the amount of A that has been made, but merely shows the ratio of formation of the two compounds.

6.3 multi-linear regression analysis

In Section 6.1 we considered a relationship between two variables where the dependent variable could be expressed in linear terms of the independent variable, and this gave us the linear relationship $y = a + bx$. Quite often we have to deal with relationships between three or more variables, and if the relationship is such that the dependent variable can be expressed in linear terms of all the independent variables, such as $y = a + bx_1 + cx_2 + dx_3$, then the relationship is known as a multiple linear regression or a multi-linear regression. Relationships between several variables which are not wholly of linear terms are not uncommon, but need an electronic computer for their derivation, and we are not concerned with these non-linear multiple regressions in this section.

Then we define multilinear regression analysis as a technique for fitting linear equations which contain several variables. It is an extremely useful statistical tool, but should not be used haphazardly and should be considered together with the following points

1 Where it is possible to design an experiment, then that experiment should be designed according to one of the standard balanced patterns of experimentation so that multilinear regression analysis is not needed. Multilinear regression analysis is a last-resort technique for use when an experiment cannot be run to design.

2 The available data must be such that it may reasonably be assumed that the majority of the experimental error lies in the dependent variable, y in the relationship

$$y = B_0 + B_1 x_1 + B_2 x_2 + \ldots + B_k x_k.$$

If this is not so, the problem is difficult and the bulk of the experimental error must be in one independent variable. If the experimental error is more or less equally shared between several independent variables, the problem is insoluble.

3 The experimental data must consist of all corresponding values of the dependent and independent variables. No set in which any entries are missing can be used, and estimation of missing values is not permissible.

4 Transformations may be used to provide a linear equation. For example, if the expected relationship is of the form

$$y = a e^{c x_1} (x_2)^d$$

then taking logarithms (base e) gives the linear equation

$$\ln y = \ln a + c x_1 + d \ln x_2$$

(and see Section 6.1.13).

5 Bitter experience leads one to believe that a multilinear regression analysis on recorded plant data is not worth while because the values calculated for the regression coefficients will depend solely on the outlying points, and these outlying points are outlying because they are freak results or because of errors in recording and reporting. Multilinear regression analysis may be a useful technique to adopt when deliberate changes are made in plant control.

The method of solution uses minimization by the method of least squares. For the equation

$$y = B_0 + B_1 x_1 + B_2 x_2 + \ldots + B_k x_k$$

it is required to derive values of B which best fit the experimental data. That is, the sum of squares of the deviations of the observations from the regression line must be a minimum. The equation is transformed to

$$y = \bar{y} + b_1(x_1 - \bar{x}_1) + b_2(x_2 - \bar{x}_2) + \ldots + b_k(x_k - \bar{x}_k)$$

and solution of this by the method of least squares leads to a set of simultaneous equations of the form

$$a_{11}b_1 + a_{12}b_2 + \ldots + a_{1k}b_k = a_{y1}$$
$$a_{21}b_1 + a_{22}b_2 + \ldots + a_{2k}b_k = a_{y2}$$
$$\cdots\cdots\cdots\cdots\cdots\cdots\cdots\cdots$$
$$a_{k1}b_1 + a_{k2}b_2 + \ldots + a_{kk}b_k = a_{yk}$$

in which the a's are numerical quantities calculated from the experimental results. The values of a are obtained from the relationships

$$a_{ii} = \sum_{1}^{n} (x_i - \bar{x}_i)^2 = \sum x_i^2 - \left(\sum x_i\right)^2/n,$$

$$a_{ij} = \sum_{1}^{n} (x_i - \bar{x}_i)(x_j - \bar{x}_j) = \sum x_{ij}^2 - \left(\sum x_i\right)\left(\sum x_j\right)/n,$$

$$a_{yi} = \sum_{1}^{n} (x_i - \bar{x}_i)(y - \bar{y}) = \sum x_i y - \left(\sum x_i\right)\left(\sum y\right)/n,$$

and in all these relationships $a_{ij} = a_{ji}$.

For example, if we are dealing with a multilinear regression of y on x_1, x_2, and x_3 then we need to calculate

$$a_{11} = \sum (x_1 - \bar{x}_1)^2; \qquad a_{12} = \sum (x_1 - \bar{x}_1)(x_2 - \bar{x}_2);$$
$$a_{13} = \sum (x_1 - \bar{x}_1)(x_3 - \bar{x}_3); \qquad a_{22} = \sum (x_2 - \bar{x}_2)^2;$$
$$a_{23} = \sum (x_2 - \bar{x}_2)(x_3 - \bar{x}_3); \qquad a_{33} = \sum (x_3 - \bar{x}_3)^2;$$
$$a_{yy} = \sum (y - \bar{y})^2; \qquad a_{y1} = \sum (x_1 - \bar{x}_1)(y - \bar{y});$$
$$a_{y2} = \sum (x_2 - \bar{x}_2)(y - \bar{y}); \qquad a_{y3} = \sum (x_3 - \bar{x}_3)(y - \bar{y}).$$

The simultaneous equations must be solved for the b's, when the regression equation can be written as

$$y = \bar{y} + b_1(x_1 - \bar{x}_1) + b_2(x_2 - \bar{x}_2) + \ldots + b_k(x_k - \bar{x}_k)$$

and it is necessary to show that this equation eliminates the variation in y by constructing the analysis of variance table.

Source of variation	Sum of squares	D.F.	Mean square	Expectation of mean square
Due to the regression	$\sum_{1}^{k} b_i a_{yi}$	k	s.s.[Reg]$/k$	
About the regression (= residual)	$a_{yy} - \sum b_i a_{yi}$	$n - k - 1$	s.s.[Res]$/$ $(n - k - 1)$	$\sigma_0^2 \rightarrow s^2$
Total	a_{yy}	$n - 1$		

If there is no real relationship between the variables, then the F-ratio will be about 1. If the F-ratio is significantly greater than 1 then the alternative hypothesis is accepted and hence the regression equation is acceptable and valid at the level of probability considered appropriate.

Finally, each of the regression coefficients must be considered and an estimate made of the accuracy with which it has been determined. This requires an estimate of the variance for each coefficient, which is given by

$$V(b_k) = s^2 . a_{kk}$$

where s^2 is the estimate of residual variance as shown in the analysis of variance table above, and is

$$s^2 = (a_{yy} - b_1 a_{y1} - b_2 a_{y2} - \ldots - b_k a_{yk})/(n - k - 1)$$

so that $100(1 - 2\alpha)$ per cent confidence limits for b_i are $b_i \pm t_\alpha . s \sqrt{a_{ii}}$, where t_α is the tabulated t-value for α probability and $(n - k - 1)$ degrees of freedom.

Similarly, confidence limits for the constant are calculated from the values

$$K \pm t_\alpha . s \sqrt{[1/n + a_{11}(\bar{x}_1)^2 + a_{22}(\bar{x}_2)^2 + \ldots + a_{kk}(\bar{x}_k)^2]}$$

in which K is the constant, n is the number of experimental runs, and t_α and s are as before. The confidence limits for predicting a further observation y_p from the reduced form of the regression equation

$$y = K + b_1 x_1 + b_2 x_2 + \ldots + b_k x_k$$

are given by the values

$$\pm t_\alpha . s \sqrt{[1 + 1/n + a_{11}(x_{p1} - \bar{x}_1)^2 + a_{22}(x_{p2} - \bar{x}_2)^2 + \ldots} \\ + a_{kk}(x_{pk} - \bar{x}_k)^2]$$

in which $x_{p1}, x_{p2}, \ldots, x_{pk}$ are the values of the variables $x_1, x_2, \ldots, x_k$ from which the prediction is to be made, and t_α, s, and n are as before.

Where the estimates $b_1 \ldots b_h$ may not be independent of one another then we must use the expression

$$V(y) = V(\bar{y}) + (x_1 - \bar{x}_1) . V(b_1) + \ldots + (x_k - \bar{x}_k) . V(b_k) \\ + 2(x_1 - \bar{x}_1)(x_2 - \bar{x}_2) . \text{cov} (b_1 b_2) + \ldots$$

which may be written as

$$V(y) = s^2 [1/n + a_{11}(x_1 - \bar{x}_1)^2 + \ldots + a_{kk}(x_k - \bar{x}_k)^2 \\ + 2a_1 a_2 (x_1 - \bar{x}_1)(x_2 - \bar{x}_2) + \ldots]$$

6.3.1 EXAMPLE CALCULATION

Table 6.3.1 gives the data for 35 experimental runs of a chemical reaction between the three reactants A, B, and C. From the data it appears likely that there is a real relationship between the yield (labelled the y-variable) and the ratio of A/B used in the reaction (labelled the x_1-variable), and possibly between the yield and the temperature at which the reaction was performed (labelled the x_2-variable). If the data are retabulated according to ascending order of variable x_1 this is seen to be the case, and a plot of the data in which values of y are plotted against the corresponding values of each x-variable in turn shows this clearly. There seems to be very little relationship between the yield and the concentration of C (labelled the x_3-variable); the relevant data points are shown in Figure 6.3.1 as small circles and these are well scattered over the experimental field.

However, we do not want to determine whether or not values of the yield may be expected to vary with variations in the x-variables considered singly, but how the yield varies with variations in the three x-variables which may occur simultaneously. Accordingly, we calculate

$$a_{11} = \sum (x_1 - \bar{x}_1)^2 = 0.026,376$$
$$a_{22} = \sum (x_2 - \bar{x}_2)^2 = 17.4929$$
$$a_{12} = \sum (x_1 - \bar{x}_1)(x_2 - \bar{x}_2) = 0.671,471$$
$$a_{23} = \sum (x_2 - \bar{x}_2)(x_3 - \bar{x}_3) = 10.428,571$$
$$a_{13} = \sum (x_1 - \bar{x}_1)(x_3 - \bar{x}_3) = 0.425,714$$
$$a_{33} = \sum (x_3 - \bar{x}_3)^2 = 198.2857$$
$$a_{yy} = \sum (y - \bar{y})^2 = 141.3297$$
$$a_{y2} = \sum (x_2 - \bar{x}_2)(y - \bar{y}) = 48.558,57$$
$$a_{y1} = \sum (x_1 - \bar{x}_1)(y - \bar{y}) = 1.915,434$$
$$a_{y3} = \sum (x_3 - \bar{x}_3)(y - \bar{y}) = 28.785,714$$

and the equations to be solved are

(1) $0.026,376b_1 + 0.671,471b_2 + 0.425,714b_3 = 1.915,434$
(2) $0.671,471b_1 + 17.492,900b_2 + 10.428,571b_3 = 48.558,570$
(3) $0.425,714b_1 + 10.428,571b_2 + 198.285,700b_3 = 28.785,714.$

Solution of these equations is straightforward, and, dropping decimal places as we go, proceeds as follows

Step 1: divide through each equation by its coefficient of b_1, to give

(1) $b_1 + 25.458b_2 + 16.140b_3 = 72.620$
(2) $b_1 + 26.052b_2 + 15.531b_3 = 72.317$
(3) $b_1 + 24.497b_2 + 465.772b_3 = 67.617$

and subtracting equation (1) from each of the others gives

(2a) $0.594b_2 - 0.609b_3 = -0.303$
(3a) $-0.961b_2 + 449.632b_3 = -5.003.$

Step 2: divide through each equation by its coefficient of b_2 to give

(2a) $b_2 - 1.025b_3 = -0.510$
(3a) $-b_2 + 467.879b_3 = -5.206$

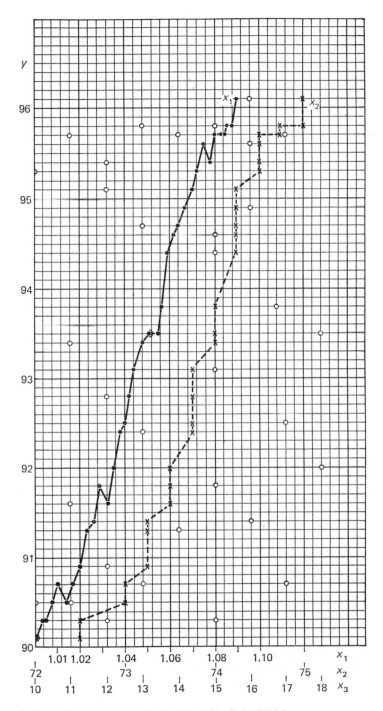

Fig. 6.3.1. EXPERIMENTAL DATA IN PAIRED RELATIONSHIPS

Table 6.3.1 Data for 35 experimental runs

Order of runs	Yield y	Ratio A/B x_1	Temperature, °C x_2	Concentration C x_3
1	94·9	1·067	74·25	16
2	91·3	1·023	73·25	14
3	95·7	1·083	74·75	17
4	92·8	1·042	73·75	12
5	91·8	1·029	73·5	15
6	90·5	1·008	73·0	11
7	94·4	1·059	74·25	15
8	96·1	1·090	75·0	16
9	90·7	1·017	73·0	17
10	92·4	1·038	73·75	13
11	90·1	1·000	72·5	10
12	93·5	1·055	74·0	13
13	95·3	1·072	74·5	10
14	91·6	1·033	73·5	11
15	95·7	1·085	74·75	11
16	94·7	1·064	74·25	13
17	90·7	1·010	73·0	13
18	90·3	1·003	72·5	12
19	93·4	1·048	74·0	11
20	95·8	1·088	75·0	13
21	93·8	1·057	74·0	17
22	95·1	1·070	74·25	12
23	90·5	1·014	73·0	10
24	95·4	1·078	74·5	12
25	90·9	1·020	73·25	12
26	90·3	1·005	72·5	15
27	95·8	1·086	74·75	15
28	93·5	1·051	74·0	18
29	95·7	1·080	74·5	14
30	94·6	1·062	74·25	15
31	93·1	1·044	73·75	15
32	95·6	1·075	74·5	16
33	92·5	1·040	73·75	17
34	92·0	1·035	73·5	18
35	91·4	1·026	73·25	16

and adding these two equations gives us that $466·854b_3 = -5·716$, that is, $b_3 = -0·0122$.

Substituting this value of b_3 in equation (2a) gives $b_2 = -0·5225$, and substituting both values in equation 1 gives $b_1 = 86·1187$. The calculated multilinear regression equation, therefore, is

$$y = \bar{y} + 86·12(x_1 - \bar{x}_1) - 0·52(x_2 - \bar{x}_2) - 0·0122(x_3 - \bar{x}_3),$$
i.e. $y = 93·2 + 86·12(x_1 - 1·047) - 0·52(x_2 - 73·83)$
$$- 0·0122(x_3 - 13·86)$$

which reduces to

$$y = 41·59 + 86·12x_1 - 0·52x_2 - 0·0122x_3.$$

Now we need to test whether or not this equation gives an acceptable fit to the data, and so calculate the sum of squares due to the regression, $\sum b_i a_{yi}$, which is

$$(86·12 \times 1·915) + (-0·52 \times 48·559) + (-0·0122 \times 28·786) = 139·3179.$$

The total sum of squares, a_{yy}, is 141·3297, so that the sum of squares about the regression is 2·0118, and the analysis of variance table may be written

Source of variation	Sum of squares	D.F.	Mean square	F-Ratio
Due to the regression	139·3179	3	46·44	714
About the regression	2·0118	31	0·065	1
Total	141·3297	34		

For 3 and 31 degrees of freedom the F-table quotes a value of 4·51 at the 0·01 level of probability. The calculated F-ratio is much greater than this and we have no hesitation in accepting the regression equation. It remains to determine the validity of the regression coefficients.

From the analysis of variance table we see that the regression variance, s^2, has a value of 0·065, so using the relationship $V(b_k) = s^2 \cdot a_{kk}$ we have

$$V(b_1) = 0·065a_{11} = 0·065 \times 0·026\ 376 = 0·0017,$$

$$\text{whence } \sqrt{V(b_1)} = 0·041.$$

For 31 degrees of freedom and 0·025 probability ($\alpha = 0·025$) the relevant t-value is 2·04, and the 95 per cent confidence limits for b_1 are 86·12 $\pm$ (2·04 × 0·041) which do not include zero and we accept the calculated value of 86·12 for b_1.

Similarly, the confidence limits for b_2 are found to be $-0·52 \pm 2·17$, which include zero; and those for b_3 are $-0·0122 \pm 7·32$, which include zero. We have reservations about these two coefficients, therefore, and we can say that within the limits of the current experimentation variation in yield is likely to be dependent on the x_1-variable – the ratio of A/B – and not on the other two variables.

This we can test easily enough by comparing estimates of y calculated from the multilinear regression of y on x_1, x_2, and x_3 and estimates of y calculated from the linear regression of y and x_1. The comparison is shown in Table 6.3.2 where estimates are calculated to two places of decimals in order to strike differences. The totals of the absolute deviations show that the linear regression is as good as the multilinear regression for the data we have considered.

However, if it is required to extrapolate outside the experimental limits, possibly as a guide for further experimentation, it is better to use the multi-linear regression equation than the linear regression equation as this makes some allowance for the possible effects of the other factors. It must be pointed out that extrapolation beyond the limits of analysis is a dangerous procedure, and estimates obtained by such a procedure should be treated with considerable reserve.

Table 6.3.2 Comparison of estimates of yield

Order of runs	Observed yield	Calculated from multilinear regression		Calculated from linear regression	
	y	$\hat{y}$	$\vert d \vert$	$\hat{y}$	$\vert d \vert$
1	94·9	94·67	0·23	94·66	0·24
2	91·3	91·43	0·13	91·46	0·16
3	95·7	95·70	0·08	95·82	0·12
4	92·8	92·83	0·03	92·84	0·04
5	91·8	91·81	0·01	91·90	0·10
6	90·5	90·31	0·19	90·37	0·13
7	94·4	94·00	0·40	94·07	0·33
8	96·1	96·26	0·16	96·33	0·23
9	90·7	91·00	0·30	91·02	0·32
10	92·4	92·47	0·07	92·55	0·15
11	90·1	89·89	0·21	89·79	0·31
12	93·5	93·81	0·31	93·78	0·28
13	95·3	95·05	0·25	95·02	0·28
14	91·6	92·20	0·60	92·19	0·59
15	95·7	96·03	0·33	95·96	0·26
16	94·7	94·45	0·25	94·44	0·26
17	90·7	90·45	0·25	90·52	0·28
18	90·3	90·12	0·18	90·01	0·29
19	93·4	93·23	0·17	93·28	0·12
20	95·8	96·13	0·33	96·18	0·38
21	93·8	94·01	0·21	93·93	0·13
22	95·1	94·95	0·15	94·87	0·23
23	90·5	90·84	0·34	90·81	0·31
24	95·4	95·54	0·14	95·45	0·05
25	90·9	91·19	0·29	91·24	0·34
26	90·3	90·26	0·04	90·15	0·15
27	95·8	96·07	0·27	96·04	0·24
28	93·5	93·31	0·19	93·49	0·01
29	95·7	95·69	0·01	95·60	0·10
30	94·6	94·26	0·34	94·29	0·31
31	93·1	92·97	0·13	92·99	0·11
32	95·6	95·23	0·37	95·24	0·36
33	92·5	92·59	0·09	92·69	0·19
34	92·0	92·28	0·28	92·33	0·13
35	91·4	91·66	0·26	91·68	0·28
		Total absolute deviation	7·59		7·81

SUGGESTIONS FOR FURTHER READING

2 YULE and KENDALL, Chapters 9–14, 1958.
3 BENNETT and FRANKLIN, Chapter 6, 1954.
5 O. L. DAVIES (ed.), Chapters 7 and 8, 1958.
12 BROOKES and DICK, Chapters 8 and 9, 1963.

CHAPTER SEVEN

ANALYSIS OF COVARIANCE

IN THOSE cases where we are required to deal with two series of measurements, such as a series of values x_i of a variable X and a series of values y_i of a variable Y, which are obtained in pairs as (x_i, y_i), statistics calculated from either series give no information regarding any possible relationship between pairs of values. Usually it is required to know how variations in the values of one variable are affected by variations in the values of the other variable. It is possible to calculate the value of a statistic, known as the covariance, to provide the information, and the covariance between two variables X and Y, written as s_{xy}, is defined as

$$s_{xy} = \frac{\sum (x_i - \bar{x})(y_i - \bar{y})}{n - 1}$$

where, as usual, $\bar{x}$ and $\bar{y}$ are the means of the series of x-measurements and y-measurements respectively and n is the number of pairs of values (x_i, y_i) in the complete set under study.

The covariance, therefore, is the sum of cross-products of the deviations of each of a pair of measurements from their respective means divided by one less than the number of pairs of values. As we have seen already, in Chapter 6, covariance terms are required in the determination of linear and multilinear regressions, and for easy computation the covariance of x and y may be expressed as

$$s_{xy} = \frac{\sum (x_i - \bar{x})(y_i - \bar{y})}{n - 1} = \frac{1}{n - 1}\left[\sum x_i y_i - \frac{(\sum x_i)(\sum y_i)}{n}\right].$$

The analysis of covariance is a procedure which has been developed to deal with those situations in which the data must be analysed by a combination of the techniques of analysis of variance and regression analysis. These situations arise in several ways: it may be that a series of responses, y, have been measured at various levels of a variable X (cross-classification analysis of variance) but some other factor Z varied during the experimentation so that any dependence of the y_i on the x_i is not straightforward and the results obtained from an analysis of variance on the data obtained during the experimentation may not be valid. It may be that in a simple case where a regression of y on x seems to be indicated, the data are derived from several different sources or periods of experimentation and it is not known whether or not there is any interference due to these different sources.

The two most common examples of the use of analysis of covariance in industry that are known to the author arise 1. when a raw material used as input to a process varies slightly in quality; the variation may be cyclic over short periods of time or may exhibit long term trends; and 2. when it is necessary to determine whether or not data may be pooled; one instance of this has been considered in the combination of regression coefficients, Section 6.1.9, and this can be extended to more than two groups.

7.1 comparison of more than two groups of paired measurements

We have a series of pairs of measurements (x_i, y_i) which can be allocated to k groups such that there are n_i pairs of measurements in the i-th group. Then we can calculate a series of values $(b_1, b_2, \ldots, b_i, \ldots, b_k)$ for the regression coefficients and another series of values $(a_1, a_2, \ldots, a_i, \ldots, a_k)$ for the regression intercepts of these groups, and it becomes necessary to test these group values for homogeneity.

For each group we calculate

$\sum_\alpha (x_{i\alpha} - \bar{x}_i)^2$, which we shall write as $s_\alpha(x_i^2)$, in which we sum over all the values in the α-th group,

$\sum_\alpha (y_{i\alpha} - \bar{y}_i)^2$, which we shall write as $s_\alpha(y_i^2)$,

$\sum_\alpha (x_{i\alpha} - \bar{x}_i)(y_{i\alpha} - \bar{y}_i)$, which we shall write as $s_\alpha(x_i y_i)$,

and $b_i = s_\alpha(x_i y_i)/s_\alpha(x_i^2)$.

Next we need to total values over all groups to give

$\sum_{\alpha i} (x_{i\alpha} - \bar{x}_i)^2$, which we shall write as $s_{\alpha i}(x^2)$,

$\sum_{\alpha i} (y_{i\alpha} - \bar{y}_i)^2$, which we shall write as $s_{\alpha i}(y^2)$,

$\sum_{\alpha i} (x_{i\alpha} - \bar{x}_i)(y_{i\alpha} - \bar{y}_i)$, which we shall write as $s_{\alpha i}(xy)$

and $b_a = s_{\alpha i}(xy)/s_{\alpha i}(x^2)$.

Also, we calculate the values

$\sum_i n_i(x_i - \bar{x})^2$, which we shall write as $s_i(x^2)$,

$\sum_i n_i(y_i - \bar{y})^2$, which we shall write as $s_i(y^2)$,

$\sum_i n_i(x_i - \bar{x})(y_i - \bar{y})$, which we shall write as $s_i(xy)$,

and $b_m = s_i(xy)/s_i(x^2)$.

Note that these calculations are based on the n_i values in the i-th group, and on $\bar{x}$ and $\bar{y}$, the overall means.

Finally, we calculate the sums for the series as a whole

$\sum_{\alpha i} (x_{i\alpha} - \bar{x})^2$, which we shall write as $S(x^2)$,

$\sum_{\alpha i} (y_{i\alpha} - \bar{y})^2$, which we shall write as $S(y^2)$,

$\sum_{\alpha i} (x_{i\alpha} - \bar{x})(y_{i\alpha} - \bar{y})$, which we shall write as $S(xy)$

and $b = S(xy)/S(x^2)$.

In those cases where we are interested only in the group effect on the individual regression coefficients the variance within sets can be estimated, since

$$\sum_{\alpha i} (y_{i\alpha} - \bar{y}_i)^2 = \sum_{\alpha i} [y_{i\alpha} - \bar{y}_i + b_i(x_{i\alpha} - \bar{x}_i)]^2 + \sum_{\alpha i} b_i^2 (x_{i\alpha} - \bar{x}_i)^2$$
$$= \sum_{\alpha i} [y_{i\alpha} - \bar{y}_i + b_i(x_{i\alpha} - \bar{x}_i)]^2$$
$$+ \sum_{\alpha i} (b_i - b_a)^2 (x_{i\alpha} - \bar{x}_i)^2 + b_a^2 \sum_{\alpha i} (x_{i\alpha} - \bar{x}_i)^2.$$

When we consider the three terms on the right-hand side of this expression we see that the first term is the sum of squares (about the regression) of the $\sum n_i (= N)$ normally distributed variates, having variance σ^2 and which is subject to $2k$ linear restraints (the total number of x- and y-values that we are handling). This term has $(N - 2k)$ degrees of freedom and is distributed as $\sigma^2 \chi^2_{N-2k}$. We shall write this term as $S_{\alpha i}(y^2) - \sum_i b_i^2 S_\alpha(x_i^2)$.

If we assume the hypothesis that all the group regression coefficients are really equal and there are no detectable differences between any of them, so that $\beta_1 = \beta_2 = \beta_3 = \ldots = \beta_k = \beta$, then the second term on the right-hand side of the expression is the sum of squares of k normally distributed variates, having variance σ^2 and which is subject to one linear constraint. This term has $(k - 1)$ degrees of freedom and is distributed as $\sigma^2 \chi^2_{k-1}$. We shall write this term as $\sum_i (b_i - b_a)^2 S_\alpha(x_i^2)$.

Finally, if we assume that there is no linear regression between groups, i.e. $\beta = 0$, the last term on the right-hand side of the expression has one degree of freedom and is distributed as $\sigma^2 \chi_i^2$. We shall write this term as $b_a^2 S_{\alpha i}(x^2)$.

Now these three terms can be included in an analysis of variance table as the sums of squares belonging to the relevant sources of variation, as

Source of variation	Sum of squares	D.F.	Mean square
A. Mean regression within groups	$b_a^2 S_{\alpha i}(x^2)$	1	$b_a^2 S_{\alpha i}(x^2)$
B. Difference between group regressions	$\sum_i (b_i - b_a)^2 S_\alpha(x_i^2)$	$k - 1$	$[\sum_i (b_i - b_a^2) S_\alpha(x_i^2)] / (k - 1)$
C. Residual corrected for group regressions	$S_{\alpha i}(y^2) - \sum_i b_i^2 S_\alpha(x_i^2)$	$N - 2k$	$[S_{\alpha i}(y^2) - \sum_i b_i^2 S_\alpha(x_i^2)] / (N - 2k)$
Total	$S_{\alpha i}(y^2)$	$N - k$	

Now we can test the hypothesis $\beta_1 = \beta_2 = \ldots = \beta_k$ from the mean square ratio B/C, and comparing the calculated F-value with the tabulated value of F for $(k - 1)$ and $(N - 2k)$ degrees of freedom determines whether or not this ratio is significant. If it is not, then we may accept the hypothesis and the sums of squares for B and C may be added together to give an estimate of residual variance based on $(N - k - 1)$ degrees of freedom. This estimate may be used to test the significance of the overall regression coefficient from the F-ratio of the mean squares $A/(B + C)$.

7.2 example of group regressions

Four research chemists were requested to examine the effect of varying the concentration of a reactant, x, on the yield obtained, y. Each chemist was asked to cover the whole range of possible concentrations of x, but unfortunately this was not done. The results obtained were

Chemist A		Chemist B		Chemist C		Chemist D	
x	y	x	y	x	y	x	y
12·5	90·3	12·9	90·6	12·2	90·2	18·2	93·1
14·0	90·8	14·7	91·5	13·7	90·7	18·8	93·2
16·0	92·1	16·7	92·1	15·5	91·6	19·3	93·7
18·0	93·1	19·0	93·3	17·2	92·3	20·5	94·1
20·0	93·8	19·8	94·0	17·5	92·8	21·2	94·5
21·7	94·7	20·8	94·3	14·2	91·5		
		21·5	94·8	13·3	90·5		

We want to know if these 25 pairs of values may be pooled to provide an estimate of the relationship between x and y. If the values are plotted on a scatter diagram there appears little doubt that there is a linear relationship between x and y, but we wish to make sure that there is no significant difference between the regression slopes for any two groups, particularly where groups C and D are involved.

(Applying the standard linear regression procedure to each group, rounding decimals to four places and accepting that this may involve some small discrepancy in the final comparison,) we have

For Group A:

$$\sum_1 (x_{i1} - \bar{x}_i)^2 = S_1(x_i^2) = 62{\cdot}3333,$$

$$\sum_1 (y_{i1} - \bar{y}_i)^2 = S_1(y_i^2) = 14{\cdot}7733,$$

$$\sum_1 (x_{i1} - \bar{x}_i)(y_{i1} - \bar{y}_i) = S_1(x_iy_i) = 30{\cdot}2467, \quad \text{and} \quad b_1 = 0{\cdot}4852.$$

For Group B:
$$\sum_2 (x_{i2} - \bar{x}_i)^2 = S_2(x_i^2) = 62 \cdot 7686,$$
$$\sum_2 (y_{i2} - \bar{y}_i)^2 = S_2(y_i^2) = 14 \cdot 8171,$$
$$\sum_2 (x_{i2} - \bar{x}_i)(y_{i2} - \bar{y}_i) = S_2(x_i y_i) = 30 \cdot 3657, \quad \text{and} \quad b_2 = 0 \cdot 4838.$$

For Group C:
$$\sum_3 (x_{i3} - \bar{x}_i)^2 = S_3(x_i^2) = 24 \cdot 12,$$
$$\sum_3 (y_{i3} - \bar{y}_i)^2 = S_3(y_i^2) = 5 \cdot 5543,$$
$$\sum_3 (x_{i3} - \bar{x}_i)(y_{i3} - \bar{y}_i) = S_3(x_i y_i) = 11 \cdot 26, \quad \text{and} \quad b_3 = 0 \cdot 4668.$$

For Group D:
$$\sum_4 (x_{i4} - \bar{x}_i)^2 = S_4(x_i^2) = 6 \cdot 06,$$
$$\sum_4 (y_{i4} - \bar{y}_i)^2 = S_4(y_i^2) = 1 \cdot 408,$$
$$\sum_4 (x_{i4} - \bar{x}_i)(y_{i4} - \bar{y}_i) = S_4(x_i y_i) = 2 \cdot 88, \quad \text{and} \quad b_4 = 0 \cdot 4752.$$

The sum of squares totals for groups are
$$\sum_{1-4} (x^2) = S_{\alpha i}(x^2) = 155 \cdot 2820; \qquad \sum_{1-4} (y^2) = S_{\alpha i}(y^2) = 36 \cdot 5527;$$

$$\sum_{1-4} (xy) = S_{\alpha i}(xy) = 74 \cdot 7524; \qquad \text{and} \quad b_a = 0 \cdot 4814.$$

The overall summations give:
$$S(x^2) = 7{,}596 \cdot 72 - (429 \cdot 2)^2/25 = 228 \cdot 2144,$$
$$S(y^2) = 214{,}164 \cdot 04 - (2{,}313 \cdot 6)^2/25 = 54 \cdot 2416,$$
$$S(xy) = 39{,}830 \cdot 52 - (429 \cdot 2)(2{,}313 \cdot 6)/25 = 110 \cdot 6352$$
$$\text{and} \quad b_0 = 0 \cdot 4848.$$

The mean regression within groups has sum of squares
$$b_a^2 \cdot S_{\alpha i}(x^2) = (0 \cdot 4814)^2 \times 155 \cdot 282$$
$$= 35 \cdot 986 \text{ for 1 d.f.}$$

The difference between group regressions has sum of squares
$$\sum_i (b_i - b_a)^2 S_\alpha(x_i^2) = (0 \cdot 4852 - 0 \cdot 4814)^2 . 62 \cdot 3333$$
$$+ (0 \cdot 4838 - 0 \cdot 4814)^2 . 62 \cdot 7686$$
$$+ (0 \cdot 4668 - 0 \cdot 4814)^2 . 24 \cdot 12$$
$$+ (0 \cdot 4752 - 0 \cdot 4814)^2 . 6 \cdot 06$$
$$= 0 \cdot 006{,}635 \text{ for 3 d.f.}$$

The residual corrected for group regressions has sum of squares
$$S_{\alpha i}(y^2) - \sum_i b_i^2 S_\alpha(x_i^2) = 36 \cdot 5527 - [62 \cdot 3333 . (0 \cdot 4852)^2$$
$$+ 62 \cdot 7686 (0 \cdot 4838)^2 + 24 \cdot 12 (0 \cdot 4668)^2$$
$$+ 6 \cdot 06 (0 \cdot 4752)^2]$$
$$= 0 \cdot 562{,}241 \text{ for 17 d.f.}$$

and the analysis of variance table is

Source of variation	Sum of squares	D.F.	Mean square	F-Ratio
A. Mean regression within groups	35·986	1	35·986	
B. Difference between group regressions	0·0066	3	0·0022	<1
C. Residual corrected for group regressions	0·5622	17	0·033	1
Total	36·5548	21		

Note that the total sum of squares calculated as $S_{ai}(y^2)$ is 36·5527; the difference between this value and the total quoted in the table is due to rounding error.

Obviously there is no difference due to group regressions and the four groups of experimental data may be pooled for determination of the linear regression between the two variables. The overall regression coefficient is $b_0 = 0·4848$ and the regression equation is

$$y = 92·544 + 0·4848(x - 17·168) \quad \text{or} \quad y = 0·4848x + 84·221.$$

7.3 treatment comparisons

In those cases where we are interested only in the group effect on the regression of y on x the procedure outlined in Section 7.1 is sufficient. Sometimes, however, we may be interested in the group effect on the constant term in the linear regression, when it becomes necessary to estimate the group means or the variance between group means. If the regression coefficients differ significantly from group to group then a comparison of the corrected group means will give a result which varies according to the value of x at which the comparison is made, and such a comparison is not likely to be of very much value.

A comparison of the group means may be made from the actual group mean values $\bar{x}_i$ and $\bar{y}_i$ and the estimated regression coefficients b_i which are used to calculate the expected value of $\hat{y}_i$ at some fixed value of x, say x_t. Then the F-ratio may be formed from the sum of squares $\sum_i n_i(\hat{y}_i - \bar{y})^2$ and the residual sum of squares. However, this method leads to an over-estimate of the significance level of the variance ratio which may lead to incorrect or unwise conclusions.

An exact test may be made using the variance–covariance values of 'between groups' and 'within groups'. We have computed the values (Section 7.1)

Source	y^2	x^2	xy	Regression coefficient
Between groups	$S_i(y^2)$	$S_i(x^2)$	$S_i(xy)$	$b_m = S_i(xy)/S_i(x^2)$
Within groups	$S_{\alpha i}(y^2)$	$S_{\alpha i}(x^2)$	$S_{\alpha i}(xy)$	$b_a = S_{\alpha i}(xy)/S_{\alpha i}(x^2)$
Total	$S(y^2)$	$S(x^2)$	$S(xy)$	$b_0 = S(xy)/S(x^2)$

and to test the significance of the mean regression within groups we have the residual variance of $S_{\alpha i}(y^2) - b_a S_{\alpha i}(xy)$ for $(N - k - 1)$ degrees of freedom, and the variance ratio is

$$\frac{b_a S_{\alpha i}(xy) \times (N - k - 1)}{S_{\alpha i}(y^2) - b_a S_{\alpha i}(xy)}.$$

If this ratio attains the accepted significance level, indicating a significant regression within groups, the hypothesis that the group means are equal implies that b_a, b_m and b_0 are estimates of a single (and common to all groups) regression coefficient. Using these estimates to calculate the residual sum of squares we have

for the estimate 'between groups', the residual sum of squares is

$$S_1 = S_i(y^2) - b_m \cdot S_i(xy) \quad \text{with } (k - 2) \text{ degrees of freedom};$$

for the estimate 'within groups', the residual sum of squares is

$$S_2 = S_{\alpha i}(y^2) - b_a \cdot S_{\alpha i}(xy) \quad \text{with } (N - k - 1) \text{ degrees of freedom};$$

and for the estimate given by the 'total' the residual sum of squares is

$$S_3 = S(y^2) - b_0 \cdot S(xy) \quad \text{with } (N - 2) \text{ degrees of freedom}.$$

The residual sum of squares divided by its corresponding number of degrees of freedom gives a residual mean square which is an estimate of the error variance σ^2.

Note that S_1 is allocated $(k - 2)$ degrees of freedom and not $(k - 1)$. It has 'lost' an extra degree of freedom because of the use of b_m as an estimate of the regression coefficient.

We see that the difference $S_3 - S_2 - S_1$ is the reduction in the residual sum of squares due to the inclusion of $(k - 1)$ independent group constants, and $S_3 - S_2 - S_1$ may be reduced to

$$\frac{(b_a - b_m)^2 S_{\alpha i}(x^2) \cdot S_i(x^2)}{S(x^2)}$$

Since the original hypothesis is that b_a and b_m are estimates of β, so that ave $(b_a - b_m) = 0$,

and

$$\sigma^2_{(b_a - b_m)} = \sigma^2 \left[\frac{1}{S_{\alpha i}(x^2)} + \frac{1}{S_i(x^2)} \right]$$

then we have that $\dfrac{(b_a - b_m)^2 . S_{ai}(x^2) . S_i(x^2)}{S(x^2)}$ or $S_3 - S_2 - S_1$ is an estimate of σ^2.

It follows that the variance ratio $\dfrac{(S_3 - S_2)}{k - 1} . \dfrac{(N - k - 1)}{S_2}$, which corresponds to the ratio

$$\frac{\text{corrected mean square between groups}}{\text{corrected mean square within groups}}$$

may be used to indicate whether or not the hypothesis should be accepted, and we can construct the analysis of variance table as follows

Source of estimate	Sum of squares	D.F.
Deviation of group means from regression of group means b_m	S_1	$p - 2$
Difference between b_a and b_m	$S_3 - S_2 - S_1$	1
Deviations from mean regression within groups b_a	S_2	$N - p - 1$
Total deviations from overall regression b_0	S_3	$N - 2$

7.4 example of application of analysis of covariance to treatment comparisons

As a result of experimentation the following sets of data were obtained

Set 1		Set 2		Set 3	
y	x	y	x	y	x
163	138	186	184	219	182
179	168	201	193	229	188
157	125	181	164	240	215
190	147	203	190	217	216
225	194	209	205	266	243
191	165	228	179	238	216
223	153	242	234	253	241
201	166	217	210	276	262
231	207	236	232	273	231
		259	222	264	214
		232	194	191	181

Each set refers to data collected in a certain reactor, x being the reaction time in minutes and y the viscosity of the batch at time of reaction x. We require to determine whether there is a relationship between viscosity and reaction time, whether this relationship is consistent over the three reactors.

We start by calculating sums of squares and of products for each set, to give

for Set 1: $\sum x_1 = 1{,}463; \sum y_1 = 1{,}760; \sum (x_1 - \bar{x}_1)^2 = 5{,}358 \cdot 2;$
$\sum (y_1 - \bar{y}_1)^2 = 5{,}778 \cdot 2; \sum x_1 y_1 = 4{,}490 \cdot 2.$

for Set 2: $\sum x_2 = 2{,}207; \sum y_2 = 2{,}394; \sum (x_2 - \bar{x}_2)^2 = 4{,}962 \cdot 5;$
$\sum (y_2 - \bar{y}_2)^2 = 5{,}864 \cdot 5; \sum x_2 y_2 = 4{,}060 \cdot 5.$

for Set 3: $\sum x_3 = 2{,}389; \sum y_3 = 2{,}666; \sum (x_3 - \bar{x}_3)^2 = 6{,}849 \cdot 6;$
$\sum (y_3 - \bar{y}_3)^2 = 7{,}240 \cdot 5; \sum x_3 y_3 = 5{,}836 \cdot 3.$

From these values we can calculate the linear regression coefficients, and for ease of manipulation we tabulate the data as follows:

Source of estimate	$\sum (y - \bar{y})^2$	$\sum (x - \bar{x})^2$	$\sum xy$	Regression coefficient	
Within Set 1	5,778·2	5,358·2	4,490·2	0·8380	(b_1)
Within Set 2	5,864·5	4,962·5	4,060·5	0·8182	(b_2)
Within Set 3	7,240·5	6,849·6	5,836·3	0·8521	(b_3)
Total within sets	18,883·2	17,170·3	14,387·0	0·8379	(b_a)
Between sets	10,940·8	15,229·4	12,448·0	0·8174	(b_m)
Total	29,824·0	32,399·7	26,835·0	0·82825	(b_0)

Note the values for 'between sets' are obtained by the difference Total − Total within sets.

To test for differences in the regression coefficients obtained in each set we require to calculate the corrected sums of squares as shown in Section 7.3. The values obtained are:

for Set 1: $S_\alpha(y_1^2) - b_1 S_\alpha(x_1 y_1) = 5{,}778 \cdot 2 - 3{,}762 \cdot 8 = 2{,}015 \cdot 4;$
for Set 2: $S_\alpha(y_2^2) - b_2 S_\alpha(x_2 y_2) = 5{,}864 \cdot 5 - 3{,}322 \cdot 3 = 2{,}542 \cdot 2;$
for Set 3: $S_\alpha(y_3^2) - b_3 S_\alpha(x_3 y_3) = 7{,}240 \cdot 5 - 4{,}973 \cdot 1 = 2{,}267 \cdot 4;$
from which the sum over the three sets is $\qquad 6{,}825 \cdot 0.$

The total within sets corrected for the mean regression is given by

$$S_{\alpha i}(y^2) - b_a S_{\alpha i}(xy) = 18{,}883 \cdot 2 - 12{,}054 \cdot 9 = 6{,}828 \cdot 3$$

and by difference, the difference between regression coefficients,

$$\sum_i (b_i - b_a)^2 S_\alpha(x_i^2) = 3 \cdot 3.$$

If we calculate the value of this last term from its components we find that

$$\sum_i (b_i - b_a)^2 S_a(x_i^2) = (0.8379 - 0.8380)^2 . 5{,}358.2$$
$$+ 4962.5(0.8379 - 0.8182)^2$$
$$+ 6{,}849.6(0.8379 - 0.8521)^2$$
$$= 0.000{,}053{,}582 + 1.925{,}897 + 1.381{,}153 = 3.3.$$

Now we can collect the results of these calculations in another table, and with the appropriate numbers of degrees of freedom, 7 for Set 1, 9 for Set 2 and 9 for Set 3, we can calculate the mean squares which we intend to use as estimates of the variance of the overall data set. We compile the table

Source of estimate	Corrected Sums of squares	D.F.	Estimate of variance
Set 1	2,015.4	7	287.9
Set 2	2,542.2	9	282.5
Set 3	2,267.4	9	251.9
Sum over sets	6,825.0	25	273.0
Difference between regression coefficients	3.3	2	1.65
Total within sets corrected for mean regression	6,828.3	27	252.9

If the relationship between reaction time and viscosity is to be consistent over the three sets of data, then our hypothesis will assume that there are equal residual variances in these sets and this assumption may be checked by Bartlett's test.

7.4.1 NOTE ON BARTLETT'S TEST

Where $s_t^2(t = 1, 2, \ldots, k)$ are independent mean square estimates of a variance, σ^2, based on d_t degrees of freedom then we can calculate

$$c_1 = \sum_{t=1}^{k} \frac{1}{d_t} - \frac{1}{N}; \quad \text{where} \quad N = \sum_{t=1}^{k} d_t$$

and

$$M = N \ln \left(\sum_{t=1}^{k} \frac{d_t s_t^2}{N} \right) - \sum_{t=1}^{k} d_t \ln s_t^2$$

in which ln indicates logarithms to the base e. Significant values of M for various c_1 and k are given in *Biometrika Tables for Statisticians*, Volume 1, Table 32.

For our example we have

$$N = 7 + 9 + 9 = 25$$
$$c_1 = \tfrac{1}{7} + \tfrac{1}{9} + \tfrac{1}{9} - \tfrac{1}{25} = 0.32$$
$$k = 3$$

$$M = 25 \ln 273 - 7 \ln 287 \cdot 9 - 9 \ln 282 \cdot 5 - 9 \ln 251 \cdot 9$$
$$= 140 \cdot 2375 - 39 \cdot 6410 - 50 \cdot 7888 - 49 \cdot 7655 = 0 \cdot 0422.$$

The tabulated values of M to indicate a significant heterogeneity of the variances are for $c_1 = 0$ and $c_1 = 0 \cdot 5$, and values are about 6 at the 15 per cent level. We may accept, therefore, that the variances estimated for the three sets are not significantly lacking in homogeneity and we may accept them as estimates of one variance. This we should have expected since the ratio largest/smallest of these variances gives a ratio of $287 \cdot 9/251 \cdot 9 = 1 \cdot 14$, and on the two-sided F-test this corresponds to a probability of about $0 \cdot 3$. Testing for group effects on the regression coefficients we see that the difference is very small and it is not really necessary to perform the calculations. We are satisfied that a regression coefficient may be applied to the overall data and that this coefficient may be applied to any of the separate sets of data, and next we need to be satisfied that the intercepts of the three regression equations are not significantly different from each other or from the intercept of the overall regression equation. From the relationship

$$a_i = \frac{S_a(y_i) - b_i S_a(x_i)}{n}$$

we calculate

$$a_1 = \frac{1,760 - (0 \cdot 8380)(1463)}{7} = 76 \cdot 3; \qquad a_2 = \frac{2,394 - (0 \cdot 8182)(2207)}{9} = 65 \cdot 3;$$

$$a_3 = \frac{2,666 - (0 \cdot 8521)(2389)}{9} = 70 \cdot 0;$$

and

$$a_0 = \frac{6,820 - (0 \cdot 82825)(6059)}{25} = 72 \cdot 1.$$

Now we can use the joint variance estimate, $\sigma^2 = 273 \cdot 0$, to calculate the variance of the predicted value of y at $x = 0$ for each regression equation, using the relationship

$$\text{var}\,(\tilde{y}_0) = \sigma^2 \left[\frac{1}{n} + \frac{(x_0 - \bar{x})^2}{\sum (x_i - \bar{x})^2} \right].$$

We calculate

$$s^2[a_1] = 273 \cdot 0 \left[\frac{1}{9} + \frac{(0 \cdot 8380)^2}{5,358 \cdot 2} \cdot \frac{1463}{9} \right] = 36 \cdot 1452$$

$$s^2[a_2] = 273 \cdot 0 \left[\frac{1}{11} + \frac{(0 \cdot 8182)^2}{4,962 \cdot 5} \cdot \frac{2207}{11} \right] = 32 \cdot 214$$

$$s^2[a_3] = 273 \cdot 0 \left[\frac{1}{11} + \frac{(0 \cdot 8521)^2}{6,849 \cdot 6} \cdot \frac{2389}{11} \right] = 31 \cdot 09$$

and F-tests show that these variances are not significantly different.

We are justified, therefore, in applying the regression equation $y = 72 \cdot 1 + 0 \cdot 82825x$ to the overall data or to any set of data obtained from a reactor. We conclude that this relationship is valid and is consistent over the three reactors.

7.5 further applications of analysis of covariance

Analysis of covariance does not seem to be widely used at the present time, and here we may mention briefly three further applications of the technique.
1 *Pooling prior data:* Very often experimentation is undertaken as a continuation of or to provide confirmation of previous experimental results which may be widely separated in space or in time. Analysis of covariance may be used to indicate whether all the prior data may be pooled and used as a single background to the new experimentation.
2 *Replication:* Where an experimental design is used as a basis for experimentation and replication is made in every cell in the design, the analysis of covariance procedure outlined in this chapter may be extended to cover the sources of estimate: 'Between replicates within cells'; 'between cells within sets'; 'between sets'; 'between groups' and 'total'.
3 *Multiple linear regression:* Where measurements are made of a number of fixed variables, leading to a multiple regression, analysis of covariance may be used to eliminate the effects of the regression of y on these variables. A series of regression coefficients for each of the x-variables is calculated.

SUGGESTIONS FOR FURTHER READING

3 BENNETT and FRANKLIN, Chapter 7, 1954.
5 O. L. DAVIES, Chapter 8, 1958.
9 K. A. BROWNLEE, Chapter 1, 1960.
10 H. SCHEFFÉ, Chapter 6, 1959.

CHAPTER EIGHT

SAMPLING AND TESTING

8.1 what makes a sample?

A sample is a portion of material or a group of individuals or specimens taken from a large mass or bulk (the population) so that a test of some sort may be made on the sample in order to make an estimate of some characteristic of the bulk. The population may be finite or infinite, real or hypothetical and the sample may consist of any fraction or any number of individuals from the population; in certain very special cases the sample may consist of the entire population. But where the population is large compared with the size of the sample abstraction of a relatively small fraction or of relatively few members will not materially affect the constitution of the remaining population, which thus may be regarded as approximately the same as the original population after the first and any subsequent sampling.

Thus a dealer buying apples may examine one or two from each barrel. A couple of ounces of sulphur may be taken from a 500-ton consignment. To determine the reactions of members of staff to certain proposals a questionnaire would be issued to every member — this is one example where the whole population constitutes the sample. To determine the reaction of the general public to a T.V. programme or to a new detergent it is not feasible to sample the whole population so that the sample may be restricted to a small fraction of the population, possibly in one area of the country.

The theory of sampling deals with obtaining from a sample estimates of certain parameters of the parent population and information derived from the sample is assumed to apply to the whole population. Generally speaking, the assumption that some specified level of accuracy can be attained only if the size of the sample is related to the size of the bulk is wrong, because truly random samples of the same size are equally reliable estimators of the characteristics of the bulk, whatever the bulk, when the sample is a small fraction of the bulk. However, as the bulk (usually referred to as the 'lot') increases, the amount at risk becomes greater and a greater precision is required. Statistical sampling theory deals with the relationships between the size of the lot for which an estimate of some characteristic is to be made, the size of the sample and the number of samples to be taken, and the accuracy with which the characteristic of the whole bulk can be estimated.

Four types of sampling are common in industry: 1. that in which the lot may be regarded as a bulk of material when a test is made on a small portion of the lot, for which economic random sampling schemes can be devised. These schemes cover such materials as powders, crystals, liquids etc., in bulk however packed. 2. that in which the lot consists of a collection of separate individuals when a test is made on a single individual or on a group of individuals, for which single and sequential sampling schemes can be devised. 3. that in which a sensory comparison is made between a sample and a standard or between two or more samples, for which special schemes have been devised. 4. that in which it is either not feasible or not economic to sample physically from a lot, for which simulated sampling schemes have been devised. This chapter deals with sampling and testing of type 1 occasions, the other three types are considered in the next chapter.

A sample may be taken from a lot in three ways

1 by selecting individuals or small portions with complete freedom of choice; this is known as *random sampling*.
2 by selecting individuals or small portions according to some pre-determined plan; this is known as *purposive sampling*.
3 by some mixture of these two methods, usually where random sampling occurs within purposive sampling.

In order to apply the theory of probability to the problem of sampling, the sample must be a random sample. That is, the sample must be selected without bias (or in a haphazard manner) so that each individual or each small portion in the lot has an equal chance of inclusion in the sample. In some cases, such as a series of trials of a chemical experiment, it may not be possible to select the trials or to carry out the trials in a strictly random order; here it may be assumed that the experimental results form a random set drawn from the population of all the possible experiments that could be made under the same conditions. Even so, the experimenter must arrange conditions so that, as far as can be foreseen, no bias is introduced; the presence of an unknown bias can be serious and can lead to wrong conclusions which may have grave consequences at a later date.

A *representative sample* (or a *stratified sample*) is a sample so taken that a specified proportion of its contents is drawn from each distinct sub-population (stratum) of the lot. The sampling of each stratum must be random. But note that if some of the strata are obviously very different from each other according to some characteristic which is to be estimated, they should not be allowed to remain in the same lot.

Samples should not be taken at regular intervals, such as every fiftieth bag or every tenth machine load, in case there is some assignable cause of variation operating with a periodicity that coincides with the interval between the taking of successive samples or successive portions which are to be combined to form a sample.

When dealing with individuals the number required to form the sample is predetermined. Only this number of individuals is taken (at random) from the lot and every member of this sample is examined. When dealing with a large bulk of solid material from which a small sample is taken, the small sample may be much too large for the purpose required. For example, the sample may consist of a 1-lb jarful taken from 10 packages in a lot of 100, and rather than spoon out 20 grams (or maybe 2 grams) for a particular test, a random sample should be obtained by the procedure of 'halving'. The sample is mixed thoroughly and divided into halves; one half is chosen and this is again mixed thoroughly and divided into halves. The procedure is continued until a final 'half' of manageable size is obtained and this may be accepted as a random sample. In any case where the material in the sample is obviously heterogeneous, the process of halving may not be satisfactory and the sample should be refused.

8.2 outliers

Dixon's Test for inclusion or exclusion of extreme values has been described in Chapter 4.1 and in Chapter 1.5 the four rules of behaviour of industrial statistics are quoted. Unfortunately it is sometimes necessary to consider whether an observation obtained from one member of a sample is so far removed from the other observations of the sample that it is likely to be incorrectly reported and not to belong to the same set as the other observations. If some error in analytical technique is *known* to have occurred which may have been responsible for the suspect outlier, then this suspect outlier should be ignored and a repeat analysis made if possible; otherwise the suspect outlier must be retained in the set. But it is important to be realistic on this point; it may be required to calculate a sum of squares (of the deviation of each result from the mean) when the contribution of one outlier to the sum of squares may be a very large fraction of the total. If the outlier is a wrong value then the sum of squares would be grossly in error. Dixon's Test presents a set of rules which enables a decision to be made whether or not the suspect outlier is to be retained in the set of sample values. See Appendix Table 1.

For example, 5 samples are taken from every lot of a chemical and each is analysed for chlorine content. The values determined are ranked as

$$x_1 = 23.2; \quad x_2 = 23.4; \quad x_3 = 23.5; \quad x_4 = 24.0; \quad x_5 = 25.7$$

from which it is desired to calculate the best value of the mean and the standard deviation. By inspection, the values x_1, x_2 and x_3 are acceptable. Then for $N = 5$ the test for $x_5 = 25 \cdot 7$ is

$$r_1 = \frac{27 \cdot 5 - 24 \cdot 0}{25 \cdot 7 - 23 \cdot 2} = \frac{1 \cdot 7}{2 \cdot 5} = 0 \cdot 68$$

But the critical value of r_1 for $N = 5$ and 95 per cent probability that the suspect outlier should be rejected is $0 \cdot 642$; the calculated value is greater than this and so we reject x_5 and next have to consider x_4. Here we have

$$r_1 = \frac{24 \cdot 0 - 23 \cdot 5}{24 \cdot 0 - 23 \cdot 2} = \frac{0 \cdot 5}{0 \cdot 8} = 0 \cdot 625.$$

Now the critical value of r_1 for $N = 4$ and 95 per cent probability that the suspect outlier should be rejected is $0 \cdot 765$. The calculated value is less than this and so x_4 is retained in the set. The set of sample values, therefore, has a mean of $\frac{1}{4}(23 \cdot 2 + 23 \cdot 4 + 23 \cdot 5 + 24 \cdot 0) = 23 \cdot 5$. The range of sample values is $0 \cdot 8$, and the estimate of the standard deviation is $0 \cdot 486 \times 0 \cdot 8 = 0 \cdot 39$ and is obtained by the use of Table 8.2.1.

Table 8.2.1 Estimate of standard deviations from range of sample values

n	s	n	s	n	s
2	0·886 w	5	0·430 w	8	0·351 w
3	0·591 w	6	0·395 w	9	0·337 w
4	0·486 w	7	0·370 w	10	0·325 w

where w is the range of n values in the set.

It is always well worthwhile ensuring that all values obtained from a sample are feasible and usable, and Dixon's Test is a very simple method of doing this.

8.3 the value of a test

When considering any test or schedule of tests applied to any raw material, process intermediate or finished product it is easy for the industrial statistician to say 'Buy the raw materials to specification and control the process to the standard operating procedure then there will be no need to perform any tests whatsoever.' It is not at all easy for the production staff to adhere to this proposition because there are small inherent variations in process operation however steady conditions may appear; there may be large variations induced by failure of some item of equipment or by human forgetfulness or misjudgment; there may be need to separate grades of an intermediate so that best quality goes to one process whereas a second process may be satisfied by a lower quality; there may be need to separate grades of a finished product according to some physical characteristic to meet the requirements of different customers; and so on. So some testing may be necessary.

The tests performed in any schedule of testing, especially if this schedule has extended over a long period of time, may be divided into four classes

1 TESTS REQUESTED BY CUSTOMERS: Special tests required by customers to ensure that the product is suitable for the particular applications must be made as long as the business is worth having. But wherever possible a customer's tests should be made only on product intended for that customer; where product is selected for a customer on the basis of such a test the testing should be stopped as soon as sufficient product has been approved to meet the customer's requirement. Note that the 'customer' may be any user of the product inside or outside the producer's organization.

2 TESTS TO DETERMINE PRODUCT QUALITY AND PROCESS CAPABILITY: Where there is any doubt regarding the constancy of product quality or process operation such tests as these are necessary. On the basis that every test must pay for itself it is obvious that unnecessary tests must be eliminated and only those tests be performed which give the information required.

3 CONFIRMATORY OR CORROBORATIVE TESTS: Cases arise where tests are made seemingly to confirm each other's reliability and accuracy. For example, any or all of the tests for assay, specific gravity, refractive index, melting point, crystallizing point, and boiling point may be made when only one test is necessary (excepting that several such associated tests may be necessary under items 1 and 2 above). Bearing in mind that any test which needs confirmation is unreliable and wasteful and should be stopped, it is possible to determine correlations between values obtained by confirmatory tests. Precision experiments should be run and that test which gives the best balance between convenience and reliability should be retained and all the other associated tests should be stopped.

4 INFORMATIONAL TESTS: From time to time additional tests may be run to provide information, not generally available, for some specific purpose. It is not unknown for such tests to be retained permanently; but unless the information generated is required on a continuing basis, when the relevant test-clause should be written into the specification, informational tests should be stopped as soon as sufficient information has been collected.

Having ensured that test schedules contain all the tests that are of value to the customer and to the producing department, and none other, it is possible to determine how variations in test results can be related to specification limits or to the importance of the test. Two schemes have been devised: one for use where a large number of test results is available, the other where relatively few (less than 50) test results are available; the 'test result' for these schemes is the numerical value obtained as the result of a test made on a random sample drawn from the lot.

I.S. 1—15

8.4 precision and accuracy of a test method

When associated tests are under consideration it is necessary to compare the precision and accuracy values for the tests and the conditions – such as manhours – required to perform the test.

The accuracy of a test method is concerned with the agreement between an observed result and the 'true value' for the quantity being measured. The precision of a test method is concerned with the agreement of the observed results among themselves. Usually only these two components of test error are considered, but if the observed result is to be the basis of a guarantee over a long period of time then a third component, reliability, which is concerned with the stability of the observed results over a period of time, must be introduced. Here we are concerned only with determination of precision and accuracy.

8.4.1 PRECISION OF A TEST METHOD

The precision of a test method is a measure of the agreement among themselves of replicate measurements. The observed results do not necessarily vary about the true value so that a test method may be precise without being accurate. Then we define the precision of a test method as 'the variation about the mean of analytical results obtained by one competent analyst, using the method in question with one set of apparatus, and controlling all factors known or expected to affect the result as closely as would be practicable if the method were in routine use by a competent analyst.' For the experimentation five subsamples from each of five carefully homogenized samples are analysed and the results examined by analysis of variance as shown in Section 5.1.1. This definition of precision is often referred to as a 'repeatability'; if several analysts using several sets of apparatus are involved in the experimentation the precision is referred to as a 'reproducibility', and one example of the calculation for this was given in the latin square experiment of Section 5.5.1. Now we can extend the definition of precision to include reliability, and an analysis of variance is made over the variables, analysts, lots and days (or some other suitable period of time; the days may, of course, be separated by several months).

Analysts are examined so that any one different from the others may be identified. Correction by means of analyst training may lead to an improvement in the precision of a test. All the analysts who may be required to perform the test as part of their routine duties should be included in the experimentation.

Different lots are examined so that the precision of the test over the whole range of the characteristic may be examined and evaluated. In some cases the test error can be shown to be dependent upon the range of values covered by the test; and here the analysis of variance should be made upon the logarithms of the observations rather than on the observations themselves.

Different days are examined to allow day-to-day variations in equipment, personnel, and laboratory to influence the test in the same manner as they influence day-to-day routine testing. Also any change in the material under test over a period of time can be evaluated. There is no limit to the number of days included in the experimentation; there must be two and four spread over three or four weeks should be sufficient to show all the variations that are likely to occur.

Table 8.4.1 shows the experimental design and observations made for a small experiment in which only two lots were examined on each of two days. The samples to be tested were randomized and numbered before being given to the analysts, who were not informed that a special investigation was in hand.

Table 8.4.1 Precision of test: experimental design and observations

	Lot 1		Lot 2		Totals for analysts
	Day 1	Day 2	Day 1	Day 2	
Analyst 1	15	18	30	31	94
Analyst 2	14	14	29	26	83
Analyst 3	19	23	45	42	129
Analyst 4	12	16	30	28	86
Subtotals for days	60	71	134	127	
Totals for lots		131		261	392

It is necessary to obtain an observation for every cell in the design. Application of the procedure to estimate missing values is not satisfactory when differences between analysts or between days may be very small. If any observation seems obviously wrong a repeat test should be made to prevent a wrong value exerting an untoward bias on the analysis. The analysis of variance is made as usual

$$\text{Correction for the mean} = (392)^2/16 = 9{,}604$$

Total sum of squares

$$= 15^2 + 18^2 + \ldots + 30^2 + 28^2 - \text{CM}$$
$$= 11{,}082 - 9{,}604 = 1{,}478$$

Sum of squares for lots

$$= \frac{(131)^2 + (261)^2}{8} - 9{,}604 = 10{,}660{\cdot}25 - 9{,}604 = 1{,}056{\cdot}25$$

Sum of squares for days

$$= \frac{(194)^2 + (198)^2}{8} - 9{,}604 = 9{,}605 - 9{,}604 = 1$$

Sum of squares for analysts

$$= \frac{(94)^2 + (83)^2 + (129)^2 + (86)^2}{4} - 9{,}604 = 9{,}940{\cdot}5 - 9{,}604 = 336{\cdot}5$$

and the analysis of variance table is

Source of variation	Sum of squares	D.F.	Mean square	F-Ratio	Expectation of M.S.
Lots	1,056·25	1	1,056·25	125·4	$\sigma_0^2 + 8\sigma_3^2$
Days	1	1	1	<1	$\sigma_0^2 + 8\sigma_2^2$
Analysts	336·5	3	112·16	13·31	$\sigma_0^2 + 4\sigma_1^2$
Residual (= experimental error)	84·25	10	8·425	1	σ_0^2
Total	1,478	15			

The F-table quotes a value of 10·04 for 1 and 10 degrees of freedom at the 0·01 level of probability and there is a highly significant difference between lots. This was expected as the lots were selected from each end of the range of values normally met and we are not interested in lot-to-lot variation in this exercise.

Obviously there is no significant variation between days, but the F-table quotes a value of 6·55 for 3 and 10 degrees of freedom at the 0·01 level of probability so that there is a highly significant difference between analysts. Inspection of the table of results shows that analyst 3 obtains consistently higher results than the others and further investigation should start with this analyst.

If we let σ_0^2 represent the experimental error and σ_1^2 the analyst error, then the estimate of test error, when a test is made by one analyst is

$$\text{Test variance} = 8{\cdot}425 + \tfrac{1}{4}(112{\cdot}16 - 8{\cdot}425) = 34{\cdot}36$$

of which the analyst variance is 25·934, 75 per cent of the total test variance.

The precision of the test, as given by the 95 per cent confidence limits for a single test, is $1{\cdot}96\sqrt{34{\cdot}36} = \pm 11{\cdot}7$; the large analyst variance has led to very wide confidence limits for the test. Note that if there had been a significant difference detected for days, the days variance σ_2^2 would have been included in the total test variance. The result of the exercise will be a statement such as the first sentence in this paragraph with the addition of the range of values, 12 to 45, covered by the experiment.

Sometimes a measurement of the error involved by the procedure of sampling is required, and this can be obtained by running an analysis of variance on lots, samples and analysts. At least three samples from each of two lots are necessary; with four analysts this means a 24-sample experiment and if more work can be entertained the number of lots should be increased rather than the number of samples.

If the experimentation is made over l lots and k samples are taken from each lot and n analysts take part then for the analysis of variance, the total sum of squares has $(kln - 1)$ degrees of freedom, there are $(n - 1)$ degrees of freedom for analysts, $(l - 1)$ degrees of freedom for lots, and $l(n - 1)$ degrees of freedom for samples within lots. The mean squares for analysts and samples within lots may be compared against the residual mean square, but the mean square for lots must be compared with the mean square for samples within lots. Table 8.4.2 shows the experimental design and observations recorded in a recent investigation.

Table 8.4.2 Sampling error: experimental design and observations

	Lot 1			Lot 2			Total for analysts
	Sample 1	Sample 2	Sample 3	Sample 4	Sample 5	Sample 6	
Analyst 1	10	8	5	20	16	24	83
Analyst 2	12	7	5	18	18	20	80
Analyst 3	10	9	6	20	20	22	87
Analyst 4	14	12	6	20	18	20	90
Totals for samples	46	36	22	78	72	86	
Totals for lots			104			236	340

Calculation of the details of the analysis of variance is left to the reader. The final analysis of variance table is

Source of variation	Sum of squares	D.F.	Mean square	F-Ratio	Expectation of M.S.
Lots	726	1	726	29·94	$\sigma_0^2 + 12\sigma_3^2$
Samples within lots	97	4	24·25	9·33	$\sigma_0^2 + 4\sigma_2^2$
Analysts	9	3	3	1·15	$\sigma_0^2 + 6\sigma_1^2$
Residual (= expmtl. error)	39	15	2·6	1	σ_0^2
Total	871	23			

Comparison with tabulated values for F shows that the variation between lots and the variation between samples within lots are significant while the variation between analysts is not significant. In this exercise we are not concerned with variance between lots, but now we can estimate the total error variance. Given the variances as shown then

$$\sigma_1^2 = \tfrac{1}{6}(3 - 2\cdot6) = 0\cdot0667$$

and
$$\sigma_2^2 = \tfrac{1}{4}(24\cdot25 - 2\cdot6) = 5\cdot4125.$$

Thus, for a single sample taken from a lot the total error variance is $0\cdot0667 + 5\cdot4125 + 2\cdot6 = 8\cdot0792$ so that the 95 per cent confidence limits for a single test are $1\cdot96\sqrt{8\cdot0792} = \pm5\cdot68$ in the range 5 to 24.

Excluding the sampling variance we have an estimate of the total test variance as $2\cdot6 + 0\cdot0667 = 2\cdot6667$, from which the precision of the test as indicated by the 95 per cent confidence limits for a single determination are $1\cdot96\sqrt{2\cdot6667} = \pm3\cdot26$ in the range 5 to 24.

Note that if three tests are run on the same sample, the estimate of precision is given by

$$t \cdot \sqrt{\left(\frac{\text{analytical variance}}{3} + \text{sampling variance} \right)}$$

whereas if three samples were blended and one test made, the estimate of precision is given by

$$t \cdot \sqrt{\left(\text{analytical variance} + \frac{\text{sampling variance}}{3} \right)}$$

8.4.2 ACCURACY OF A TEST METHOD

The accuracy of a test method is determined by making a number of synthetic mixtures that cover the expected range of composition over which the test method is likely to be used. About 15 synthetic mixtures should cover most ranges and these should be fairly distributed over the range. After analysing these mixtures by the test method under investigation, a *discrepancy* is obtained for each mixture where

Discrepancy = Value found − Value known to be present.

The discrepancies should be distributed evenly about a zero mean if the test is carried out in the absence of any personal or experimental bias. If the test method is accurate then the discrepancies should be distributed evenly about zero mean and there should be no great difference between the discrepancy values in any sections of the range. From the discrepancies the mean discrepancy and the standard error of this mean are calculated, and the accuracy of the test method is expressed in the numerical values of the mean discrepancy ± standard error.

For example, Table 8.4.3 shows the observations made in three accuracy investigations. The discrepancies found for test method 1 show zero mean and a standard error of ±0·35 so that the expected accuracy of a test in the range of values shown is reported as ± 0.35. This test method is shown to be accurate over the whole range of the investigation with equal discrepancies spread over the range.

Table 8.4.3 Determinations for accuracy of a test method

Test Method 1

Found	33	32	34	43	58	64	68	75	79	84	91	96	108	115	127
Actually present	32	33	34	43	59	64	68	75	78	84	91	96	107	115	128
Discrepancy	1	−1	—	—	−1	—	—	—	1	—	—	—	1	—	−1

From which $\Sigma x = 0$; $\bar{x} = 0$; $N = 15$; $\Sigma x^2 = 6$; $s = 0.6325$; $t_{14,95} = 2.145$ and

$$\text{S.E.M.} = \frac{2.145 \times 0.6325}{\sqrt{15}} = 0.35$$

and the accuracy is ± 0.35 in the range 32 to 128.

Test Method 2

Found	820	928	994	1044	1126	1694	1710	1897	2010	2366	2934	3300	3375	3574	3692
Actually present	853	1037	1041	1052	1129	1716	1728	1944	2021	2413	2973	3470	3431	3597	3801
Discrepancy	−33	−109	−47	−8	−3	−22	−18	−47	−11	−47	−39	−170	−56	−17	−109

From which $\Sigma x = -736$; $\bar{x} = -49$; $N = 15$; $\Sigma x^2 = 66{,}326$; $s = 46.45$ and

$$\text{S.E.M.} = \frac{2.145 \times 46.45}{\sqrt{15}} = 25.7$$

and the accuracy is $-49(\pm 26)$ in the range 853 to 3,801.

Test Method 3

Found	12	10	10	16	15	14	18	17	17	21	21	20	25	25	25
Actually present	8	8	8	13	13	13	18	18	18	23	23	23	28	28	28
Discrepancy	4	2	2	3	2	1	—	−1	−1	−2	−2	−3	−3	−3	−3

The discrepancies show a gradual change from 4 (when 8 are actually present) to −3 (when 28 are actually present) and depend on the composition. It is not possible to determine an accuracy over the whole range and the best that can be done without further investigation is to report that

in the range 8 to 18 the accuracy may be expected to lie in the interval 0 to +4;
in the range 18 to 28 the accuracy may be expected to lie in the interval 0 to −3.

On the other hand with test method 2 all the discrepancies have been found to be negative; there is some bias present in the test and this should be investigated as it may result from a small but consistent error in the test procedure or from a misapplication of the test method. However, as far as the accuracy of the test is concerned, within the range of values examined the method would be expected to yield a result 49 units below the true result (on average), but likely to vary somewhere in the range 23 to 75 below the true result.

In the observations for test method 3 we note a gradual transition in discrepancies from positive for the low values to negative for the high values. It is obvious that the test method is not particularly good and no accuracy figure should be quoted for any test method which gives a series of discrepancies such as this.

In any case where the discrepancy values differ significantly between sections of the range of compositions studied it becomes necessary to determine the accuracy of the method over each section of the range. As many additional synthetic mixtures should be made up and analysed to give an adequate cover of each section of the range.

In any case where all, or the great majority (say 12 or more out of 15), of discrepancy values have the same sign, that is these values will be all negative or all positive, and the mean is heavily weighted from zero, some bias is present and is concealing the true experimental error. Wherever possible, this bias should be the subject of further work leading to its identification and elimination.

With a knowledge of the precision and accuracy of every test in the schedule associated tests can be compared and the less valuable tests dropped from the schedule. Each of the tests finally allowed in the schedule can be submitted to a simple statistical analysis to determine the optimum frequency of performing the test.

8.5 frequency of testing

Two methods of statistical analysis are used: one where there is a large number of test results, as will be the case if lots are submitted daily, the other where there is only a small number of test results following infrequent submission of lots for testing.

8.5.1 DESIRABLE FREQUENCY OF TEST: MANY VALUES

Where a large number of test results is available as a consequence of a test having been performed on successive lots of material, the test results will have a normal distribution. It is important that the results be obtained from successive lots; unless there is a valid reason for excluding any results all should be used. The statistician must investigate carefully any breaks in the sequence of test results and refuse to deal with data presented on a selective basis.

With results in a normal distribution the standard deviation provides a measure of the dispersion of the values and may be used to predict the probability that future values obtained by the test may be expected to fall in any given range. From this probability it may be decided whether or not to accept the chance of not detecting an unsatisfactory lot of material; if the chance is acceptable then an arbitrary division of test frequencies may be assigned to each probability range. This procedure requires that the process which produces the material remains at all times under statistical control so that an unsatisfactory lot, if it occurs, will be due solely to random deviations within the process and not to some imposed manipulation of the process variables.

The following table gives the division which has been used successfully for many years in the testing of raw materials, process intermediates, and finished products in chemical industry.

Table 8.5.1 Frequency of testing based on mean value and standard deviation of test results

Where the test specification limit is at

Mean value $\pm 3\sigma$:	Test every lot.	This range covers 99·73 per cent probability.
Mean value $\pm(3\sigma$ to 3·5 σ):	Test every other lot.	This range covers 99·95 per cent probability and excludes about 1 in 2,000.
Mean value $\pm(>3·5\sigma$ to 4·0 σ):	Test 1 lot in 5.	This range covers 99·994 per cent probability and excludes about 1 in 16,000.
Mean value $\pm(>4·0\sigma$ to 4·5 σ):	Test 1 lot in 10.	This range covers 99·999,3 per cent probability and excludes about 1 in 140,000.
Mean value $\pm(>4·5\sigma$ to 5·0 σ):	Test 1 lot in 25.	This range covers 99·999,94 per cent probability and excludes about 1 in 1,600,000.
Mean value $\pm(>5·0\sigma$ to 6·0 σ):	Test 1 lot in 100.	This range covers 99·999,998 per cent probability and excludes about 1 in 50,000,000.
Mean value $\pm$(over 6·0 σ):	Stop testing.	

If any specification limit is at more than 6σ from the calculated mean value there is no point in attempting to locate the limit more closely as this means that the test characteristic is being controlled a long way from the specification limit. In cases such as this the value of the specification limit should be queried.

The mean value and standard deviation are calculated from the lesser number of test results involved in the values reported for the last 400 lots or the values reported over the last 3 years as long as there are more than 50 values in this period. Of course there must have been no change imposed on the process or in the method of testing during the interval chosen.

The recommendation to reduce the frequency of testing is made in the following terms: 'The test specification is at $n\sigma$ from the calculated mean value of N test results. This corresponds to a probability of a per cent, so that as long as manufacture and process operation continue as they were during the period under survey, a per cent of the values of this characteristic re ported for future tests will be expected to lie within the specification limits. This is sufficient probability to permit a reduction in the frequency of testing, and it is recommended that the frequency of performing this test be reduced to 1 lot in k selected at random.' In this recommendation the actual values for n, N, a, and k will be used.

If a lot tested on a reduced frequency schedule is found to be outside specification, then every lot up to the next scheduled lot is tested; if all these test results agree with the limits previously determined then testing returns to the frequency schedule, but if there is any disagreement a new frequency schedule is calculated. Wherever possible, lots previous to the out-of-specification lot are inspected to determine whether the one lot is on its own or followed some number of out-of-specification lots; in the latter case failure of process control or imposition of a process change would be suspected.

For example, the test results reported for the last 268 (successive) lots gave a mean value of 95·1 and a standard deviation of 0·14. The specification for this particular characteristic is 94·5 (minimum). Then we see that the specification minimum is $(95·1 - 94·5)/0·14 = 4·28\sigma$ from the calculated mean value and the recommendation made is to reduce the frequency of testing to 1 lot in 10 selected at random. This means that a schedule is prepared randomizing the numbers 1 to 10 and lots are examined according to this schedule; it does not mean that every tenth lot is examined.

8.5.2 DESIRABLE FREQUENCY OF TEST: FEW VALUES

Where only a few values (say, below 50) are recorded for any test made on a material, or where there has been a change in the manufacturing process or in the test method so that only the few most recent values should be considered, it is very unlikely that these values will indicate a normal distribution, or any other regular distribution. The standard deviation as a measure of the dispersion of these values must be estimated by a different method, and the method of successive differences may be used.

In this method the differences between successive test values, regardless of sign, are used and the procedure may be described as

1 Calculate the average difference between successive values (and let this be d);
2 Estimate the standard deviation as $0·88d$ (and let this be s);
3 Calculate the *precontrol factor* as $2·33s$ (and let this be f);
4 Then the *precontrol limit* is: specification limit $- f$ (where specification limit is a maximum) or specification limit $+ f$ (where specification limit is a minimum).

The number of values lying outside the precontrol limit is counted and compared with the 'State of Control Chart' shown in Table 8.5.2. The appropriate frequency of testing for future lots is recommended according to the value assigned to the test. If a lot tested on a reduced frequency schedule is found to be outside specification the same procedure described in Section 8.5.1, last-but-one paragraph, is followed.

For example, suppose that for a particular test only 20 values are available, and let these be the last 20 values shown in the third chart of the Dottograph in Chapter 3, Figure 3.3.7, and we have the sum of the 19 differences $= 70$, so that

$$d = 70/19 = 3·684,$$
$$s = 0·88 \times 3·684 = 3·242,$$
$$f = 2·33 \times 3·242 = 7·554, \text{ which is to be taken as } 8$$

and $\qquad$ PCL $= 20 - 8 = 12.$

There is one point on this limit and there are two points above it. Entering the state of control chart at 19 (number of tests) and 3 (number of outsiders) we find that the test is to be placed in Class (or Area) C, and the frequency of

State of Control Chart

Number of Points lying outside one P.C.L.

Number of Tests carried out, excluding the selected starting Point.

Tests	0	1	2	3	4	5	6	7	8	9	10	11	12	13	14	15	16	17	18	19	20	21	22	23	24	25	26	27	28	29	30
X	X																														
1	A	A																													
2	A	A	A																												
3	B	A	A	A																											
4	C	B	A	A	A																										
5	C	B	B	A	A	A																									
6	C	C	B	B	A	A	A																								
7	C	C	B	B	B	A	A	A																							
8	C	C	C	B	B	B	A	A	A																						
9	D	C	C	C	C	B	B	A	A	A																					
10	D	C	C	C	C	B	B	B	A	A	A																				
11	D	C	C	C	C	B	B	B	B	A	A	A																			
12	D	D	C	C	C	B	B	B	B	A	A	A	A																		
13	D	D	C	C	C	C	B	B	B	B	A	A	A	A																	
14	D	D	C	C	C	C	B	B	B	B	B	A	A	A	A																
15	D	D	D	C	C	C	B	B	B	B	B	B	A	A	A	A															
16	D	D	D	C	C	C	B	B	B	B	B	B	A	A	A	A	A														
17	D	D	D	C	C	C	C	B	B	B	B	B	B	A	A	A	A	A													
18	D	D	D	C	C	C	C	B	B	B	B	B	B	A	A	A	A	A	A												
19	D	D	D	C	C	C	C	C	B	B	B	B	B	B	A	A	A	A	A	A											
20	D	D	D	C	C	C	C	C	B	B	B	B	B	B	A	A	A	A	A	A	A										
21	D	D	D	C	C	C	C	C	C	B	B	B	B	B	B	A	A	A	A	A	A	A									
22	D	D	D	D	C	C	C	C	C	B	B	B	B	B	B	B	A	A	A	A	A	A	A								
23	D	D	D	D	C	C	C	C	C	C	B	B	B	B	B	B	B	A	A	A	A	A	A	A							
24	D	D	D	D	C	C	C	C	C	C	B	B	B	B	B	B	B	B	A	A	A	A	A	A	A						
25	D	D	D	D	C	C	C	C	C	C	B	B	B	B	B	B	B	B	A	A	A	A	A	A	A	A					
26	D	D	D	D	C	C	C	C	C	C	B	B	B	B	B	B	B	B	B	A	A	A	A	A	A	A	A				
27	D	D	D	D	C	C	C	C	C	C	C	B	B	B	B	B	B	B	B	B	A	A	A	A	A	A	A	A			
28	D	D	D	D	C	C	C	C	C	C	C	B	B	B	B	B	B	B	B	B	B	A	A	A	A	A	A	A	A		
29	D	D	D	D	C	C	C	C	C	C	C	C	B	B	B	B	B	B	B	B	B	B	A	A	A	A	A	A	A	A	
30	D	D	D	D	C	C	C	C	C	C	C	C	B	B	B	B	B	B	B	B	B	B	A	A	A	A	A	A	A	A	A
35	E	D	D	D	D	C	C	C	C	C	C	C	C	B	B	B	B	B	B	B	B	B	B	B	A	A	A	A	A	A	A
40	E	D	D	D	D	C	C	C	C	C	C	C	C	C	C	B	B	B	B	B	B	B	B	B	B	B	B	B	B	A	A
45	E	E	D	D	D	C	C	C	C	C	C	C	C	C	C	C	B	B	B	B	B	B	B	B	B	B	B	B	B	B	B
50	E	E	D	D	D	D	C	C	C	C	C	C	C	C	C	C	C	C	B	B	B	B	B	B	B	B	B	B	B	B	B

Value of Test	Frequency for Testing in Areas				
	A	B	C	D	E
Extremely critical	1	1	1	3	5
Critical	1	1	3	5	10
Important	1	3	5	10	25
Informational	3	5	10	25	100

Fig. 8.5.2. STATE OF CONTROL CHART

testing to be recommended will be reported from the table below the chart according to the value of the test, that is,

> if the test is thought to be extremely critical (a customer's test) then every lot is to be tested;
> if the test is thought to be critical (a process control or sales specification test) then one lot in three is to be tested;
> if the test is thought to be important (minor control variable or lot comparator) then one lot in five is to be tested; and
> if the test is required only to derive information (long term process variations) then only one lot in ten need be tested.

In any case where a specification has both an upper limit and a lower limit, their respective precontrol limits must be calculated separately. The number of points outside each PCL must be considered, and any recommendation made will be based on the poorer classification. Where this procedure is applied to a test for which no specification limit has been established, then a limit of mean value $\pm 4s$ is assumed as a specification limit.

Note that in the above calculation the factor 2·33 is an approximation of the value 2·326, which is the value of Student's t for 98 per cent probability and infinite degrees of freedom. When the precontrol factor is calculated and found to be a fraction which does not agree exactly with any point on the test result scale, it must be rounded up to the next acceptable value.

8.6 how big is a sample?

Usually when we talk of taking a sample from a lot of raw material or finished product we imagine a large bulk of absolutely homogeneous material. This may be a heap of powder or crystal which has been blended thoroughly before packing into bags or kegs, or it may be a large volume of liquid which has been agitated to ensure homogeneity. With such a lot any very small portion is as good as any other very small portion, so we just take as much material in a sample as will permit the necessary tests to be made and leave some over as a 'retained sample' for future reference. To our random samples and their analyses we apply probability theory to compare the test results and the specification limits and thereby determine suitable test frequencies. Unfortunately, lots are not always homogeneous and a common question is 'How big should the sample be?' or 'How many drums per lot of 50 should we sample?'

In many cases where no prior information is available the only answer that can be made is that the sample should be of sufficient size to be representative, though this may not always be feasible, or that the number of samples to be taken should be such that they can be dealt with satisfactorily in the time and with the effort available. As one might expect, this is not often accepted as an adequate answer, and to the industrial statistician the sample is of very little use unless the sample data are valid; the sample data are reliable; and the sample data may be subjected to statistical analysis that proves its reliability. Sometimes, as in a work sampling study where a binomial distribution holds, the sample size can be specified exactly and corrected sequentially as observations are made. Occasionally a sampling level of N samples per lot is specified, where N is the maximum number of samples that can be handled, then two other sampling levels such as $N/4$ and $N/2$ are used; when sufficient lots have been examined the means and standard deviations are calculated for each sampling level and if agreement is noted $N/4$ is accepted as a sufficient sample.

Analysis of variance techniques permit us to determine the best sampling level to be taken for any given test according to the analytical results obtained. For any sequence of testing, be it on lots of raw materials, process intermediates, or finished products, an analysis of variance can be made on test results which will apportion the total variance among

1 the variance among lots, σ_2^2,
2 the variance among packages, σ_1^2, and
3 the variance due to testing error, σ_0^2,

so that for any situation where n lots are to be considered, with samples to be taken from p packages per lot, and r replicates of test are to be made on each sample, the analysis of variance results in the following table

Source of variation	Sum of squares	D.F.	Mean square	Quantity estimated by M.S.
Among lots	SS[Lots]	$(n-1)$	$\dfrac{SS[Lots]}{(n-1)}$	$\sigma_0^2 + r\sigma_1^2 + pr\sigma_2^2$
Among packages within lots	SS[Packages]	$n(p-1)$	$\dfrac{SS[P]}{n(p-1)}$	$\sigma_0^2 + rr\sigma_1^2$
Testing error	SSE	$np(r-1)$	$\dfrac{SSE}{np(r-1)}$	σ_0^2
Total	TSS	$npr-1$		

The precision of the sampling and testing scheme, as indicated by the standard error, can be determined easily from the variances shown in the above table.

For example, consider the following set of analytical test results, relating to duplicate tests made on samples from each of three packages taken from each of ten lots

Table 8.6.1 Analytical test results for assay

Lot	Package 1	Package 2	Package 3
1	98·4, 98·1	97·9, 97·5	98·1, 98·3
2	93·4, 93·6	93·6, 93·7	93·4, 93·3
3	92·6, 92·4	92·7, 92·9	92·6, 92·7
4	96·9, 97·2	97·4, 97·2	97·3, 97·0
5	93·9, 94·1	94·0, 93·8	93·0, 94·0
6	94·8, 94·9	94·8, 94·6	94·6, 94·6
7	97·5, 97·4	97·2, 97·4	97·6, 97·4
8	97·0, 96·6	97·1, 97·0	96·9, 97·1
9	95·7, 95·5	95·6, 95·7	95·7, 95·5
10	94·4, 94·8	94·4, 94·7	94·7, 94·6

Subtracting 92·0 from each result to simplify the working, and providing totals for packages and lots gives

Lot	Package 1		Totals	Package 2		Totals	Package 3		Totals	Totals for Lots
1	6·4	6·1	12·5	5·9	5·5	11·4	6·1	6·3	12·4	36·3
2	1·4	1·6	3·0	1·6	1·7	3·3	1·4	1·3	2·7	9·0
3	0·6	0·4	1·0	0·7	0·9	1·6	0·6	0·7	1·3	3·9
4	4·9	5·2	10·1	5·4	5·2	10·6	5·3	5·0	10·3	31·0
5	1·9	2·1	4·0	2·0	1·8	3·8	1·9	2·0	3·9	11·7
6	2·8	2·9	5·7	2·8	2·6	5·4	2·6	2·6	5·2	16·3
7	5·5	5·4	10·9	5·2	5·4	10·6	5·6	5·4	11·0	32·5
8	5·0	4·6	9·6	5·1	5·0	10·1	4·9	5·1	10·0	29·7
9	3·7	3·5	7·2	3·6	3·7	7·3	3·7	3·5	7·2	21·7
10	2·4	2·8	5·2	2·4	2·7	5·1	2·7	2·6	5·3	15·6

Grand Total: 207·7

The analysis of variance is carried out in the usual manner.

Correction for the grand mean

$$= (207·7)^2/60 = 718·99$$

Total sum of squares $= 906·55 - 718·99 = 187·56$ [for 59 d.f.]

Sum of squares for packages

$$= \frac{(12·5)^2 + (3·0)^2 + \ldots + (7·2)^2 + (5·3)^2}{2} - CM$$

$$= 905·825 - 718·99 = 186·835 \text{ [29 d.f.]}$$

Sum of squares for lots $= \dfrac{(36·3)^2 + \ldots + (15·6)^2}{6} - CM$

$$= 905·01 - 718·99 = 186·02 \text{ [9 d.f.]}$$

Sum of squares within packages (replication)

$$= 187 \cdot 56 - 186 \cdot 835 = 0 \cdot 725 \, [30 \text{ d.f.}]$$

Sum of squares for packages within lots

$$= 186 \cdot 835 - 186 \cdot 02 = 0 \cdot 815 \, [20 \text{ d.f.}]$$

and the analysis of variance table is

Source of variation	Sum of squares	D.F.	Mean square	Quantity estimated by M.S.
Among lots	186·02	9	20·67	$\sigma_0^2 + 2\sigma_1^2 + 6\sigma_2^2$
Among packages within lots	0·815	20	0·04075	$\sigma_0^2 + 2\sigma_1^2$
Within packages (replication)	0·725	30	0·02417	σ_0^2
Total	187·56	59		

The mean square ratio shows that the analytical test may be expected to distinguish between lots such as those quoted in Table 8.6.1, but here the main interest lies in the variances. The best estimates of these variances are

$$
\begin{aligned}
\sigma_0^2 &= 0 \cdot 02417 & &\text{whence } \sigma_0 = 0 \cdot 1554, \\
\sigma_1^2 &= \tfrac{1}{2}(0 \cdot 04075 - 0 \cdot 02417) & &\text{whence } \sigma_1 = 0 \cdot 0911, \\
\text{and} \quad \sigma_2^2 &= \tfrac{1}{6}(20 \cdot 67 - 0 \cdot 04075) & &\text{whence } \sigma_2 = 1 \cdot 854
\end{aligned}
$$

If we accept σ_0 to be the standard error of analytical testing (as determined by replicate analyses of the samples), and σ_1 to be the standard error of sampling (as determined among packages within lots), then it is possible to devise a suitable sampling and testing scheme to meet any desired precision of the analytical estimate. Where p packages of a lot are sampled, and r independent tests are made on each sample, the variance of the average for the lot will be

$$V = \frac{\sigma_0^2}{pr} + \frac{\sigma_1^2}{p},$$

which for our example would be

$$\frac{0 \cdot 02417}{pr} + \frac{0 \cdot 00829}{p}.$$

For any values of p and r the standard errors can be calculated, and the sampling procedure which gives an acceptably low value for the standard error can be adopted. Table 8.6.2 shows the standard errors calculated from various values of p and r and the variances σ_0^2 and σ_1^2 of our example:

Table 8.6.2 Calculation of standard errors for various sampling procedures

p	r	Variance of average for the lot	Standard error
1	1	0·02417 + 0·00829 = 0·03246	0·1802
	2	0·01208 + 0·00829 = 0·02037	0·1427
	3	0·00806 + 0·00829 = 0·01635	0·1279
2	1	0·01208 + 0·00414 = 0·01622	0·1274
	2	0·00604 + 0·00414 = 0·01018	0·1009
	3	0·00403 + 0·00414 = 0·00817	0·0939
3	1	0·00806 + 0·00276 = 0·01082	0·1040
	2	0·00403 + 0·00276 = 0·00679	0·0824
	3	0·00269 + 0·00276 = 0·00545	0·0738
4	1	0·00604 + 0·00207 = 0·00811	0·0901
	2	0·00302 + 0·00207 = 0·00509	0·0713
	3	0·00201 + 0·00207 = 0·00408	0·0639
10	1	0·00242 + 0·00083 = 0·00325	0·0570
	2	0·00121 + 0·00083 = 0·00204	0·0452
	3	0·00081 + 0·00083 = 0·00164	0·0405

From this tabulation we see that if a standard error of 0·1 is required, the sampling and testing procedure can be either duplicate testing on 2 packages per lot or single testing on 3 packages per lot.

The table shows that, for this particular example, the variance of the average for the lot may be reduced more effectively by increasing the number of packages sampled rather than by increasing the test replication per sample. We see, for example, that it is better to make one test on each of ten packages per lot than to make three tests on each of four packages per lot.

8.7 the cost of sampling and testing

In the previous section we considered how a sampling and testing scheme can be determined from the analytical results of the test and on a precision requirement. In many cases this procedure will be satisfactory, but sometimes the cost of carrying out a test is quite big and it is important to provide an adequate safeguard for minimum cost; it becomes necessary to consider sampling and testing costs as well as the sampling and testing variances.

The variance of the mean of the sampling procedure by which p samples are taken from a lot and r tests are carried out on each sample was stated (in the previous section) to be

$$V = \frac{\sigma_1^2}{p} + \frac{\sigma_0^2}{pr}, \quad \text{which can be rewritten as} \quad \frac{1}{p}\left[\sigma_1^2 + \frac{\sigma_0^2}{r}\right] \quad (1)$$

If we let c_1 represent the cost of taking a sample and c_0 the cost of performing the analytical test on one sample, then the total cost incurred per lot, which involves p samples and pr tests, is given by

$$c = pc_1 + prc_0 \quad \text{or} \quad c = p(c_1 + rc_0) \tag{2}$$

Substituting the value of p from equation (1) in equation (2) gives

$$c = (c_1 + rc_0) \cdot \frac{\left[\sigma_1^2 + \dfrac{\sigma_0^2}{r}\right]}{V} = \frac{1}{V}\left[c_1\sigma_1^2 + c_0\sigma_0^2 + \frac{c_1\sigma_0^2}{r} + rc_0\sigma_1^2\right] \tag{3}$$

and this is the total cost involved in sampling and testing for any given variance V; the only unknown quantity in this expression is the value of r.

Then differentiating equation (3) with respect to r and equating to zero to provide the minimum gives

$$\frac{d\,c}{d\,r} = \frac{1}{V}\left[c_0\sigma_1^2 - \frac{c_1\sigma_0^2}{r^2}\right] = 0, \quad \text{whence} \quad r = \frac{\sigma_0}{\sigma_1}\sqrt{\frac{c_1}{c_0}}.$$

It follows that

$$V = \frac{1}{p}\left[\sigma_1^2 + \frac{\sigma_0^2}{(\sigma_0/\sigma_1)\sqrt{(c_1/c_0)}}\right] \quad \text{so that} \quad p = \frac{1}{V}\left[\sigma_1^2 + \sigma_0\sigma_1 \cdot \sqrt{\frac{c_0}{c_1}}\right].$$

If we can consider the cost of analytical testing to be 25 times the cost of taking a sample, so that $c_1/c_0 = 0.04$, then for the variances calculated in the example in the previous section where $\sigma_0 = 0.1554$ and $\sigma_1 = 0.0911$, we have $r = 0.1554 \times 0.2/0.0911 = 0.3$ and it is sufficient to take 3 samples per lot, bulk these, and perform one analytical test on the bulked sample. If in any case it is not permissible to bulk samples then any value of r calculated to be less than 1 must be taken as 1.

In most cases the desired standard error of the sampling and testing procedure will be known. If this were 0.5, so that $V = 0.25$, with the above values for σ_0 and σ_1 we have

$$p = \frac{1}{0.25}[0.0829 + (0.0911)(0.1554)\sqrt{25}]$$

$$= 3.2 \text{ (which must be taken as 4)}$$

so that with $r = 1$ and $p = 4$ the sampling scheme requires that 4 samples be taken per lot and that each sample is to be tested once. But if the samples can be bulked then we have $r = 0.3$,

$$p = \frac{1}{V}\left[\sigma_1^2 + \frac{\sigma_0^2}{r}\right] = \frac{1}{0.25}\left[0.0829 + \frac{0.02417}{0.3}\right]$$

$$= 0.65 \text{ (which must be taken as 1)}$$

and we have the situation where we should take one sample from a lot and bulk three samples for testing. This has reduced the frequency of testing very effectively.

8.7.1 EXAMPLE: SAMPLING SCHEME FOR A CHEMICAL PRODUCT

The analytical data for many lots of the product are available, and in this example data for a per cent moisture test are considered. Two assumptions are made: 1. Lots of the product are homogeneous so that stratified sampling is not necessary, and 2. The process concerned is operated consistently and is under statistical control so that the analytical test results may be regarded as results obtained from random samples all drawn from the same set or population of available samples.

For this test the variances that have been determined are

$$\text{Testing variance: } \sigma_0^2 = 0\cdot0004$$
$$\text{Sampling variance: } \sigma_1^2 = 0\cdot0008$$

and the ratio of costs $c_0:c_1 = 25$, so that

$$r = \frac{\sigma_0}{\sigma_1}\sqrt{\frac{c_1}{c_0}} = \frac{0\cdot02}{0\cdot028} \times 0\cdot2 = 0\cdot143,$$

and we can take a sample from each of 7 packages in the lot, bulk the 7 samples and carry out one test on the bulked sample.

However, the specification limit for this particular test is 0·2 per cent (max.) and the average of the test results considered is 0·113 per cent, so the range available for error is $0\cdot2 - 0\cdot113 = 0\cdot087$ per cent. At 99·73 per cent confidence, the permissible standard error is $0\cdot087/3 = 0\cdot029$, and the permissible variance, therefore, is $(0\cdot029)^2 = 0\cdot000,841$.

Then using the relationship

$$V = \frac{1}{p}\left[\sigma_1^2 + \frac{\sigma_0^2}{r}\right] \quad \text{we have} \quad 0\cdot000841 = \frac{1}{p}\left[0\cdot0008 + \frac{0\cdot0004}{0\cdot143}\right]$$

whence $p = 0\cdot036/0\cdot000,841 = 4\cdot28$, which we must take as 5.

It should be sufficient to sample 5 packages per lot, bulk these 5 package samples into 1 lot sample and carry out a single analytical test on this lot sample.

8.8 simulated sampling

Frequently situations arise where some method of sampling is indicated, but where the actual taking of a sample is prohibitively expensive if not impossible. In many such situations it is possible to derive useful information from some type of simulated sampling.

Simulated sampling involves replacing the actual population of items by its theoretical counterpart, a population described by some assumed probability distribution, and then sampling from this theoretical distribution by means of a table of random numbers. The methods of taking such a sample, as well as the discussion of decision problems which rely on such sampling methods, are referred to as Monte Carlo Methods.

Where the distribution of the population concerned is rectangular or normal, tables of random deviates are available (tables of random numbers and random normal numbers respectively) and small sections of these are given in the Appendix, Tables 11 and 12. In all other cases the procedure to be used is as follows

1 First plot the cumulative probability function

$$y = F(x) = \int_{-\infty}^{\infty} f(u).d\,u$$

but note that the complement, $1 - F(x)$, may be plotted if this is more convenient.

2 Using a table of random numbers, choose a random decimal between 0 and 1, to as many decimal places as desired or can be handled by the scales used.

3 Project horizontally the point on the y-axis (see Figure 8.8.1) corresponding to this random decimal until the projection line intersects the cumulative probability function curve $y = F(x)$.

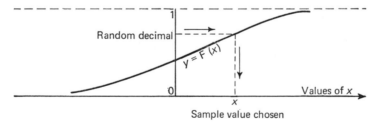

Fig. 8.8.1. SELECTION OF RANDOM SAMPLE VALUE IN A SIMPLE CASE

4 The value of x corresponding to the point of intersection is taken as the value of x. For a rectangular distribution where values between 0 and 1 are required, tables of random numbers are used and any number from an arbitrary location in the table is read as a decimal. Sometimes it is required to obtain a series of random values within a certain range and here the procedure is a little different: the decimal value is multiplied by

the rectangular range and added to the lower limit to provide the sample value. If, for example, we need to derive six random values between 18 and 25 we compile a table such as

Selection of random numbers	Decimal multiplied by range	Add lower limit	Random value
62	→ 0·62 × 7	→ 4·34 + 18	→ 22·34
06	→ 0·06 × 7	→ 0·42 + 18	→ 18·42
20	→ 0·20 × 7	→ 1·40 + 18	→ 19·40
93	→ 0·93 × 7	→ 6·51 + 18	→ 24·51
35	→ 0·35 × 7	→ 2·45 + 18	→ 20·45
51	→ 0·51 × 7	→ 3·57 + 18	→ 21·57

and these six values in the last column are the six required random values.

For a normal distribution tables of random normal numbers are used. These are derived from a population with zero mean ($\mu = 0$) and unit standard deviation ($\sigma = 1$). For any known mean and standard deviation the corresponding sample value is obtained by multiplying the random normal number by the known value of the standard deviation and adding the known mean. Tables 11 and 12 in the Appendix give a selection of random numbers and random normal numbers.

Simulated sampling is used extensively in calculations involving life curves and queue theory, where actual sampling might need several years. A simulation model permits reliable estimates to be made in a very short time, and this simulation model can be regarded as an experimental device in which a single run represents an experiment and the output of the simulation represents a single observation. The input to the simulation model contains some random variables so that the output would vary even if the simulation run were to be repeated with the same values of model parameters. In this sense the result of a simulation run is not reproducible, and variability in the model depends on

1 The sequence of random numbers used in making a simulation run.
2 The length of the run (sample size) during which data are collected (a simulated year, etc.).
3 The initial or starting values of the system variables at the beginning of the simulation run.
4 The duration of the initialization period during which the simulation is run but data are not collected. This may be done so that the system will reach some kind of equilibrium during this period.

The variability caused by these factors must be reduced as far as possible. Some variation in the results is a natural characteristic of the system and at times it may be useful to run a simulation for the sole purpose of determining the cause and examining the magnitude of this inherent variation.

The validity of the entire simulation model as a decision-making tool may be tested by applying it to the appropriate historical data, when the behaviour of the model may be compared with the actual historical performance. When making such a comparison it must be borne in mind that both the result of a simulation model and the historical performance of the real system are statistical samples. Often it is possible only to verify that the behaviour of various components of the model is consistent with the conditions in the remainder of the system at all times, especially in such fields as production scheduling which has to account for variations in factors such as inventory levels, orders on hand, expected demand, etc.

In this chapter we are concerned only with the actual sampling, and two simple examples follow.

8.8.1 TO ESTIMATE THE RANGE OF A SAMPLE OF FIVE VALUES

From the table of random normal numbers a sample of 5 consecutive values is $1\cdot119$, $-0\cdot792$, $0\cdot063$, $0\cdot484$, and $1\cdot045$, which has a range of $1\cdot911$. Further samples of five show ranges of

1·334	3·013	1·292	3·783	1·633	2·796	2·633	3·825
2·390	3·353	2·827	3·883	3·089	1·073	2·828	1·730
2·274	2·621	3·844	2·488	1·433	1·112	2·841	2·250

and the mean range of the 25 samples of 5 is $2\cdot490$.

Thus the estimate of the mean range in samples of 5 from a normal distribution with standard deviation σ [and any mean, μ] is $2\cdot490\sigma$. This may be compared with the exact value for the mean range in samples of 5 of $2\cdot326\sigma$, and as the number of samples increases the estimate will approach this value more closely.

8.8.2 TO ESTIMATE STOCK REQUIREMENTS FOR MANUFACTURE OF A NEW PRODUCT

Sales are anticipated of a blend which requires Product X, not currently manufactured. Product X can be made in one manufacturing department which is likely to have a varying capacity available for Product X each month. Orders for the blend are expected to vary between 5 and 10 each month and an order can require blend equivalent to 1,000, 2,000, or 3,000 lb. of Product X. The situation can be described by the distributions

1 AVAILABLE CAPACITY FOR MANUFACTURE OF PRODUCT X:

Capacity in 1,000 lb. units per month	Probability	Cumulative probability
10	0·05	0·05
11	0·10	0·15
12	0·20	0·35
13	0·30	0·65
14	0·20	0·85
15	0·10	0·95
16	0·05	1·00

2 EXPECTED DISTRIBUTION OF ORDERS FOR BLEND

Number of orders per month	Probability	Cumulative probability
5	0·10	0·10
6	0·15	0·25
7	0·20	0·45
8	0·40	0·85
9	0·10	0·95
10	0·05	1·00

3 EXPECTED REQUIREMENT OF PRODUCT X PER ORDER:

1,000 lb. units of Product X	Probability	Cumulative probability
1	0·4	0·4
2	0·4	0·8
3	0·2	1·0

These three cumulative probability distributions are shown in Figure 8.8.2. From these it is required to estimate whether or not any Product X should be bought in before manufacture begins, and if so, how much.

Consider activities over any 12-month period; note that the longer the period chosen the more reliable will be the estimate, but for start-up on a new product in spare manufacturing capacity a 12-month period should be sufficient. First we tackle manufacturing capacities, and we make a selection of 12 consecutive numbers from the table of random numbers, write a decimal point in front of each number and accept these as a random selection of probabilities which we can apply to the capacity table or the cumulative probability distribution plot to obtain a sequence of manufacturing quantities

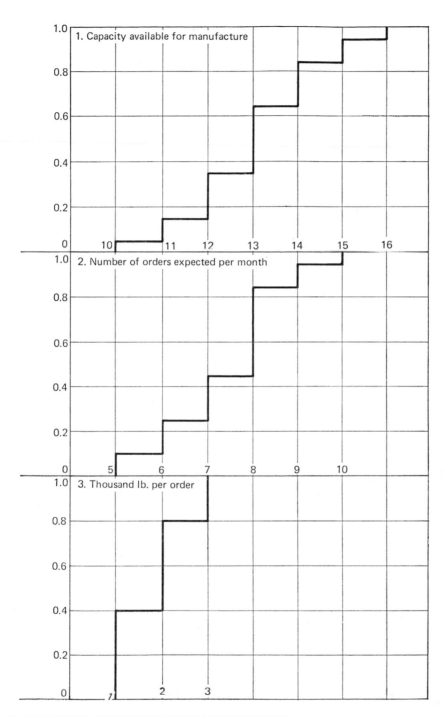

Fig. 8.8.2. CUMULATIVE PROBABILITY DISTRIBUTIONS

Month	Random number	Manufacture	Month	Random number	Manufacture
1	0·0652	11 (units)	7	0·0468	10
2	0·7436	14	8	0·9523	16
3	0·7410	14	9	0·2158	12
4	0·5539	13	10	0·5486	13
5	0·4155	13	11	0·8250	14
6	0·8037	14	12	0·9087	15

Next we make another selection of 12 random numbers and apply these to the cumulative probability distribution of the number of orders expected per month

Month	Random number	No. of orders expected	Month	Random number	No. of orders expected
1	0·6155	8	7	0·0495	5
2	0·4535	8	8	0·3506	7
3	0·3681	7	9	0·4518	8
4	0·0379	5	10	0·3578	7
5	0·8862	9	11	0·9957	10
6	0·9551	10	12	0·3426	7

and now the comparative estimates may be tabulated as

Month:	1	2	3	4	5	6	7	8	9	10	11	12
No. of orders:	8	8	7	5	9	10	5	7	8	7	10	7
Require units of X, 1:	3	3	3	2	4	4	2	3	3	3	4	3
2:	3	3	3	2	3	4	2	3	3	3	4	3
3:	2	2	1	1	2	2	1	1	2	1	2	1
Total X required:	15	15	12	9	16	18	9	12	15	12	18	12
Availability:	11	14	14	13	13	14	10	16	12	13	14	15
Excess to stock:	−4	−1	2	4	−3	−4	1	4	−3	1	−4	3
Cumulative excess:	−4	−5	−3	1	−2	−6	−5	−1	−4	−3	−7	−4

From which we see that either 4 units (4,000 lb.) of Product X should be bought in before manufacture is started, or the plant should endeavour to manufacture 15,000 lb. instead of 11,000 lb. in the first month's operation

SUGGESTIONS FOR FURTHER READING

See Chapter 9.

CHAPTER NINE

SOME SPECIAL SAMPLING AND TESTING PROCEDURES

CHAPTER EIGHT dealt with some of the topics met in the more usual procedures of sampling and testing which are most often employed in chemical industry. These topics, however, do not meet all the requirements and in this chapter we shall consider some special procedures related to the fields of work sampling, sensory testing, sampling and testing for defectives, and sampling for stores accounting. These procedures seem to be used very little at present and it is hoped that this chapter will stimulate thought and lead to further applications of the procedures.

9.1 work sampling

In most works there are many instances of non-repetitive and irregularly occurring activities for which complete method and frequency descriptions are not available and probably are not worth the effort involved in their compilation. In such cases the technique of work sampling may be used to provide a quantitative analysis, in terms of time, of the activity of men, machines, or of any observable state or condition of operation; in this connection work sampling is often referred to as 'activity sampling'.

Also, work sampling may be applied to sections or groups of men or machines engaged in repetitive work or work which occurs fairly regularly, but which is widely distributed in place or in time so that the men (or machines) are not expected to be working in one location throughout the working day.

A work sampling study consists of taking a large number of observations of the individuals concerned and allocating the observations into conditions or states of activities. The industrial statistician's main interests are in determining how many observations should be made, in evaluating the data, and in presentation of the data so that they may be understood and appreciated by all concerned.

9.1.1 SETTING UP A WORK SAMPLING STUDY

Any work sampling study may be divided conveniently into four sections, and for the study to succeed the sections must be completed in order as listed

1 *Planning:* involves
   a the *choice of objectives.* A work sample study is not a method study or a work study, although it can be a useful preliminary to a method study. Objectives must be simple and should be restricted to estimation of the proportion of time that is used profitably, or spent in some other way. Various comparisons between areas of work or periods of time may be proposed.
   b *the measurements to be made.* As far as possible arrangements must be made so that every individual in the section or group is observed a large number of times. Observations may be divided among any number of classifications, but the three classifications of *working, waiting* (resting or standing may be desired here), and *walking* (travelling or forced idleness may be desired for this classification) usually are sufficient for a general study. Each classification must be defined clearly; for instance if an item of equipment is not in use because of repair work or because it is an 'installed spare' it would be classified as standing, but if that item is not in use because of repair work to another item it could be classified as forced idleness.

2 *Preparation:* involves
   a *making the necessary announcements* to all concerned. An announcement by the department or works manager should be followed by detailed announcements and discussions within the sections concerned so that everyone is aware of the position.
   b *selection and training of personnel.* The persons chosen to act as observers and record the data should be selected carefully and should be acceptable to all the individuals concerned in the study. Observers should be fully conversant with the objectives of the study and the methods used to make measurements.
   c *selection of places.* Where the section or group under study is small and reasonably compact, no trouble is met. Each of the individuals has a chance of being observed at any time, and all the individuals are likely to be observed most times. Where the section or group under study comprises a large number of individuals, possibly spread over a large area of

the works, then it is convenient to subdivide this area into zones such that each zone can be traversed by the observer in the agreed time interval.

d *selection of time intervals*. The need is to obtain a large number of observations in a reasonably short time so that time intervals should be short. Where the area or zone is small and compact, quarter-hour observation periods should be sufficient. For widespread areas or zones, half-hour periods may be necessary. Longer periods of observation should not be considered.

e *compilation of forms*. Forms on which observations are to be recorded should be kept as simple as possible. Headings for Date; Time of inspection; Number of observations for Working, Walking and Waiting; and Area or Zone inspected provide for all the data required. Where outside workers are involved a statement on weather conditions may be necessary. Data will be rearranged as required for statistical analysis and this should not be the concern of the observers.

3 *Performance* involves making the inspections and recording observations. The following points should be noted

a Where a section or group is divided among several zones the zones should contain approximately equal numbers of individuals and the zones may be selected for inspection by random sampling. Where the zones cannot be arranged to contain approximately equal numbers of individuals systematic sampling should be used so that each cycle of inspections includes one inspection of each zone; in this case zone observations are totalled to give a measurement for the whole section or group.

b Each inspection should consist of a complete traverse of a zone, preferably using different traverses at various times. Observers should not 'double back' to locate individuals they think may have been missed during the traverse, and should not go looking for individuals they think should be in the zone. The object of work sampling is to sample the work being done and not attempting to locate individuals 'not at work'.

e Observations should be recorded immediately they are made and afterthoughts should not be permitted.

d Each work sampling study should be made with several observers, all of whom cover all the zones.

4 *Evaluation of data* involves

a *the validity of the data*. A random sampling scheme is acceptable only when every individual concerned has an equal chance of being observed with every other individual in any zone and at any time-interval during the day. To eliminate the possibility of bias creeping into the observations an overall systematic sampling scheme should be drawn up so that each zone may be inspected as often as each other zone, and so that the same number of inspections are made of each zone in each time interval of the day. Inspections may be carried out according to random selection from the systematic scheme.

b *the reliability of the data.* Usually it is satisfactory to take 95 per cent confidence limits which gives one chance in 20 of reaching a wrong conclusion.

c *analysis of results.* Results may be expressed in terms of individuals, times, classifications, weather conditions, etc., and may be presented in tabular or graphical form. On completion of a systematic sampling plan it should be possible to distinguish between observers; between zones of an area or between areas; between time periods of the day; between days of the week or any other chosen periods. Possibly the best representation of data is given by a Shewhart dottograph-type chart for zone measurements (see Figure 9.1.1), a cumulative-sum chart comparing major time intervals such as weeks or months (see Figure 9.1.2), and a block diagram comparing measurements for time periods during the day (see Figure 9.1.3).

9.1.2 USE OF DATA OBTAINED IN A WORK SAMPLING STUDY

Work sampling is only a technique for estimating the proportion of time spent working (or in some other activity); it cannot improve or control results. The data obtained during a work sampling study may be used to show

1 the allocation of individuals (numerically or proportionally) to each classification in each zone, in each area or for the works as a whole;
2 the allocation of individuals within each time-period of the day, the variation in this allocation during the week, and any variation in this allocation over major time intervals;
3 any seasonal effect on the allocation and any effect of weather or any unusual occurrences on the allocation;
3 an estimate of the efficiency of any established system of work accounting and a suggestion as to areas which are most likely to benefit from a detailed method study investigation.

Based on the analysis, it may be possible to recommend some line of action leading to an improvement in the proportion of individuals 'at work'. If the recommendation is implemented a further study would appraise the effect of the change. One study that should always be in mind is to investigate the nature and extent of long-term cycles and how these are affected by renewals.

9.1.3 STATISTICAL BASIS OF WORK SAMPLING

Observations may be allocated among any number of classifications, but the total of the observations made may be regarded as the sum of the observations in one classification and the sum of the observations in all the other classifications. For observations in any one classification, therefore, we may apply the binomial distribution, and for all observations covering all classifications we can say $[p + (1 - p)]^n = 1$, where p is the probability of an observation falling in any one classification. The variance of a binomial distribution is given by $s^2 = \dfrac{p(1 - p)}{n - 1}$, where n is the number of observations made, and where n is large, and usually any value greater than 30 is accepted to be large in this context, the expression $s^2 = p(1 - p)/n$ may be used. We use this expression to estimate the number of observations necessary in any work sampling study, as follows:

1 WHERE A SMALL NUMBER OR COMPACT GROUP OF INDIVIDUALS IS CONCERNED: Let the estimated probability of occurrence be p and the allowable margin of error be y. Then the estimated standard error (the 'limit of accuracy') will be py.

   To achieve a confidence limit of 95 per cent (and here we use a t-factor of 2 instead of the tabulated value of 1·96) the standard error is $2s$, where s is the standard deviation, so that s will be equal to $py/2$ and substituting this in the expression derived above for the variance, we have

$$n = \frac{4p(1 - p)}{p^2 y^2}.$$

This expression for n is independent of the number of individuals concerned and can apply only to a small number of individuals, working in a compact area, all of whom may be observed on each inspection. Such compact areas might be analytical laboratories, production departments, workshops, etc.; this expression for n is particularly suitable to a study on items of equipment in such areas.

   For example, where p is estimated to be 40 per cent ($=0·4$) and a 5 per cent margin of error is permissible, then the number of observations required would be estimated as

$$n = \frac{(4)(0·4)(0·6)}{(0·4)^2(0·05)^2} = 2,400.$$

We see that:

   if only 1 individual is involved in the study, he (or it) would be observed 2,400 times;
   if 5 individuals are involved in the study, they would be observed about 480 times each;
   if 30 individuals are involved in the study, they would be observed about 80 times each; and
   if 3,000 individuals were to be involved in the study, some would not be observed at all.

This derivation of n, therefore, must be retained for a small number of individuals working in a compact area, such that all the individuals can be observed on each inspection.

2 WHERE A LARGE NUMBER OF INDIVIDUALS IS CONCERNED: Let the estimated probability of occurrence be p, and let the total number of individuals involved in the study be M.

Then at any given moment during the working day we would expect to observe pM individuals in the classification concerned (say 'working'), and the probability of this happening is the term in p^{pM} in the binomial expansion of $[p + (1 - p)]^M$ which is

$$\binom{M}{pM} \cdot p^{pM} \cdot (1 - p)^{M-pM}$$

and this is the probability factor to be used in the expression for n quoted in the preceding section.

For example, if the probability of finding a man working is estimated (or hoped!) to be 0·4, and 440 men who may be working over widespread areas of the works are involved in the study, the required probability factor is

$$\binom{440}{176} \cdot (0·4)^{176} \cdot (0·6)^{264} \quad \text{or} \quad \frac{440!}{176! \, 264!} \cdot (0·4)^{176} \cdot (0·6)^{264} = 0·04061,$$

and the number of observations to be made in the study is

$$n = \frac{4 \times (0·04061) \times (0·95939)}{(0·04061)^2 \times (0·05)^2} = 37,799.$$

This is a very large number of observations, but means that, on average, each individual may expect to be observed about 86 times; and as we saw previously each member of a compact group of 30 individuals could expect to be observed 80 times so that the very large increase in the number of individuals to be observed has resulted in quite a small proportion of observations per individual.

This large number of observations obviously will require a long period of time for completion. However, there is no time limit to the duration of the study; always bearing in mind, of course, that to be of most use the information derived from the study must be made available as quickly as possible. As the number of complete inspections of the section or group concerned increases, the estimated value of p becomes more accurate and the value of n to be achieved so that reasonably accurate inferences may be made from the data may be calculated more accurately. But we may expect the required number of observations, n, to become smaller only if the estimated value of p becomes larger.

9.1.4 RECORDING THE DATA

The observations may be recorded on forms or in a notebook, but should be recorded as soon as they have been made. Whichever is used the information needed consists of

1 Date: Day of the Week: Time of Day;
2 Area (and zone if the area has been divided);
3 Number of observations in each classification (such as working, waiting, or walking);
4 Weather conditions and any abnormal circumstances (such as fire alarm, group meetings, emergency job, etc.).

Observations should be grouped in cycles which cover the whole area or section concerned and overall percentage values for each cycle should be plotted on a Shewhart type chart as shown in Figure 9.1.1, on which the average value and 95 per cent confidence limits are drawn for the classification '% Working'. The values plotted in Figure 9.1.1 are the overall values for a section as observed over 44 complete inspections.

Where the study may extend over several months, or other convenient time intervals, cumulative sum charts as shown in Figure 9.1.2 offer the best method of comparing the observations made in successive time intervals. The datum for each month is the average value achieved in the preceding month, so that at any time during a month the chart shows whether the observations infer an improvement or a deterioration compared with the previous month's performance.

When sufficient observations have been made in each period of the working day, a block diagram as shown in Figure 9.1.3 may be drawn to show the variation within and among classifications throughout the day. The block diagrams may be drawn at full height, or truncated as shown, and should be brought up to date at regular intervals.

On completion of the study an analysis of variance of the data may be made showing the variations between areas or zones; between days; between weeks, months or seasons; between observers; between trades; and between working conditions. This analysis should be used to supplement the data on the charts.

9.1.5 EXAMPLE OF A WORK SAMPLING STUDY

One section of the works contains 110 men, any of whom may be required to work in any of five areas of the works. Work performance was thought to be about 60 per cent, and the study was initiated to confirm or correct this estimate and to derive data which could be used as a basis for modifications and innovations leading to an improvement in work performance.

For 110 men and an estimate of 60 per cent working at any time we have

$$p = \binom{110}{66} \cdot (0\cdot6)^{66} \cdot (0\cdot4)^{44} = \frac{110!}{66!44!}(0\cdot6)^{66} \cdot (0\cdot4)^{44} = 0\cdot07834$$

whence $\qquad n = \dfrac{4 \times 0\cdot07834 \times 0\cdot92166}{(0\cdot07834)^2 \times (0\cdot05)^2} - 18{,}824$ observations to be made.

The working day is from 7.30 a.m. to 4.30 p.m. with a lunch break between midday and 1 p.m. Each area of the works could be traversed in a quarter of an hour and so the working day was divided into $32 \times \frac{1}{4}$-hour periods. The study was required to be complete in three months and so 5 observers were selected and each observer requested to observe 22 areas each week; the area and time of observation were selected at random from a master tabulation which gave equal coverage to all areas and all time intervals.

Observations were examined weekly, and charts were prepared or brought

Table 9.1.1 Summary of observations in 10-week work sampling study

1. *Observations by area:*

Area	Number Working	Walking	Waiting	Total	No. of inspections	Percentages Working	Walking	Waiting
1	5,697	1,641	1,290	8,628	220	66·0	19·0	15·0
2	648	138	216	1,002	220	64·7	13·8	21·5
3	3,798	1,377	825	6,000	220	63·3	23·0	13·7
4	600	231	144	975	220	61·5	23·7	14·8
5	1,098	387	324	1,809	220	60·7	21·4	17·9
Overall	11,841	3,774	2,799	18,414	220	64·3	20·5	15·2

2. *Observations by days:*

	Number Working	Walking	Waiting	Total	No. of inspections	Percentages Working	Walking	Waiting
Mon.	2,284	703	388	3,375	220	67·7	20·8	11·5
Tues.	2,164	799	675	3,638	220	59·5	22·0	18·5
Wed.	2,480	723	572	4,075	220	60·9	17·7	21·4
Thurs.	2,464	810	570	3,844	220	64·1	21·1	14·8
Fri.	2,449	739	594	3,782	220	64·8	19·5	15·7
Overall	11,841	3,774	2,799	18,414	220	64·3	20·5	15·2

3. *Observations by observers:*

	Numbers Working	Walking	Waiting	Total	No. of inspections	Percentages Working	Walking	Waiting
Obs. 1	2,421	762	531	3,714	220	65·2	20·5	14·4
2	2,079	720	498	3,297	220	63·0	21·8	15·2
3	2,396	770	572	3,738	220	64·1	20·6	15·3
4	2,455	734	585	3,774	220	65·1	19·4	15·5
5	2,490	788	613	3,891	220	64·0	20·2	15·8
Overall	11,841	3,774	2,799	18,414	220	64·3	20·5	15·2

up to date weekly. Figure 9.1.1 shows the plot of observations for the first two weeks of the study, and Figure 9.1.2 shows the weekly comparison of percentage working data for the first four weeks of the study. Figure 9.1.3 shows the distribution of observations during the quarter-hour periods of the day; the early morning build-up of work performance is most noticeable.

In the event, the study was terminated after ten weeks and the observations made are summarized in Table 9.1.1. During the period under survey there were no untoward occurrences and the weather was the usual British weather; there was one practice fire alarm and no observations were recorded during the quarter of an hour in which that occurred.

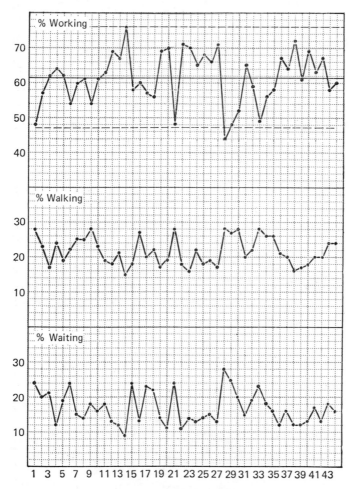

1 3 5 7 9 11 13 15 17 19 21 23 25 27 29 31 33 35 37 39 41 43

Sequence of complete inspections

Fig. 9.1.1. SHEWHART CHARTS FOR OBSERVATIONS OVER WHOLE SECTION
I.S. 1—17

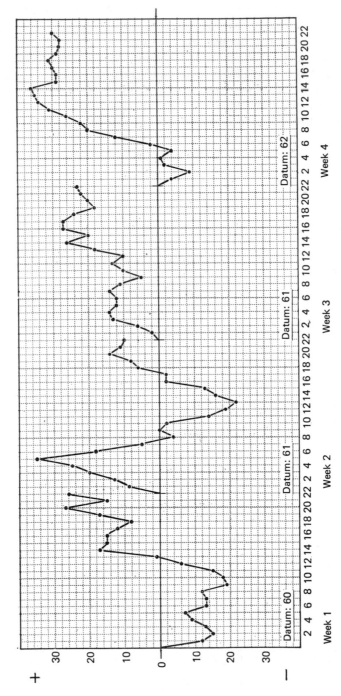

Fig. 9.1.2. CUMULATVE SUM CHART SHOWING COMPARISONS OF % WORKING IN FOUR SUCCESSIVE WEEKS

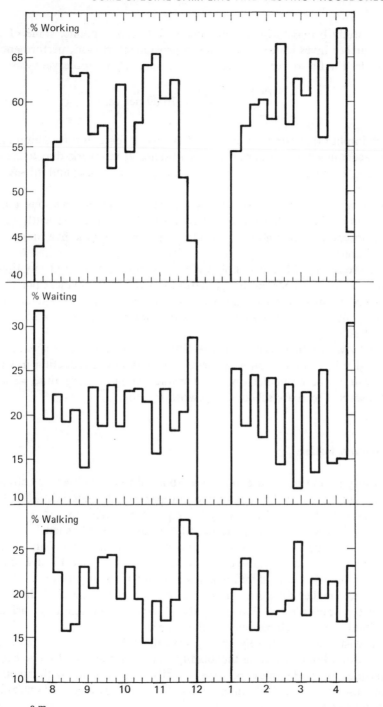

Fig. 9.1.3. BLOCK DIAGRAMS SHOWING % OBSERVATIONS IN EACH
TIME PERIOD OF THE DAY

The study brings to light a number of interesting points, some of which need further investigation before an improvement in work performance can be made. Firstly we see that the coverage made by the observers was

$$\frac{18,414 \times 100}{220 \times 110} = 76 \cdot 09 \text{ per cent,}$$

which implies that almost a quarter of the work force in this section has not been accounted. This quarter covers absence from work due to sickness, holidays, etc.; temporary absence from the place of work; and misses by the observers.

Next we see that observer 2 has recorded fewer observations than the others, and it seems that this observer 'missed' far more frequently than the other observers, although the percentages recorded by the five observers are very similar.

The areas quite obviously hold different numbers of men at any time and there is a small but perceptible gradation in work performance; possibly this is related to distance from the work centre. For some reason or another Tuesday and Wednesday are poor days in work performance, while Monday is the best.

Finally we see that very nearly one-fifth of the men's time is spent in walking, and this is the first subject for review; possibly a reduction in walking time will be accompanied by some reduction in waiting time, especially where several men are scheduled to work together.

9.2 sensory testing

A sensory testing procedure may be established to meet either or both of two objectives: 1. it may be required to compare some materials with the appropriate standard; and 2. it may be required to detect the presence of undesirable inclusions in the material. Standards are established because it is believed that the consumer expects consistency and associates an acceptable quality with a product whose quality does not vary beyond his discriminable limits. In theory, a consistent quality is achieved through an expert tester who can detect smaller differences than the average consumer, and the ultimate product is controlled so that its limits of variation — where any variation is permitted — are detectable only by the expert.

It is customary not to rely on a single expert, but to set up a panel of experts all of whom have been thoroughly trained in the art — that is, each one has acquired considerable experience, usually in conjunction with the others — so that they are more likely than not to agree on assessments or scores in any particular test.

A number of methods have been devised for use by panels of experts, but in this chapter we shall restrict discussion to those tests which use paired comparisons, triangular comparisons and block comparisons.

9.2.1 PAIRED COMPARISONS TO INDICATE A PREFERENCE OR A DIFFERENCE

Sometimes it is required to know whether or not a sample may be identified as being different from an established standard, or maybe whether or not a difference can be detected between two samples from the same or different sources. For a test such as this a simple paired comparison may be made; each tester in the panel is given the two samples and he is asked to indicate whether or not there is a difference between them, though on occasion he may be asked to indicate a preference for one sample rather than the other.

The value of the test results reported by the panel may be estimated by means of a Chi-square $[\chi^2]$ test (see Chapter 4.2), which will show whether or not the set of results reported by the panel differs significantly from a set of results which would be obtained by chance. In this context a set of results would be obtained by chance if each member of the panel were unable to exercise discrimination and merely made a guess, and this notion of guessing a chance set is retained throughout this section.

Then given a pair of samples, A and B, there is a probability p that a tester will guess A to be better in some respect, or to have a higher quality, than B, and an equal probability p that he will guess B to be better than A. There is, therefore, a probability of $2p$ that the tester will guess that there is a difference between A and B. This may be stated as 'From any set of panel results the probability that a given proportion indicating a difference between the samples is a chance selection is twice the probability that the same proportion indicating a preference for one sample is a chance selection', or Pr (difference) = 2 Pr (preference); for any given set.

Each set of panel results may be examined by a χ^2-test as follows

If there are n testers in the panel, and these all guessed the results they reported, then in the long run for each pair of samples A and B we would expect a proportion $n/2$ testers to express a preference for sample A and an equal proportion $n/2$ to express a preference for sample B. Then if, in any one set of results k of the testers express a preference for one sample (so that $n - k$ testers express a preference for the other sample) the calculation to be made is

$$\chi^2 = \frac{(k - n/2)^2}{n/2} + \frac{(n - k - n/2)^2}{n/2}$$

and this calculated value of χ^2 is compared with the tabulated values for 1 degree of freedom and various probabilities. If the calculated value of χ^2 is greater than the tabulated value at some desired level of probability then the set of reported results is likely (at that level of probability) to be purposeful and not obtained by chance. Usually this is reported as 'there is (the quoted level of) probability that a significant indication of preference has been made'. A selection of useful values of χ^2 for 1 degree of freedom is given in Table 9.2.1.

For example, 10 testers of a 12-member panel indicate that there is a difference between the two samples submitted to them. Here the guessing datum is $\frac{12}{2} = 6$ and the χ^2-test is given by

$$\chi^2 = \frac{(10 - 6)^2}{6} + \frac{(2 - 6)^2}{6} = \frac{32}{6} = 5 \cdot 33.$$

Arithmetic interpolation in Table 9.2.1 [note that arithmetic interpolation in the χ^2 table is not correct, but gives a usable value which is not far wrong] shows that the double-sided probability, that one sample is of a higher quality than the other, equivalent to this value of χ^2 is 0·021. This means that there is a probability of 0·021 (equivalent to 21 in 1,000 or 2·1 per cent) that the panel members obtained their preferences by guessing, or a probability of 0·979 that there exists a real preference. That is, there is a probability of 0·042 that the panel members indicated a difference between the samples by sheer guesswork, or a probability of 0·958 that the members of the panel were able to detect a real difference between the samples. The probability of guessing, 0·042, is small enough for us to accept that there is a real difference, significant at the 95·8 per cent level of probability, between the two samples.

Table 9.2.1 Double-sided probability values of χ^2: for 1 d.f.

χ^2	p	χ^2	p	χ^2	p	χ^2	p
0·001	0·97477	0·7	0·40278	4·2	0·04042	9·0	0·00270
0·002	0·96433	0·8	0·37109	4·4	0·03594	9·2	0·00242
0·003	0·95632	0·9	0·34278	4·6	0·03197	9·4	0·00217
0·004	0·94957	1·0	0·31731	4·8	0·02846	9·6	0·00195
0·005	0·94363	1·1	0·29427	5·0	0·02535	9·8	0·00175
0·006	0·93826	1·2	0·27332	5·2	0·02259	10·0	0·00157
0·007	0·93332	1·3	0·25421	5·4	0·02014	10·5	0·00119
0·008	0·92873	1·4	0·23672	5·6	0·01796	11·0	0·00091
0·009	0·92442	1·5	0·22067	5·8	0·01603	11·5	0·00070
0·01	0·92034	1·6	0·20590	6·0	0·01431	12·0	0·00053
0·02	0·88754	1·7	0·19229	6·2	0·01278	12·5	0·00041
0·03	0·86249	1·8	0·17971	6·4	0·01141	13·0	0·00031
0·04	0·84148	1·9	0·16808	6·6	0·01020	13·5	0·00024
0·05	0·82306	2·0	0·15730	6·8	0·00912	14·0	0·00018
0·06	0·80650	2·2	0·13801	7·0	0·00815	14·5	0·00014
0·07	0·79134	2·4	0·12134	7·2	0·00729	15·0	0·00011
0·08	0·77730	2·6	0·10686	7·4	0·00652	15·5	0·00008
0·09	0·76418	2·8	0·09426	7·6	0·00584	16·0	0·00006
0·1	0·75183	3·0	0·08327	7·8	0·00522	16·5	0·00005
0·2	0·65472	3·2	0·07364	8·0	0·00468	17·0	0·00004
0·3	0·58388	3·4	0·06520	8·2	0·00419	17·5	0·00003
0·4	0·52709	3·6	0·05778	8·4	0·00375	18·0	0·00002
0·5	0·47950	3·8	0·05125	8·6	0·00336	19·0	0·00001
0·6	0·43858	4·0	0·04550	8·8	0·00301	20·0	0·00001

A probability of 0·05 (5 per cent level) is usually taken as the maximum by which a set of chance results may be accepted to indicate a difference between two samples; this gives a probability of 0·95 (a 95 per cent level of significance) that there is a real difference between the two samples. This probability corresponds to a value of $\chi^2 = 5·03$ for 1 degree of freedom, and the numbers of testers who must report a difference between the two samples to achieve this level of probability are

6 members of a panel of 6	14 members of a panel of 18
8 members of a panel of 8	16 members of a panel of 20
9 members of a panel of 10	17 members of a panel of 22
10 members of a panel of 12	18 members of a panel of 24
12 members of a panel of 14	19 members of a panel of 26
13 members of a panel of 16	20 members of a panel of 28
	22 members of a panel of 30

Figure 9.2.1 shows the various probabilities of chance selection associated with panels of 6, 10, 12, 16, 20 and 30 members. The required number of testers, k, in a panel of n members who must indicate a difference for the set of results to achieve 95 per cent significance may be obtained by equating the value of χ^2 in the n, k equation to 5·03 and is

$$k = \frac{n + \sqrt{(5·03n)}}{2}.$$

9.2.2 TRIANGULAR COMPARISONS TO INDICATE A PREFERENCE OR A DIFFERENCE

Triangular testing may be performed under any of four different conditions

1 Two standard stimuli, different from one another, are presented to the tester and are followed by one variable which is identical with one of the two standards. The tester is told that the two standards are different and is asked to say which one the third sample resembles. Here each member of the panel is given the two standards and the single sample is varied randomly among the members of the panel.

2 One standard stimulus is presented to the tester and is followed by two variable stimuli one of which is identical with the standard. After testing the standard the tester is told that one of the two samples to follow is the same as the standard and he is asked to say which one it is. This is almost the reverse of 1.

3 Three stimuli are presented to the tester. The tester is informed that one is an odd sample while the other two are identical with one another and he is asked to identify the odd sample. This is the easiest form of triangular testing procedure to operate and analyse and is the one used most often. The odd sample is randomized among members of the panel.

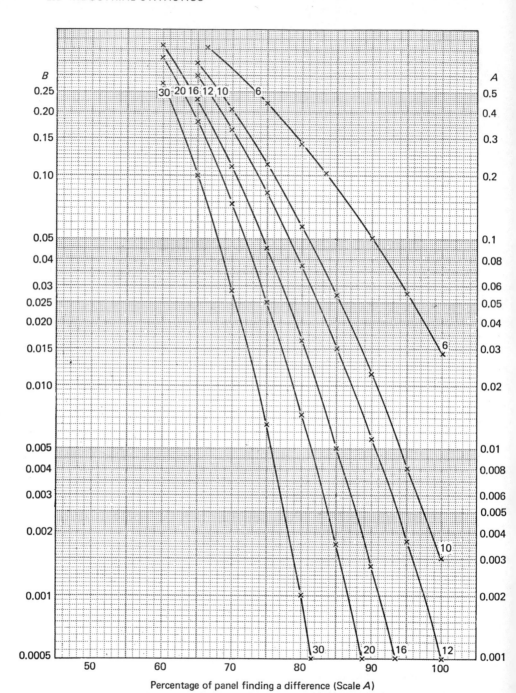

Percentage of panel finding a difference (Scale A)
or percentage of panel finding a higher quality rating in one sample (Scale B)

Fig. 9.2.1. SIGNIFICANCE LEVELS FOR PAIRED COMPARISONS: PANEL SIZES 6 TO 30

4 Three stimuli are presented to the tester together with a card bearing the three statements: 'All the same'; 'All different'; 'Two the same and one different'. The tester is required to decide which statement is true before proceeding either to identify the odd sample or express a preference. This form of triangular tests is the most difficult for testers to perform correctly and demands a panel of highly-skilled experts; this is no test for raw testers.

Discussion in this section is restricted to condition 3, and we shall consider the methods of analysis that may be applied to the results declared by the panel. Analysis of results under the other conditions follows much the same pattern with modifications as required to suit the conditions.

If we neglect the possibility of correlation in performance between successive triangles examined by the same tester, then with the three stimuli presented of form ABB there is a probability (on average and over a long run of tests) of 1 in 3 that the odd sample may be selected by chance alone. The distribution of selection by chance in some number m of successive triangular tests is the binomial expansion of $(p + q)^m$ where

$p = \frac{1}{3}$ = the probability of guessing correctly in one triangular test, and
$q = \frac{2}{3}$ = the probability of guessing incorrectly in the same triangular test.

For example, if there are 4 triangles to be tested in succession we would expect to find, purely by chance, that

$^4C_0 \cdot (\frac{1}{3})^4$ i.e. $\frac{1}{81}$ of the panel select all 4 of the odd samples;
$^4C_1 \cdot (\frac{1}{3})^3 \cdot (\frac{2}{3})$ i.e. $\frac{8}{81}$ of the panel select 3 of the odd samples;
$^4C_2 \cdot (\frac{1}{3})^2 \cdot (\frac{2}{3})^2$ i.e. $\frac{24}{81}$ of the panel select 2 of the odd samples;
$^4C_3 \cdot (\frac{1}{3}) \cdot (\frac{2}{3})^3$ i.e. $\frac{32}{81}$ of the panel select only 1 of the odd samples; and
$^4C_4 \cdot (\frac{2}{3})^4$ i.e. $\frac{16}{81}$ of the panel fail to select an odd sample.

This, of course, provides a good procedure for establishing the panel in the first place, since it enables us to select the most discriminative testers from all those available.

Suppose that in a test run the proportions of the panel selecting the odd samples (in the order given above) were $1:6:20:37:17$, and we wish to know whether or not this differs significantly from a chance selection. Then we apply the χ^2-test using the chance values as our datum points, giving

$$\chi^2 = \frac{(1 - 1)^2}{1} + \frac{(8 - 6)^2}{8} + \frac{(24 - 20)^2}{24} + \frac{(32 - 37)^2}{32} + \frac{(16 - 17)^2}{16} = 2 \cdot 011.$$

For four degrees of freedom the χ^2-table quotes a value of $9 \cdot 488$ at the $0 \cdot 05$ level of probability, so that we can be 95 per cent sure that the selections made by the panel are not significantly different from a chance set of selections that could have been obtained by guessing.

As with paired comparisons the value of the test results reported by a panel may be estimated by means of a χ^2-test. Given a triangle of samples ABB there is a probability p that a tester will guess A to be better than either of the B's, and an equal probability that he will guess each of the B's (in turn) to be better than either of the other two samples. Therefore there is a probability of $3p$ that the tester will guess that there is a difference between one sample and the other two samples included in the test, or

$$\text{Pr (difference)} = 3 . \text{Pr (preference); for any given set.}$$

The χ^2-test for a triangular test is made as follows

If there are n testers in the panel, and these guessed the results they reported, then in the long run for each triangle ABB we would expect a proportion $n/3$ of the testers to express a preference for sample A, and a proportion $2n/3$ of the testers to express a preference for one or other of the samples B. Then if in any one test k of the testers express a preference for the odd sample, the statistic to be calculated is

$$\chi^2 = \frac{(k - n/3)^2}{n/3} + \frac{(n - k - 2n/3)^2}{2n/3}$$

and the calculated value of χ^2 may be compared with the values listed in Table 9.2.1. If the calculated value is greater than the tabulated value at some desired level of probability then the set of reported results is likely, at that level of probability, to be purposeful and not obtained by chance.

For example, given a triangle ABB, if 9 testers out of a panel of 12 correctly identify the odd sample, then

$$\chi^2 = \frac{(9 - 4)^2}{4} + \frac{(3 - 8)^2}{8} = \frac{75}{8} = 9 \cdot 375.$$

Arithmetic interpolation in Table 9.2.1 shows that the probability for preference equivalent to this value of χ^2 is 0·0022. This means that there is a probability of 0·0022 for each of the samples that the panel guessed that sample to be the best, or a probability of 0·0066 that the panel identified the odd sample by guessing. This is an acceptably small probability so we may say, with 99·34 per cent probability of being correct, that the panel detected a real difference between the odd sample and the other two samples.

As previously, the maximum probability by which a set of chance results may be accepted to indicate a real difference between the odd sample and the other two samples in any triangular test is taken at the 0·05 level; this gives a probability of 0·95 (or 95 per cent) that a real difference has been detected between the odd sample and the other two. This probability corresponds to a value of $\chi^2 = 5 \cdot 73$, and the numbers of testers who must identify the odd sample to achieve this level of probability are

5 members of a panel of 6	11 members of a panel of 18
6 members of a panel of 8	12 members of a panel of 20
7 members of a panel of 10	13 members of a panel of 22
8 members of a panel of 12	14 members of a panel of 24
9 members of a panel of 14	15 members of a panel of 26
10 members of a panel of 16	16 members of a panel of 28
	17 members of a panel of 30

Figure 9.2.2 shows the various probabilities of chance selection associated with panels of 6, 10, 12, 16, 20 and 30 members. The required number of testers, k, in a panel of n members who must indicate a difference for the set of results to achieve 95 per cent significance may be obtained by equating the value of χ^2 in the n, k equation to 5.73 and is

$$ k = \frac{n + \sqrt{(11 \cdot 46n)}}{3}. $$

Note that this test is more efficient than the paired comparison test. For example, 9 members of a panel of 10 must indicate a difference between two samples to achieve 95 per cent probability in a paired comparison test, but only 7 members of a panel of 10 are required to identify the odd sample to achieve 95 per cent probability in a triangular test. This apparent increase in efficiency is due to the fact that the triangular test is more difficult to perform than the paired comparison.

Although the statistical analysis of triangular testing is based on the assumption that the tester guesses a preference for one member of a triangle rather than the other two, it is felt that triangular testing should not be used as a measure of preference test because every test is biased and it is not possible to separate this bias. In every test one item of one material, A, is tested against two items of another material, B, and a tester may express a preference or a dislike for the second material, B, merely because he has tested it twice and perhaps recognized it on the second test. Thus when considering results expressed by the panel in a large number of cases we find that there is a correlation between identification of the odd sample and expressed preference for the odd sample; but whether or not such correlation can be demonstrated, there is no means of determining whether or not any bias is included in the test; every tester is confident that he exerts an unbiased judgment.

For example, in a test carried out with a triangle containing one sample of A and two samples of B the scoring was

7 members of a panel of 12 correctly identified the odd sample; while
4 of these 7 considered this odd sample to be better than the other two.

Then setting up a 2 × 2 contingency table for these results we have

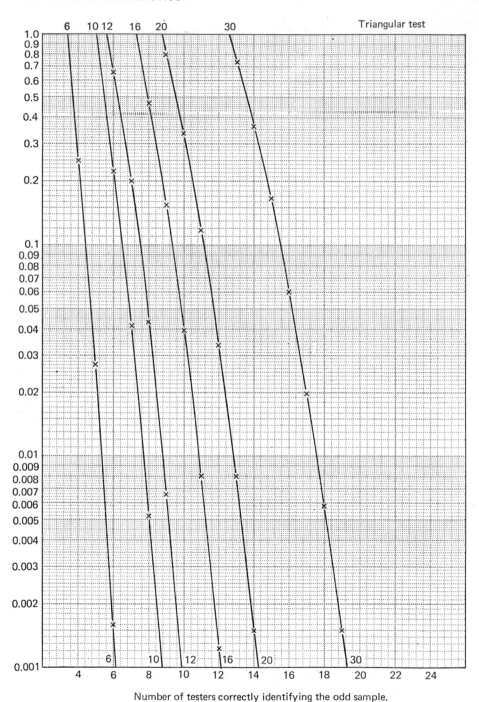

Number of testers correctly identifying the odd sample.

Fig. 9.2.2. PROBABILITIES FOR IDENTIFYING THE ODD SAMPLE BY CHANCE: TRIANGULAR TEST

	Preferred odd sample	Preferred others	Total
Correct identification	4	3	7
Failed to identify	3	2	5
Total	7	5	12

From which the calculated value of χ^2 is approximately 0·01, and there is no significant correlation between identification of the odd sample and preference of the odd sample. Though there does seem to be a slight tendency to favour sample A.

But when, a few days later, the test was reversed so that the triangle contained two samples of A and one sample of B, the scoring was

10 members of a panel of 11 correctly identified the odd sample, while 9 of these 10 considered the odd sample to be not as good as the other two,

and the 2 × 2 contingency table for these results is

	Preferred odd sample	Preferred others	Total
Correct identification	1	9	10
Failed to identify	1	0	1
Total	2	9	11

and the calculated value of χ^2 is 4·5. For 1 degree of freedom the corresponding probability is about 0·34, and the inference is that there is a real correlation, with 96·6 per cent probability, between identification of the odd sample and preference of the other samples. Although this second panel was one member short, we see that altering the triangle from ABB to AAB was followed by an increase in the preference for sample A, and it may have been due simply to the fact that sample A was tested twice in the second triangle.

Thus, in order to establish whether or not a difference is likely to be detectable between two materials a triangular test should be used, but the triangular test is of doubtful value for expression of a preference.

9.2.3 BLOCK COMPARISONS

The previous sections have dealt with those cases in which two materials are compared with each other and we have considered the two usual methods of making comparisons between two materials. Sometimes it is necessary to determine a preference from three or more materials, and it is suggested that in these cases block comparisons provide a satisfactory method of determining preferences.

A block comparison is a system of paired comparisons in which each material is compared in turn with each other material, so that over the whole block every pair of materials is compared twice. For instance, in a test to determine the best out of 4 materials A, B, C and D, the six comparisons are made twice, giving the block

	A	B	C	D
No. of panel members who say A is better than				
B is better than		—		
C is better than			—	
D is better than				—

We exclude the diagonal comparisons AA, BB, CC and DD from this test, though they can be included any time a more searching test is required. For this test each member of the panel is given three samples and is told that they are all different. Then he is given a fourth sample, is told that it is different from the other three samples and is asked to score whether or not the fourth sample is better (in some way) than the other three. The total scores for the panel are inserted in the appropriate cell and a χ^2-test is made on the totals for preference of each material.

For example, members of a panel of 12 express preferences as follows

	A	B	C	D	Total preferences
A is better than	—	10	10	9	29
B is better than	3	—	7	5	15
C is better than	1	6	—	11	18
D is better than	2	2	3	—	7

If each member of the panel guessed his preferences, then we would expect a total vote of 18 for each material so that the χ^2-test is

$$\chi^2 = \frac{(29-18)^2}{18} + \frac{(15-18)^2}{18} + \frac{(18-18)^2}{18} + \frac{(7-18)^2}{18} = \frac{251}{18} = 13 \cdot 94.$$

The χ^2-table quotes a value of $11 \cdot 34$ for 3 degrees of freedom at the $0 \cdot 01$ level of probability; the calculated value is greater than this so we may conclude with 99 per cent probability of being correct that the totals indicate a real preference which was not obtained by chance. As a result of this test we would accept A as being the best material and D the worst, with B and C at some intermediate quality and probably not distinguishable from each other as their total scores are very near each other.

Note that in this plan the testers are not told which sample is the comparator and very often the recorded values are not complementary. The test can be simplified by testing only that part of the plan above and to the right of the diagonal line, and writing in the complementary values in the appropriate cells. In this test a report indicating that two samples are equally good is scored $\frac{1}{2}$, and with half the plan in use the complement cell is given the $\frac{1}{2}$ rating as well. Then if, for example, 10 members of a 12-member panel assert A to be better than B, we would write the complement, 2, as having declared B to be better than A. Under such a scheme the four-sample plan shown above would reduce to the plan in which only six comparisons were made, giving the results

	A	B	C	D	Total preferences
A is better than	—	10	10	9	29
B is better than	2	—	7	5	14
C is better than	2	5	—	11	18
D is better than	3	7	1	—	11

for which the χ^2-test is

$$\chi^2 = \frac{(29 - 18)^2}{18} + \frac{(14 - 18)^2}{18} + \frac{(18 - 18)^2}{18} + \frac{(11 - 18)^2}{18} = \frac{186}{18} = 10 \cdot 33$$

which the χ^2-table shows to be significant at 98 per cent probability.

This half-plan involves half the time and effort of the full block comparison and with expert testers or in cases where a preference may be expressed without much doubt is very little less efficient than the full block comparison. Whenever a half-plan is under test and the testers indicate equality of samples the plan should be extended to the full block comparison.

9.3 sampling and testing for defective items

Statistical sampling theory deals with the relationships between the size of the lot for which an estimate of some characteristic is to be made, the size of the sample and the number of samples to be taken, and the accuracy with which the characteristic of the whole bulk can be estimated. In Chapter 8 we dealt with the case in which a test is made on a portion of the lot for which reduced frequency rates or economic sampling schemes can be devised; now we shall consider the case in which the lot consists of a collection of separate items when a test is to be made on a single individual or on each member of a group of individuals.

An individual which fails the test is known as a defective, and there are three methods which may be used to estimate the proportion of defective items in a lot: Single Sampling, Sequential Sampling, and Variable Sampling. Obviously, the limits of sampling a lot of distinct items are 1. take no sample at all, in which case the customer carries all the risk that all the items in the lot meet the specification requirements, and 2. sample the whole lot, that is test every item in the lot, in which case the producer carries all the risk of ensuring that every item in the lot meets the specification requirement. In some cases the customer may request full testing and if the business is profitable then full testing must be made; in some cases variation in the finished items may be so great that full testing is necessary; in all other cases it is necessary to undertake sufficient testing to offer the customer an acceptable guarantee without overloading the producer's testing facilities.

The three methods listed above provide optimum sampling and testing schemes to meet this guarantee; the difference in the methods may be described as follows

Single sampling consists of taking one sample from the lot, where the sample consists of a random selection of items. Every item in the sample is tested and the lot is accepted or rejected on the test data. Here the test data are the number of items in the sample and the number of defectives found in this sample.

Sequential sampling entails taking a sample from the lot, where the sample consists of a random selection of items. Every item in the sample is tested and then the lot is accepted or rejected or a decision is made to examine a further sample according to the test data. Sampling continues as indicated by the cumulative test data, and here the test data are the total number of defectives found in these samples.

Variable sampling demands exactly the same procedure as sequential sampling; the difference between these two methods lies in the data required to formulate a decision. In variable sampling the data required are the cumulative number of items tested and the total of the values of the variable tested for these items. We shall consider these methods separately.

9.3.1 SINGLE SAMPLING

First, it is necessary to establish an agreement between producer and consumer that a lot of items (total number N) shall be expected to contain not more than some stated proportion (or percentage), p, of items which lie outside the agreed specification limits. This proportion is referred to as the proportion (or percentage) defective, and immediately fixes the work to be done in making the necessary tests. The producer will know the capacity available for testing the items, so that with items allocated to lots in approximately equal number it will be possible to test some quantity, n, of items per lot, where obviously $n \leq N$, and the expected number of defectives in the sample under test will be pn. For example, if the agreed percentage defectives in a lot is to be 0·5, and the producer is able to test 220 items per lot, then if the lots submitted for approval are likely to meet the requirement we would expect the number of defectives per sample to average out at $0·5 \times 220/100 = 1·1$.

The probabilities with which 0, 1, 2, 3, ..., x defectives are likely to be found in a sample of n items when the expected average number of defectives in the lot is known are defined by the Poisson distribution. The individual terms of the Poisson distribution are given in *Biometrika Tables for Statisticians*, Volume 1, Table 39, and we see that for an expected average of 1·1 ($m = 1·1$)

the probability of finding 0 defective in the sample is 0·332,871,
the probability of finding 1 defective in the sample is 0·366,158,
the probability of finding 2 defectives in the sample is 0·201,387,
the probability of finding 3 defectives in the sample is 0·073,842, and
the probability of finding 4 defectives in the sample is 0·020,307, etc.

Forming cumulative totals of these probabilities we can say that we would expect one-third of all the samples examined to be free from defectives; 70 per cent of them to contain one or nil defective; 90 per cent of them to contain two or less defectives; 97 per cent of them to contain three or less defectives; and so on through the table.

We see from the Poisson distribution table that if the producer were able to test 1,200 items in every lot, giving an average expected defective count of 6 per sample ($m = 6$), there would be a probability of 0·916 that a sample would contain 9 or less defectives. This indicates, as we might expect, that the bigger the sample the more defectives are likely to be found with the expected average number of defectives remaining constant. Now the probability factors can be turned to good account.

In the first paragraph of this section we mentioned an agreed percentage defective per lot of 0·5. Now this should be coupled with an agreement between producer and consumer that the agreed percentage defective per lot will be met with some stated probability, and for the example data quoted, 0·9 is a reasonable probability. If this is agreed, it means that the consumer wants lots of these particular items to contain no more than 0·5 per cent defectives and he will accept a probability of 0·9 that this condition be met; that is, at least 90 per cent of the lots are to contain no more than 0·5 per cent defectives. Referring to the extract of the Poisson distribution table, we see that for the expected average of 1·1 defective per sample of 220 items, 90 per cent probability corresponds to 2 defectives, and we can quote the final sampling scheme as 'Sample 220 items per lot and examine every item in the sample. If two or less defectives are found in the sample, approve the lot for dispatch to the customer. As soon as three defectives are found in the sample, reject the lot'. In practice, an 'approved' sample is returned to its parent lot, and the whole lot dispatched; while if a lot is 'rejected' then every item in the lot is examined, defective items are removed and the remaining good items submitted for inspection.

However, the Poisson distribution table shows that 10 per cent of the samples will show 3 or more defectives even when the lot average is 0·5 per cent defectives (giving 1·1 defective per sample), and this means that acceptance of this sampling plan imposes on the producer a risk that if the lots really contain 0·5 per cent defectives then one-tenth of the lots will be rejected needlessly. Searching through the Poisson distribution table we find that 2 or fewer defectives in a sample may occur with a probability of 0·1 when the lot has an expected percentage defective of 5·3 ($m = 5$·3). Thus from these data, the consumer has accepted a risk of 0·1 that a lot may contain more than 0·5 per cent defectives, and the upper limit is expected to be 5·3/2·2 = 2·4 per cent defectives per lot.

A single sampling plan, therefore, for any lot requirement, is defined by the size of the sample and the maximum permissible number of defective items that may be detected in the sample. Related to this definition are the probabilities of accepting or of rejecting a lot containing any given percentage of defective items, and these probabilities can be calculated from the Poisson distribution. These probabilities can be plotted and an operating characteristic curve drawn; the operating characteristic curve in itself gives no information on the quality of an accepted lot, it merely indicates the probability of accepting a lot containing some specified percentage defective when such product is inspected. Defence Specification DEF-131-A 'Sampling Procedures and Tables for Inspection by Attributes' includes many operating characteristic curves for single sampling plans.

9.3.2 FIXING THE SAMPLE SIZE IN A SINGLE SAMPLING PLAN

In the example above we started with a statement regarding the permissible percentage defectives in a lot and the agreed sampling plan, and we used the Poisson distribution to determine the consumer's risk and the producer's risk that would result from these stated values. It seems to be most usual in industry to agree the consumer's and producer's risks and calculate the sampling plan, and this is simple enough, but is done on a trial basis. Enough sample size values are calculated for acceptance and rejection levels until the sample size for a particular acceptance–rejection level are equal; this level is the required sampling plan.

For example: a customer expects very frequent stoppages — which entail heavy wastage of material as well as loss of production — if lots of a particular item exceed 2·0 per cent defectives, and the agreed consumer risk was 0·1 probability of receiving a lot containing 2·0 per cent defectives. The producer could not undertake full inspection without incurring heavy expenditure for additional testing facilities, which would lead to a considerable increase in the cost of the item, and as rejection involved very high reworking costs it was obvious that unnecessary rejection was to be equated to a very low probability; the producer risk was fixed at a probability of 0·025 of rejecting a lot containing 0·5 per cent defectives.

Table 9.3.2 shows the upper and lower confidence limits at various probabilities for a range of defective item counts per sample; this table is an extract from Table 40, 'Confidence Limits for the expectation of a Poisson Variable' in *Biometrika Tables for Statisticians*, Volume 1. For any given set of risks it is necessary to choose a count per sample such that the acceptance count (x defectives) and the rejection count ($x + 1$ defectives) lead to approximately the same sample size.

From Table 9.3.2 we see that the upper limit at 0·1 probability for 2 defectives per sample is 5·32. This should be read as 'if the maximum expected number of defectives is 5·32 then the probability of obtaining 2 or less defectives per sample is 0·1.' The value of 5·32 is to be related to a lot percentage of 2·0 (the customer's maximum allowance) and so the estimated sample size is

$$\frac{5\cdot32 \times 100}{2\cdot0} = 266.$$

Similarly, the lower limit for 0·025 probability and 2 defectives per sample is 0·242, and this value is to be related to a lot percentage defective of 0·5, and so the estimated sample size would be

$$\frac{0\cdot242 \times 100}{0\cdot5} = 48.$$

Then for the set of risks quoted a trial sample size table can be compiled, such as

Acceptance count	Probability	Sample size	Rejection count	Probability	Sample size
2	0·1	266	3	0·025	124
3		334	4		218
4		400	5		324
5		463	6		440
6		525	7		562
7		590	8		690

and we settle for the sampling plan which states

Sample size 463, accept the lot with 5 or less defectives per sample, reject the lot with 6 or more defectives per sample.

For inspection of any given product, where a single sampling plan is desired, the sampling plan and the set of risks must be related in this manner. It is no use assuming a 'convenient' sampling plan and expecting it to agree with some stated (or assumed) risks; such agreement never occurs. Note that the size of the sample may be reduced by increasing the consumer's or the producer's risk.

Table 9.3.2 Confidence limits for the number of defective items per sample

Number of defectives per sample	Lower limits Pr = 0·005	0·01	0·025	0·1	Upper limits Pr = 0·1	0·025	0·01	0·005
0	0	0	0	0	2·30	3·69	4·61	5·30
1	0·005	0·010	0·025	0·105	3·89	5·57	6·64	7·43
2	0·103	0·149	0·242	0·532	5·32	7·22	8·41	9·27
3	0·338	0·436	0·619	1·100	6·68	8·77	10·05	10·98
4	0·672	0·823	1·09	1·74	7·99	10·24	11·60	12·59
5	1·08	1·28	1·62	2·43	9·27	11·67	13·11	14·15
6	1·54	1·79	2·20	3·15	10·5	13·06	14·57	15·66
7	2·04	2·33	2·81	3·89	11·8	14·42	16·00	17·13
8	2·57	2·91	3·45	4·66	13·0	15·76	17·40	18·58
9	3·13	3·51	4·12	5·43	14·2	17·08	18·78	20·00
10	3·72	4·13	4·80	6·22	15·4	18·39	20·14	21·40
11	4·32	4·77	5·49	7·02	16·6	19·68	21·49	22·78
12	4·94	5·43	6·20	7·83	17·8	20·96	22·82	24·14
13	5·58	6·10	6·92	8·65	19·0	22·23	24·14	25·50
14	6·23	6·78	7·65	9·47	20·1	23·49	25·45	26·84

9.3.3 SEQUENTIAL SAMPLING

As we have seen in the two previous sections, a single sampling plan requires that the size of the sample is fixed before any inspection takes place; this may involve a lot of unnecessary sampling and testing with consequent wastage of effort. To reduce this wastage as far as possible — and the amount of reduction depends to a large extent on the quality of the product — sequential sampling schemes have been devised. In a sequential sampling plan more than one sample may be taken from a lot and a test of 'goodness or badness' is applied to the accumulated data after inspection of each sample; sampling is stopped as soon as the data indicate that the lot may be accepted (or rejected, as the case may be) with the desired degree of certainty. Sampling continues as long as the accumulated data remain in the 'uncertain' area.

Like a single sampling plan, a sequential sampling plan is based on a definition of the consumer's risk and the producer's risk, and these two risks may be stated generally as

'Let α be the risk of rejecting a lot in which the proportion defective is p_1, and β the risk of accepting a lot in which the proportion defective is p_2.

These four parameters define explicitly the acceptance–rejection limits of a sequential sampling plan in which if the percentage defective is $> 100p_2$ the lot is most likely to be rejected, and if the percentage is $< 100p_1$ the lot is most likely to be accepted. Between $100p_1$ and $100p_2$ either acceptance or rejection may occur. Of the four parameters α is the producer's risk and β the consumer's risk; p_1 and p_2 are the limiting proportions. The big advantage of sequential sampling is that for any given set of parameters the total number of items examined before an accept or reject decision is made is (usually) less than that of any other system of sampling with no reduction in the guarantee offered.

If we define

$$h_1 = \frac{\ln\left[(1-\alpha)/\beta\right]}{\ln\,(p_2/p_1)}; \qquad h_2 = \frac{\ln\left[(1-\beta)/\alpha\right]}{\ln\,(p_2/p_1)}; \qquad s = \frac{p_2 - p_1}{\ln\,(p_2/p_1)}$$

in which ln stands for natural (or Napierian) logarithms, then sequential sampling theory enables us to calculate the acceptance–rejection divisor-lines which separate the regions of acceptance and uncertainty and the regions of uncertainty and rejection respectively.

When n items have been inspected, d_1 is the maximum permissible (cumulative) number of defectives for the lot to be accepted and d_2 is the minimum permissible (cumulative) number of defectives for the lot to be rejected, where d_1 and d_2 are defined by the equations of the two lines we have referred to in the previous paragraph as the divisor-lines

$$d_1 = -h_1 + sn$$
$$d_2 = h_2 + sn$$

For lots containing a proportion defective, p_1, the average sample size required will be

$$\bar{n}_1 = [(1-\alpha)h_1 - \alpha h_2]/(s - p_1),$$

and for lots containing a proportion defective, p_2, the average sample size required will be

$$\bar{n}_2 = [(1-\beta)h_2 - \beta h_1]/(p_2 - s),$$

and usually the total number of items required to be sampled will be less than the greater of $\bar{n}_1$ and $\bar{n}_2$. If the actual proportion defective lies between p_1 and p_2 then the amount of sampling necessary before a decision can be made may be very high and in such cases it may be desirable to consider whether or not some or all of the values of the parameters α, β, p_1 and p_2 can be modified. This means reaching a compromise between the degree of protection and the amount of testing and the two factors to be given consideration are the real proportion defective and the cost of sampling and testing. The average sample size may be decreased by increasing α or β or the interval between p_1 and p_2.

As testing of the lot continues, the total number of defectives found in all the samples examined can be compared with tabulated values or plotted on a graph and a decision made to accept the lot, take a further sample, or reject the lot. A graph may be drawn very easily for any sequential sampling plan (one such graph is shown in Figure 9.3.4) and sampling continues if the cumulative data point falls between the two divisor-lines and is stopped if the cumulative data point falls on a divisor-line or outside the enclosed region.

Table 9.3.3 gives a collection of values for $\ln\left[(1-\alpha)/\beta\right]$ and $\ln\left[(1-\beta)/\alpha\right]$ corresponding to some of the more usual values of α and β, and the table may be useful in calculating the acceptance and rejection limits for a sequential sampling plan, which plan is to be based on stated values for the

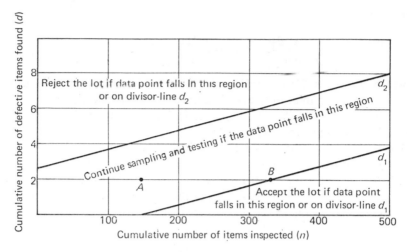

Fig. 9.3.4. SEQUENTIAL SAMPLING PLAN FOR EXAMPLE 9.3.4 ($\alpha = 0.025$, $p_1 = 0.005$; $\beta = 0.1$, $p_2 = 0.02$)

Table 9.3.3 Useful values for calculation of divisor lines

α	0.0005	0.001	0.005	0.01	0.02	0.025	0.04	0.05	0.10	0.20	0.25	0.40	0.50
β													
0.0005	7.600	7.600	7.596	7.591	7.581	7.576	7.560	7.550	7.496	7.378	7.313	7.090	6.908
	7.600	6.907	5.298	4.605	3.911	3.688	3.218	2.995	2.302	1.609	1.386	0.916	0.693
0.001	6.907	6.907	6.903	6.898	6.888	6.882	6.867	6.856	6.802	6.685	6.620	6.397	6.215
	7.600	6.907	5.297	4.604	3.911	3.688	3.218	2.995	2.302	1.608	1.385	0.915	0.692
0.005	5.298	5.297	5.293	5.288	5.278	5.273	5.257	5.247	5.193	5.075	5.011	4.787	4.605
	7.596	6.903	5.293	4.600	3.907	3.684	3.214	2.991	2.298	1.604	1.381	0.911	0.688
0.01	4.605	4.604	4.600	4.595	4.585	4.580	4.564	4.554	4.500	4.382	4.317	4.094	3.912
	7.591	6.898	5.288	4.595	3.902	3.679	3.209	2.986	2.293	1.599	1.376	0.906	0.683
0.02	3.911	3.911	3.907	3.902	3.892	3.887	3.871	3.861	3.807	3.689	3.624	3.401	3.219
	7.581	6.888	5.278	4.585	3.892	3.669	3.199	2.976	2.282	1.589	1.366	0.896	0.673
0.025	3.688	3.688	3.684	3.679	3.669	3.664	3.648	3.638	3.583	3.466	3.401	3.178	2.996
	7.576	6.882	5.273	4.580	3.887	3.664	3.194	2.970	2.277	1.584	1.361	0.891	0.668
0.04	3.218	3.218	3.214	3.209	3.199	3.194	3.178	3.168	3.114	2.996	2.931	2.708	2.526
	7.560	6.867	5.257	4.564	3.871	3.648	3.178	2.955	2.262	1.569	1.345	0.875	0.652
0.05	2.995	2.995	2.991	2.986	2.976	2.970	2.955	2.944	2.890	2.773	2.708	2.485	2.303
	7.550	6.856	5.247	4.554	3.861	3.638	3.168	2.944	2.251	1.558	1.335	0.865	0.642
0.10	2.302	2.302	2.298	2.293	2.282	2.277	2.262	2.251	2.197	2.079	2.015	1.792	1.609
	7.496	6.802	5.193	4.500	3.807	3.583	3.114	2.890	2.197	1.504	1.281	0.811	0.588
0.20	1.609	1.608	1.604	1.599	1.589	1.584	1.569	1.558	1.504	1.386	1.322	1.099	0.916
	7.378	6.685	5.075	4.382	3.689	3.466	2.996	2.773	2.079	1.386	1.163	0.693	0.470
0.25	1.386	1.385	1.381	1.376	1.366	1.361	1.345	1.335	1.281	1.163	1.099	0.875	0.693
	7.313	6.620	5.011	4.317	3.624	3.401	2.931	2.708	2.015	1.322	1.099	0.629	0.405
0.40	0.916	0.915	0.911	0.906	0.896	0.891	0.875	0.865	0.811	0.693	0.629	0.405	0.223
	7.090	6.397	4.787	4.094	3.401	3.178	2.708	2.485	1.792	1.099	0.875	0.405	0.182
0.50	0.693	0.692	0.688	0.683	0.673	0.668	0.652	0.642	0.588	0.470	0.405	0.182	0.000
	6.908	6.215	4.605	3.912	3.219	2.996	2.526	2.303	1.609	0.916	0.693	0.223	0.000

upper value gives $\ln\left(\dfrac{1-\alpha}{\beta}\right)$; lower value gives $\ln\left(\dfrac{1-\beta}{\alpha}\right)$.

four parameters α, β, p_1 and p_2 and not on some assumed (even if convenient) sampling fraction.

9.3.4 FIXING THE SAMPLE SIZE IN A SEQUENTIAL SAMPLING PLAN

The size of the first sample of items to be examined may be obtained from the tabulated values or from the graph of the agreed sequential sampling plan, and is the smallest number of items which will permit acceptance of the lot if no defective is found in the sample. Perhaps this may be demonstrated more easily in an arithmetic example and we shall consider the set of risks quoted in Section 9.3.2

for the producer's risk we have $\alpha = 0.025$, $p_1 = 0.005$; and
for the consumer's risk we have $\beta = 0.1$, $p_2 = 0.02$.

Then $p_2/p_1 = 4$; ln $4 = 1.3863$; and using Table 9.3.3 we have $h_1 = 2.277/1.3863 = 1.642$; $h_2 = 3.583/1.3863 = 2.585$; $s = 0.015/1.3863 = 0.0108$; from which the equation

of the acceptance divisor-line is $d_1 = -1.642 + 0.0108n$, and
of the rejection divisor-line is $d_2 = 2.585 + 0.0108n$.

Now the acceptance–rejection values may be tabulated by substituting 0, 1, 2, 3, 4, ..., k in turn in the equations for d_1 and d_2 and calculating the appropriate values of n. It is simpler, and seems more satisfying, to plot these lines on a graph, and this has been done in Figure 9.3.4.

Line d_1 cuts the horizontal axis at $n = 155$ (the actual solution of the equation $0.0108n - 1.642 = 0$ is 152) and so the first sample taken under this plan could be as few as 155 items, which is just over one-third of the sample size calculated for the single sampling plan from this set of risks. If no defective item is found in this sample the lot is accepted; if 4 or more defective items are found in the sample then the lot is rejected. If the sample is found to contain 1, 2, or 3 defectives the data point will fall in the 'Continue Sampling' region and another sample must be taken. The minimum size of this second sample is the number of items to be examined if no further defective item is found in the second sample.

For example, suppose the first sample of 155 items was found to contain 2 defective items, corresponding to the plot of Point A in Figure 9.3.4. Then if the second sample is likely to be free of defective items, to permit acceptance of the lot the next plot must be at Point B on line d_1; this corresponds to about 335 items (in practice we would use 335 items) and so the second sample would be at least $335 - 155 = 180$ items. Of course, one might decide to 'make an allowance' in the first sample and allow for 1 defective, in which case the sample size would be 240. On the grounds that the product in a lot should be reasonably good, one imagines that the first sample will be fixed at minimum size; if the product is unreasonably bad testing may be stopped very quickly, and the lot rejected, as soon as the 'reject number' of defectives is counted.

In the example used for sections 9.3.2 and 9.3.4 we have taken a set of risks and developed both a single sampling plan and a sequential sampling plan and obtained the results

1 Single sampling plan: accept the lot on 5 or less defectives in a sample of 463, reject the lot on 6 or more defectives in a sample of 463.

2 Sequential sampling plan: accept the lot on nil defectives in a sample of 155, reject the lot on 5 defectives in a sample of 155, continue sampling on 1, 2, 3 or 4 defectives in a sample of 155,

and we see from Figure 9.3.4 that the sequential sampling plan will permit acceptance of a lot when a sample contains 5 defectives only when the sample size is somewhat more than 500 (the actual value is 615).

The figure 463 is considerably more than 155, and considerably less than 615. Even though two different procedures are involved it seems fair to ask if any discrepancy is present. It must be remembered that the customer fixed 2·0 per cent defective as the maximum he was prepared to tolerate, and most of the time he would expect lots with nil defective. When lots contain very small percentages of defectives, 463-item samples are exorbitant as this sample size is fixed at the maximum permissible percentage defective. On the other hand, the value of 155 is a minimum sample size and 615 approximates to a maximum sample size, but the average expected sample size for the sequential sampling plan can be estimated from

$$\bar{n}_1 = \frac{(1 - 0·025)1·642 - (0·025 \times 2·585)}{0·0108 - 0·005} = 265.$$

and

$$\bar{n}_2 = \frac{(1 - 0·1)2·585 - (0·1 \times 1·642)}{0·025 - 0·0108} = 82$$

and the average size expected would be about 265. The difference between the 463-item sample of the single sampling plan and the 265-item average sample of the sequential sampling plan is a measure of the increase in efficiency of the sequential sampling procedure over the single sampling procedure.

9.3.5 VARIABLE SAMPLING

The procedures discussed in Sections 9.3.1 and 9.3.3 permit the development of sampling plans based on the proportion of defective items that may be found in a lot, and an item may be classed as defective according to the measurement of some variable (weight, diameter, etc.) or the inspection of some attribute (number of chips or scratches, surface gloss, etc.). A sampling plan may be based on the measured values of a variable (resistivity, breaking load, etc.) and where such a sampling plan is worked sequentially it is called a variable sampling plan to distinguish it from the sequential sampling plan already mentioned.

For a variable sampling plan the following five parameters must be specified:

q_1 is to be the average value for material which should not be rejected;

q_2 is to be the average value for material of barely acceptable quality;

α is the producer's risk of rejecting material when in fact it has an average value of q_1;

β is the consumer's risk of accepting material when in fact it has an average value of q_2; and

σ is the standard deviation of actual test values obtained under the product specification.

Then the probability of acceptance of lots of quality worse than q_2 will be less than β, and the probability of rejecting lots of quality better than q_1 will be less than α; q_1 may be greater than q_2 according to whether the specification limit is a minimum or a maximum. The difference between q_1 and q_2, and the values of α and β should be decided from technical and economic considerations.

As one might expect, the size of the sample to be examined before a decision is reached will depend on the quality of the lots presented for inspection. Small samples will be enough for lots of very good or very bad quality which will show a level of acceptance or rejection very quickly. Lots of intermediate quality will need larger samples, and if the quality lies between q_1 and q_2 very large samples may be required.

Average sample sizes to be expected are

$$\frac{2\sigma^2 . [(1 - \alpha)b - \alpha a]}{(q_2 - q_1)^2} \text{ for lots whose mean value of quality is } q_1,$$

$$\frac{2\sigma^2 . [(1 - \beta)a - \beta b]}{(q_2 - q_1)^2} \text{ for lots whose mean value of quality is } q_2, \text{ and}$$

$$\frac{ab . \sigma^2}{(q_2 - q_1)^2} \text{ for lots whose mean value of quality is } \frac{q_1 + q_2}{2},$$

in which, and in the formulae which follow,

$$a = \ln\left(\frac{1 - \beta}{\alpha}\right) \quad \text{and} \quad b = \ln\left(\frac{1 - \alpha}{\beta}\right).$$

Sample sizes should not exceed three times the largest of these, and if the amount of testing becomes excessive then α, β, or the difference between q_1 and q_2 should be increased; note that if such an increase is made the risk of making a wrong decision is also increased.

Tables of acceptance–rejection levels can be prepared from the equations

$$x_1 = \frac{n}{2}(q_1 + q_2) + h_1$$

$$x_2 = \frac{n}{2}(q_1 + q_2) - h_2$$

in which $h_1 = b\sigma^2/(q_1 - q_2)$ and $h_2 = a\sigma^2/(q_1 - q_2)$ and n is the number of observations made. Note than n is the total number of items inspected, and not the number of samples taken from the lot.

Where the specification limit is a minimum value the lot is rejected when the cumulative total of measurement is less than x_2 or accepted when the cumulative total of measurements is greater than x_1. Between x_1 and x_2 further sampling is required. A graph may be drawn, as in Figure 9.3.6,

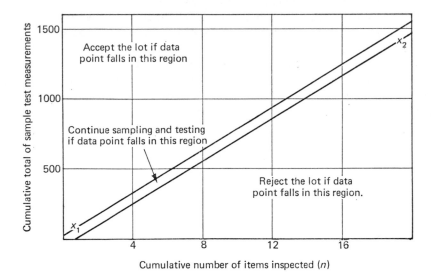

Fig. 9.3.6. VARIABLE SAMPLING PLAN FOR EXAMPLE 9.3.6

where x_1 and x_2 are plotted against n as the acceptance–rejection limit lines.

Where the specification limit is a maximum value the lot is accepted when the cumulative total of measurements is less than x_2 and rejected when the cumulative total of measurements is greater than x_1. If a specification has both minimum and maximum limits then values of α, β, q_1, and q_2 must be established for each limit; the one value of σ, derived from a large number of test measurements made in the immediate past, is applicable to both limits. A graph for such a specification would have two pairs of parallel lines.

9.3.6 FIXING THE SAMPLE SIZE IN A VARIABLE SAMPLING PLAN

The size of the first sample of items to be examined is obtained by calculation from the formulae for average sample sizes given in the previous section, and use of these formulae may be demonstrated by the following example.

The specification for items of a certain product is 75 (minimum) and customers will not accept product testing less than 75. Rejection of a lot would mean full testing to identify and remove defectives and this would be very expensive. Then we fix

q_1, the value which should not cause rejection, at 77,
q_2, the value which is barely acceptable, at 75,
α, the risk of rejecting material of average quality 77, at 0·005,
β, the risk of accepting material of average quality 75, at 0·1, and
σ, the standard deviation of the last 200 measurements, at 2·5.

From Table 9.3.3 we see that $a = 5·193$ and $b = 2·298$, and we have

average sample size expected for q_1

$$= \frac{[(1 - 0·005)2·298 - (0·005 \times 5·193)] \times 2 \times 2·5^2}{(75 - 77)^2} = 8$$

average sample size expected for q_2

$$= \frac{[(1 - 0·1)5·193 - (0·1 \times 2·298)] \times 2 \times 2·5^2}{(75 - 77)^2} = 15$$

average sample size expected for $\dfrac{q_1 + q_2}{2} = \dfrac{5·193 \times 2·298 \times 2·5^2}{(75 - 77)^2} = 20$

[Note that in each case we have declared the average sample size to the next highest whole number], and based on inspection of the data from recent tests, we decide to take a first sample of 10 items.

For these values we have

$$h_1 = \frac{2·298 \times 6·25}{77 - 75} = 7·18 \quad \text{and} \quad h_2 = \frac{5·193 \times 6·25}{77 - 75} = 16·23,$$

whereon the acceptance–rejection equations are

$$x_1 = \frac{(75 + 77)n}{2} + 7·18 \quad \text{or} \quad x_1 = 76n + 7·18$$

and

$$x_2 = \frac{(75 + 77)n}{2} - 16·23 \quad \text{or} \quad x_2 = 76n - 16·23$$

and these lines are plotted in Figure 9.3.6. [Please note that the lines drawn in the Figure are not quite correct. The distance between the lines should be

7.18 + 16·23 = 23·41 units; the lines have been displaced a little to create a continue sampling region large enough to see on this diagram.]

From the equations we find for our sample of 10 items ($n = 10$) that $x_1 = 767·18$ and $x_2 = 743·77$. So that if the cumulative measurements of the 10 items

> exceeds 767·18, the lot is accepted,
> is less than 743·77, the lot is rejected,
> is between 743·77 and 767·18, a further sample must be taken.

It is possible for one abjectly low value to cause rejection of a lot when a variable sampling plan is used, but this is not likely to occur when the product is made under controlled conditions.

9.3.7 SOME COMMENTS ON THE USE OF A SAMPLING PLAN

1 Agreement must be reached with the customer before any sampling plan can be introduced. Once the parameters have been established they should not be modified unless there is a real change in the customer's requirement or in the quality of the items produced.

2 Once a sampling plan has been agreed, whether it be for single sampling, sequential sampling or variable sampling, the plan must be adhered to and no 'fiddling' of any sort is to be permitted. If a sample indicates that the lot in question should be rejected, then the lot is to be rejected and not judged on the results obtained from any additional or alternative sample.

3 Items included in a sample are to be obtained by random selection from all the items in the lot. Stratified sampling (with a lot divided into sections) and systematic sampling (such as every 25th item produced) should not be encouraged. Items which are obviously different from each other should be accumulated in different lots.

4 In many cases it will be feasible to judge lots by either a sequential sampling plan or a variable sampling plan. The variable sampling plan involves a little more work per item inspected than the sequential sampling plan—the measurements have to be made exactly as a pass-fail indication is of no use, the measurements have to be recorded and not merely a count made of the number of defectives, and a little arithmetic must be performed—but usually the variable sampling plan will require examination of many fewer items than would be required by a sequential sampling plan.

5 Where items in a lot are to be judged on more than one test, all items in the sample should be submitted to the first test, and then to the second test, and so on until the lot can be sentenced. The tests should be arranged in order of priority with the most important test first.

6 After examination of the sample it seems to have become the practice—

where the sample indicates that the lot should be accepted – to return the whole sample, including defectives, to the lot for dispatch to customers. The writer believes this to be bad practice and recommends that known defectives be removed. This recommendation is based on two premises: firstly, that it is immoral and a bad business principle knowingly to dispatch defective items to customers; and secondly, the return of defectives to the manufacturing department should lead to an improvement in quality.

9.4 sampling for stores accounting

In chemical industry failure of a particular item of equipment and lack of a replacement could result in serious loss of production, so that it is customary to hold large stocks of a great variety of equipment to minimize this loss of production. The cost of the items held in stock may vary from a few pence each to several thousand pounds each; there are likely to be many of the cheaper varieties and very few of the more costly varieties in store. It is customary to maintain some kind of stores ledger record for each kind of item in the store, and every intake and delivery of the item is entered on this record, which, at any moment should provide knowledge of the availability, rate of usage, etc. of that item.

Usually the total value of stores is assessed at the end of the financial year. The obvious procedure is to obtain the required figure from inspection of the stores ledger records which show the balance in stock and purchase cost of the items. If the records are correct, or can be assumed to be correct, the total value of the stores can be deduced very quickly. Unfortunately, many of the records are likely to be inaccurate for any of a multitude of reasons, including the following

1 the previous inventory may have been wrong, giving a wrong starting balance for the year and a wrong record throughout the year;
2 some receipts or issues may have been made and not recorded, especially during 'closed hours';
3 some items may have been lost, or stolen, or discarded;
4 records may have been entered wrongly, especially so for somewhat similar items.

If these and any other sources of error can be eradicated, the stores ledger record will be exact. Failing this, the ledger record must be checked by actual physical counting of the numbers of all the items in stock, and of course this must be done in a very short time. The counting is a tedious, time-consuming procedure which is not necessarily free from error, especially if carried out by personnel drafted for the occasion who have no continuing interest in the stores.

Two procedures have been proposed to reduce the work involved in checking the ledger record by means of statistical sampling techniques. The first is a sequential sampling procedure suitable for use at the annual inventory check, the second offers a continuous sampling procedure for use throughout the year; these are discussed separately and in detail.

9.4.1 SEQUENTIAL SAMPLING PROCEDURE FOR ANNUAL INVENTORY CHECK

We use a procedure developed by James (*Applied Statistics*, VIII, 1959, pp. 145–157). The store is likely to contain a large number of items of low value, and usually the number of items held decreases as the value per item increases until there are only a few of the large costly items held in stock. A plot of the value of all items up to and including items of value x against the cost, x, per item gives a graph such as that shown in Figure 9.4.1.

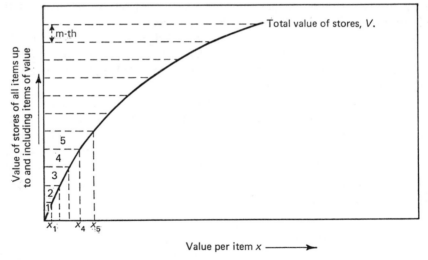

Fig. 9.4.1. DISTRIBUTION OF VALUE OF STORES

The vertical axis in Figure 9.4.1 can be divided into m equal parts and this corresponds to a division of the total stores inventory into m groups of equal value, with the ranges of values shown on the horizontal axis. Then the value of the stores in each group is $V/m = u$, and for any given group the following information is known

1 the total value of the group, u,
2 the number of items in the group, n,
3 the range of values of the items in the group.

It must be agreed between the company and the auditors that the accuracy required in the estimate of the value of the stores, as given by the stores ledger, shall be such that it will not differ by more than some figure, a per cent, from its real value. Thus for each of the m groups into which the inventory has been divided the stores ledger value must not differ from its real value by more than a per cent.

Consider any group, say the i-th group, and let x_i be the maximum value of any item in this group. Then if k items of this group are missing the maximum error that could arise by accepting the stores ledger value of the group would be kx_i; but this value must not exceed a per cent of u, so that equating these two values gives, at the maximum

$$kx_i = \frac{au}{100} \quad \text{or} \quad k = \frac{au}{100x_i}.$$

As long as no more items than this are missing, whatever their individual values may be, the stores ledger may be accepted as the maximum error involved cannot be more than a per cent of the actual group value.

In practice, the stores ledger may be in error due to a book deficit or a book surplus. Also, the items surplus to or missing from the book record of any group of items are not likely to belong wholly to the dearest category in that group; in general they will be distributed randomly over all categories in the group. Instead of considering the numbers of items surplus or missing it is more convenient to consider differences, and we shall consider all differences as being additive regardless of sign; the signs used would be $+$ for items surplus to the book record and $-$ for items missing from the book record, but we are interested in the total likely error and not in the possibility of eliminating error by balancing surplus items against missing items. Then it is reasonable to assume that provided the sum of differences from the stores ledger over all the categories of the i-th group does not exceed $2au/100x_i$, the stores ledger value of the i-th group can be accepted as being within the accuracy required.

Then the quantity $2au/100x_i$ represents the permissible error in terms of the difference in the number of items, surplus plus missing, from the stores ledger. If n_i is the actual number of items totalled over all categories in the i-th group, this permissible error may be represented as the proportion $0.02au/(n_i x_i)$, and the permissible error in terms of the proportion of items surplus to and missing from the stores ledger for each group is

$$\frac{0.02au}{n_1 x_1}; \quad \frac{0.02au}{n_2 x_2}; \quad \cdots; \quad \frac{0.02au}{n_m x_m}.$$

But here we note that u is the actual value of a group, and n_i is the actual number of items in the i-th group, and we do not know these actual values. What is known is the maximum number of items held in store of each category, and their values, and these figures provide an acceptable approximation. Alternatively, the stores ledger records may be used; the error involved in using either is negligible.

Using the 'permissible errors' for the m groups of stores in terms of the proportion of items surplus plus missing allows us to establish a sequential sampling scheme, and from this scheme it will be possible to decide to a high degree of certainty whether or not the stores ledger gives a sufficiently accurate estimate of the value of all items in any group. If now we write A_i for the permissible error in the i-th group ($A_i = 0.02au/n_i x_i$), then the following conditions must apply

1 the risk of accepting the stores ledger as correct when the real error in the group is as big as A_i must be very small;
2 the risk of not accepting the stores ledger as correct when the real error in the group is some value less than A_i (say $\frac{1}{2}A_i$) must be very small;

and if each of these risks be taken as 0.01 (allowing 1 chance in 100 of being wrong), then the four numerical values $[0.01, A_i, 0.01, \frac{1}{2}A_i]$ establish the limits for the sequential sampling scheme as shown in Figure 9.4.2.

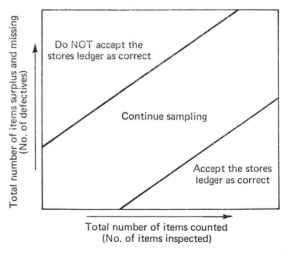

Fig. 9.4.2. LIMITS FOR SEQUENTIAL SAMPLING SCHEME

The procedure to be adopted is as follows: from any one group choose one category of items at random and count the number of items of this category in store. Compared with the stores ledger the count may provide a ledger value surplus or missing. The corresponding point is plotted on a graph similar to Fig. 9.4.2, and if

1 the point lies on or below the lower line, then accept the stores ledger as correct for that group; or

2 the point lies on or above the upper line, then count all items in all categories of that group; or

3 the point lies between the two lines, select another category of items and plot the cumulative total; sampling and counting is stopped as soon as 1. or 2. is attained.

This scheme means that if the actual error in a group, in terms of the proportion of items surplus plus missing, is greater than the permissible error A_i, there is at least a 99 per cent chance that the stores ledger will be found to be unacceptable. If the actual error is less than $\frac{1}{2}A_i$ there is at least a 99 per cent chance that the stores ledger will be accepted. Between these limits of error either possibility is likely. The scheme allows only a 1 per cent chance of using the stores ledger record for a group when it is incorrect by too great an amount, and of course this applies, in any group, only to a fraction $1/m$ of the total value of stores.

The problem is to decide on a value for m, the number of groups to be taken. The number required is that which will give, on average, the smallest amount of total stores counting. Always remembering that those groups which contain only a few expensive items will be counted completely every time.

We have seen in Section 9.3.3 that sequential sampling theory requires statements such as 'Let α be the risk of rejecting a lot in which the proportion defective is p_1, and β be the risk of accepting a lot in which the proportion defective is p_2', and these four parameters define explicitly the boundary lines which may be drawn, as on Figure 9.4.2, to describe the sequential sampling plan. If the percentage defective is greater than $100p_2$ the lot is most likely to be rejected, and if it is less than $100p_1$ the lot is most likely to be accepted. Between $100p_1$ and $100p_2$ either acceptance or rejection may occur.

Now we transform the theory so that a 'defective' becomes 'an item surplus to or missing from the stores ledger record', and the 'number of items inspected' becomes the 'number of items listed in the stores ledger record'. Then instead of 'accept the lot' we read 'use the stores ledger record', and instead of 'reject the lot' we have 'count all items in the group'. 'Continue sampling' becomes 'continue counting by choosing another category of items in the group'.

The permissible error expressed as a proportion of items surplus plus missing, A_i for the i-th group, becomes $_ip_2$, and some fraction of A_i (and it is convenient to take $\frac{1}{2}A_i$) becomes $_ip_1$, so that our data list is

$$_ip_1 = \tfrac{1}{2}A_i = \frac{0 \cdot 01au}{n_i x_i}; \qquad _ip_2 = A_i = \frac{0 \cdot 02au}{n_i x_i}$$

where

$u = V/m = $ the value of a group of categories of items,

$a\% = $ the permissible error in the value of a group when estimated from the stores ledger,

x_i = the maximum value of an item in the i-th group,

n_i = the total number of items in the i-th group,

α = the risk of refusing to use the stores ledger record when in fact the proportion of items surplus plus missing is $\frac{1}{2}A_i$,

β = the risk of using the stores ledger record when in fact the proportion of items surplus plus missing is A_i.

As in the usual sequential sampling procedures we have the boundary lines

$$d_1 = -h_1 + sn \quad \text{(lower line)}$$

and

$$d_2 = +h_2 + sn \quad \text{(upper line)}$$

in which d = the total number of discrepancies, and n = the total number of items counted.

$$h_1 = \frac{\log\left[(1 - \alpha)/\beta\right]}{\log\left[A_i(1 - \frac{1}{2}A_i)/\frac{1}{2}A_i(1 - A_i)\right]} = \frac{\log\left[(1 - \alpha)/\beta\right]}{\log\left[(2 - A_i)/(1 - A_i)\right]}$$

$$h_2 = \frac{\log\left[(1 - \beta)/\alpha\right]}{\log\left[(2 - A_i)/(1 - A_i)\right]} \quad \text{and} \quad s = \frac{\log\left[(1 - \frac{1}{2}A_i)/(1 - A_i)\right]}{\log\left[(2 - A_i)/(1 - A_i)\right]}$$

and from these the sequential sampling control chart may be drawn as in Figure 9.4.3.

Thus we can calculate a sequential sampling scheme for each of the m groups. It remains necessary to determine the value of m, and this must be that value which results in the minimum amount of total counting.

Sampling techniques can be used only if the stores ledger records are sufficiently good, because a decision to 'reject the lot' means that all items have to be counted. For the sampling scheme to work the proportion of items

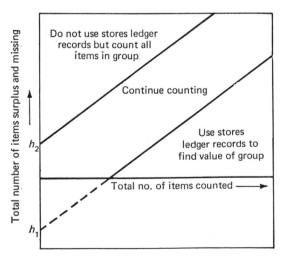

Fig. 9.4.3. SEQUENTIAL SAMPLING CONTROL CHART

surplus plus missing must be no more than $\frac{1}{2}A_i(p_1)$ otherwise a large proportion of the items will have to be counted. Then if the stores ledgers are accurate the average sample number, $\bar{n}_i$, for a group may be taken as that corresponding to $\frac{1}{2}A_i$, that is

$$\bar{n}_i = \frac{(1 - \alpha)h_1 - \alpha h_2}{s - \frac{1}{2}A_i}$$

where h_1, h_2 and s are as defined above. Any group for which $\bar{n}_i$ is greater than the actual number of items in the group must be counted; such groups are likely to be those containing only a few expensive items and counting for these groups will not be particularly onerous.

The value of m must be found which minimizes the sum of the values of $\bar{n}_i$ plus the actual total number of items for those groups which cannot be sampled. This may be done by finding the 'total average sample number' for different values of m and plotting these values against m to locate the minimum. If the minimum is located in a flat region, as shown in Figure 9.4.4, there is no point in attempting to locate the absolute minimum, and for a case represented by Figure 9.4.4 a value of $m = 12$ is good enough.

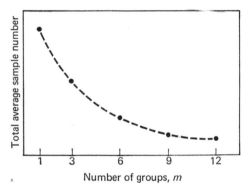

Fig. 9.4.4. MINIMUM AVERAGE SAMPLE NUMBER

EXAMPLE CALCULATION: Given that the maximum permissible error is to be 1 per cent, and each of the risks is to be 0·01. The items in the stores have been divided into groups, each of total value £4,500, and in the group we are to consider there are 15,000 items whose values range between 3s. and 15s.

Then for this group

$$A_i = \frac{0·02 \times 1 \times 4,500 \times 20}{15,000 \times 15} = 0·008$$

and of course $\frac{1}{2}A_i = 0·004$. It follows that

$$s = \frac{\log \left[(1 - 0·004)/(1 - 0·008)\right]}{\log \left[(2 - 0·008)/(1 - 0·008)\right]} = \frac{\log \left[0·996/0·992\right]}{\log \left[1·992/0·992\right]} = 0·00594,$$

and $\qquad h_1 = h_2 = \dfrac{\log 99}{\log (1{\cdot}992/0{\cdot}992)} = 6{\cdot}5905$ (take as 6·6)

The average number of items we would expect to count is

$$\bar{n}_i = \frac{0{\cdot}98 \times 6{\cdot}5905}{0{\cdot}00594 - 0{\cdot}004} = 3{,}399$$

and the boundary lines for our sequential sampling scheme are

> lower line is $d_1 = -6{\cdot}6 + 0{\cdot}00594n$, and
> upper line is $d_2 = 6{\cdot}6 + 0{\cdot}00594n$

where d is the total number of discrepancies in the n items counted, and the sampling plan may be described in a chart such as Figure 9.4.5.

The actual counts made show that

1 The first category chosen by random selection showed a count of 498 against the stores ledger record of 500. The corresponding point (500, 2) is plotted, A in Figure 9.4.5, and is found to lie between the limit lines, so another sample is required.

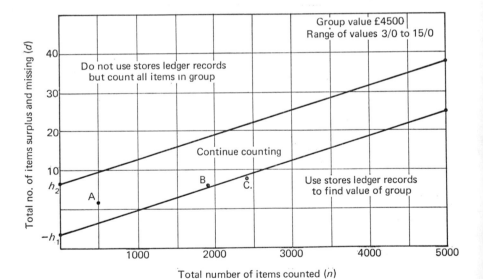

Fig. 9.4.5. STORES SAMPLING PLAN

2 The count of the second category, again chosen by random selection, was 1,404 against the stores ledger record of 1,400. The total discrepancy is now 2 + 4 for a total count of 500 + 1,400. The corresponding point (1,900, 6) is plotted at B in Figure 9.4.5 and this, too, lies between the limit lines so a further sample is required.

3 The third category, again chosen by random selection, showed a count of 502 against the stores ledger record of 500. The total discrepancy is now 2 + 4 + 2 for a total count of 500 + 1,400 + 500. The corresponding point (2,400, 8) is plotted at C in Figure 9.4.5 and as this lies in the 'accept' region sampling was stopped and the stores ledger record for this group was accepted as likely to be within the 1 per cent limit of accuracy required.

If we were to examine our allocation of items into groups and calculate the expected average number of items to be counted in each group we obtain data such as

Scheme a				Scheme b			
Group	u	x_i	n_i	Group	u	x_i	n_i
1	£4,500	£4,500	1	1	£9,000	£4,500	4
2	,,	2,000	3				
3	,,	400	30	2	,,	400	96
4	,,	150	66				
5	,,	100	120	3	,,	100	370
6	,,	50	250				
7	,,	25	475	4	,,	25	1,490
8	,,	12	1,105				
9	,,	5	2,300	5	,,	5	6,720
10	,,	3	4,420				
11	,,	25/-	9,000	6	,,	25/-	24,000
12	,,	15/-	15,000				
	$\bar{n}_i = 15,460$				$\bar{n}_i = 13,658$		

Scheme c				Scheme d			
Group	u	x_i	n_i	Group	u	x_i	n_i
1	£13,500	£4,500	34	1	£18,000	£4,500	100
2	,,	150	436	2	,,	100	1,800
3	,,	25	3,790	3	,,	5	30,720
4	,,	3	28,420		$\bar{n}_i = 19,298$		
	$\bar{n}_i = 16,294$						

We find that Scheme b gives the smallest average sample total and adopt this scheme for the annual inventory check.

9.4.2 A CONTINUOUS SAMPLING PROCEDURE TO ELIMINATE THE ANNUAL CHECK

The sequential sampling scheme described in Section 9.4.1 is intended for use at the annual stock accounting and, initially, involves considerable effort in the construction of the necessary charts or tables; the reduction in actual counting of items depends on the accuracy found in the stores ledger records, and this reduction can vary from nil to about 60 per cent. As an alternative procedure it is possible to develop a continuous sampling procedure intended for regular use throughout the year, so that the stores ledger records are kept at a high degree of accuracy at all times, and this eliminates the need for an annual stock accounting. This alternative procedure does not lead to any reduction in counting but spreads the load so that the counting does not have to be rushed.

The basic idea is the continuous quality control of the stores, again using discrepancy from the stores ledger record as the control parameter. The stores are divided (stratified) into separate locations (lots) all of which contain approximately the same number of items (giving equal lot size) which may be of different categories in any location. The initial plan assumes that one-quarter of the lots will be examined in each quarter of the year — or one-twelfth of the lots examined every month — so that the whole store is covered in a year. Any lot thought to be out of control is rechecked, and any lot found to lie outside the agreed control limit is checked completely by counting all the items; this serves the same purpose as 100 per cent inspection of a rejected lot of items from a manufacturing line.

A 'permissible error', being the maximum discrepancy between an actual count and the stores ledger record that can be tolerated, must be agreed. As before, a figure of 1 per cent of the stores ledger record is suggested.

A random sample of categories is selected from each lot, and a physical count made of the items in each category. Each count is compared with the stores ledger record and if the count disagrees with the record by more than the permissible error, the category is said to be 'in error'. An estimate of the percentage of categories in each lot which are in error is obtained from the simple binomial estimator

$$\hat{P}_i = \frac{100d_i}{n_i}$$

where $\hat{P}_i$ is the estimated error rate in the i-th lot,
          d_i is the number of categories in error in the i-th lot,
and n_i is the number of categories in the sample chosen from the i-th lot.

It follows that the variance of the estimator, which may be required for significance testing, is

$$\text{var } \hat{P}_i = \frac{\hat{P}_i(100 - \hat{P}_i)}{n_i}$$

An acceptable limit for the estimated error rate must be established, and 10 per cent is suggested as a start; this may depend on the results obtained from the sample, and can be modified as required. If more lots have an estimated error rate above 10 per cent than can be rechecked by the available effort in the given time period, only those of the highest error-rate lots are rejected that will require about one-quarter of the inventory time for rechecking; the remainder of the lots with estimated error-rate above 10 per cent are accepted temporarily. When there are insufficient lots with error-rate above 10 per cent to constitute a full quarter's work the acceptable limit can be reduced or the working party reduced or both.

The following procedure is based on time periods of a quarter; any other convenient time period may be used but the time period should be determined by the number of categories to be counted and the time available to do the counting. It is useless to guess these factors.

An initial sample of about one-tenth of the number of categories in each lot is chosen by some process of random selection, and the items in each category are counted. Some lots may be 'accepted' (i.e. have an estimated error-rate below 10 per cent), other lots may be 'rejected' (i.e. have an estimated error-rate above 10 per cent).

In the first quarter, those lots rejected on the initial sample are counted completely. A sample is chosen from all the other lots, which will include those 'accepted' from the initial sample, and from this sample the check list for the second quarter is prepared, and so on. Lots counted in one quarter cannot be counted again in the following quarter as they will not be included in the list from which the sample is drawn.

When a sample has been chosen for counting in any quarter the procedure adopted for each category in the sample is as follows

1 Count all the items in that category.
2 Compare the count with the stores ledger record. If the count and the record agree within the acceptable limit, then report the category as 'acceptable'.
3 If the count and the record disagree, they may do so because
   a a miscount has occurred,
   b a recent receipt into or issue from the stores has not been recorded, or
   c the category is in error.
   Judgment is postponed for a week, then
4 Recount the items in this category and compare with the stores ledger record. If the count and the record agree within the acceptable limit, report the category as 'acceptable'. If they disagree by the same amount as previously, report the category as 'rejected'. If they disagree by some different amount, postpone judgment for a further week, then
5 Recount the items in this category. If the count and the record agree within the acceptable limit, report the category as 'acceptable'. If they

disagree then a detailed investigation must be made to reconcile the account.

Note that no count should be accepted unless it agrees with the record or with a previous count; this virtually eliminates the possibility that a miscount will be accepted. The record must be adjusted for categories shown to be in error, and although the adjustment on paper may be made easily, the cause should be investigated.

Compared with the once-a-year stock reconciliation the advantages of this continuous procedure are thought to be

1 It permits normal store operation throughout the year; there is no 'dead' period for stocktaking.
2 At any given time the records have a higher degree of accuracy, and the state of actual stocks and recorded stocks is constantly under review.
3 Inefficient procedures, or those likely to lead to errors, may be identified and eliminated before errors become very large.

The two schemes described in Section 9.4 offer alternative procedures (though since one scheme deals with the monetary value of the stores and the other deals with the number of items held the two procedures could be considered to be complementary), which are likely to be of great value when applied to a very large store containing thousands of categories of items and where much effort is required to provide a physical check on the stores ledger record. As the size of the store decreases the savings likely to result from the use of statistical control methods also decrease, and given the data it is possible to estimate the size of store (in terms of the number of categories held) where the statistical effort involved equals the saving in checking effort; below this size it is not worth even considering the introduction of a statistical scheme.

If the requirements of the stores ledger record are taken to be
1 to show how many items of whatever categories are available at any time, and
2 to enable an estimate to be made of the value of stock at any time,

then a continuous sampling scheme is likely to be better than an annual check if information regarding stores transactions is passed to records quickly and accurately, and the records are made carefully and accurately. In such cases the estimated error-rates will be very low so that recounting of categories will not be necessary; occasional recounts may be requested to prove the point.

It is possible to institute a procedure which can be transformed into a statistical control scheme as and when the need arises. Some categories will contain few items, probably expensive and slow-moving items, and these can be left for annual check as errors in the stores ledger records of these categories are not likely to occur. The remaining categories can be used to estimate whether or not the stores ledger records may be accepted at any given time.

Firstly it is necessary to decide how much effort is to be given to the stores checking, and if for example two men are to be allocated for two days a month, then a procedure can be devised according to the size of the store

1 WITH COMPLETE COUNTING: where the store is small, so that one-twelfth of the stores can be counted within the limit of effort allowed (one-tenth, or one-eighth, or even one-sixth could be used if thought more convenient) the recommended procedure is as follows: A random sample of one-twelfth of the categories held in the store is chosen each month, all categories counted, any errors noted and resolved. If at the annual stock-taking time the total of the monthly errors over all categories is less than the maximum permissible error the stores ledger record is accepted as correct. If the total error is greater than the maximum permissible error then sequential sampling is started using the latest count as datum point.

The sample of categories chosen each month must be completely random. If any category is known to be continually in error, that category should be the subject of a separate inquiry; it must not be included in successive months' samples as deliberate policy.

2 FOR PARTIAL COUNTING: where the store is too big to permit one-twelfth of the categories to be counted within the limit of effort allowed the recommended procedure is as follows. The categories are arranged in groups so that the groups are of approximately equal total value; for each group a sequential sampling control chart, as in Figure 9.4.5, is prepared. Each month one category, and more if effort permits, is chosen by random selection from each group, the items counted and the cumulative error plotted. Acceptance or rejection of the stores ledger record as accurate within the permissible error limit is indicated by the final point plotted on the control chart.

SUGGESTIONS FOR FURTHER READING

2 YULE and KENDALL, Chapters 17, 18, 19 and 21, 1958.
5 O. L. DAVIES (ed.), Chapter 11, 1958.
6 L. M. DEBING (ed.), Chapter 6, 1957.
7 FREUND and WILLIAMS, Chapters 8 and 12, 1959.
11 COCHRAN, 1964.
13 DEF-131-A, 1966.
14 MIL-STD-414, 1957.

STATISTICAL TABLES

Table A1 is reprinted from 'Critical Values and Criteria for Testing for Extreme Values,' *Biometrics* 9 (1953), p. 89, by kind permission of Prof. W. J. Dixon and the managing editor of *Biometrics*.

Tables A2, A3 and A4 have been compiled from various publications. For more exact values see *Biometrika Tables for Statisticians*, Volume 1.

Tables A5 and A6 are reprinted from 'The use of Range in Place of Standard Deviation in the *t*-test', *Biometrika* 34 (1947), 41, by kind permission of E. Lord and the *Biometrika* Trustees.

Table A7 is reprinted from 'The two-sample *t*-test based on Range,' *Biometrika* 44 (1957), 482, by kind permission of Prof. P. G. Moore and the *Biometrika* Trustees.

Tables A8, A9 and A10 are reprinted from *Some Rapid Approximate Statistical Procedures*, by Dr. Frank Wilcoxon by kind permission of American Cyanamid Company.

Table A1 Critical values and criteria for testing for extreme values

Number of values n	Probability that the extreme value be accepted							Criterion to to be used
	0·3	0·2	0·1	0·05	0·02	0·01	0·005	
	Percentage probability that the extreme value be rejected							
	70	80	90	95	98	99	99·5	
3	0·684	0·781	0·886	0·941	0·976	0·988	0·994	
4	0·471	0·560	0·679	0·765	0·846	0·889	0·926	$r_1 = \dfrac{x_n - x_{n-1}}{x_n - x_1}$
5	0·373	0·451	0·557	0·642	0·729	0·780	0·821	
6	0·318	0·386	0·482	0·560	0·644	0·698	0·740	
7	0·281	0·344	0·434	0·507	0·586	0·637	0·680	
8	0·318	0·385	0·479	0·554	0·631	0·683	0·725	
9	0·288	0·352	0·441	0·512	0·587	0·635	0·677	$r_2 = \dfrac{x_n - x_{n-1}}{x_n - x_2}$
10	0·265	0·325	0·409	0·477	0·551	0·597	0·639	
11	0·391	0·442	0·517	0·576	0·638	0·679	0·713	
12	0·370	0·419	0·490	0·546	0·605	0·642	0·675	$r_3 = \dfrac{x_n - x_{n-2}}{x_n - x_2}$
13	0·351	0·399	0·467	0·521	0·578	0·615	0·649	
14	0·370	0·421	0·492	0·546	0·602	0·641	0·674	
15	0·353	0·402	0·472	0·525	0·579	0·616	0·647	
16	0·338	0·386	0·454	0·507	0·559	0·595	0·624	
17	0·325	0·373	0·438	0·490	0·542	0·577	0·605	
18	0·314	0·361	0·424	0·475	0·527	0·561	0·589	$r_4 = \dfrac{x_n - x_{n-2}}{x_n - x_3}$
19	0·304	0·350	0·412	0·462	0·514	0·547	0·575	
20	0·295	0·340	0·401	0·450	0·502	0·535	0·562	
21	0·287	0·331	0·391	0·440	0·491	0·524	0·551	
22	0·280	0·323	0·382	0·430	0·481	0·514	0·541	
23	0·274	0·316	0·374	0·421	0·472	0·505	0·532	
24	0·268	0·310	0·367	0·413	0·464	0·497	0·524	
25	0·262	0·304	0·360	0·406	0·457	0·489	0·516	

Table A2 Values of χ^2

D.F.	Probability of a larger value of χ^2							
	0·995	0·990	0·980	0·975	0·950	0·900	0·800	0·750
1	0·000	0·00	0·00	0·00	0·00	0·02	0·06	0·10
2	0·010	0·02	0·04	0·05	0·10	0·21	0·45	0·58
3	0·072	0·12	0·18	0·22	0·35	0·58	1·01	1·21
4	0·207	0·30	0·43	0·48	0·71	1·06	1·65	1·92
5	0·412	0·55	0·75	0·83	1·15	1·61	2·34	2·67
6	0·676	0·87	1·13	1·24	1·64	2·20	3·07	3·45
7	0·989	1·24	1·56	1·69	2·17	2·83	3·82	4·25
8	1·344	1·65	2·03	2·18	2·73	3·49	4·59	5·07
9	1·735	2·09	2·53	2·70	3·33	4·17	5·38	5·90
10	2·156	2·56	3·06	3·25	3·94	4·87	6·18	6·74
11	2·603	3·05	3·61	3·82	4·57	5·58	6·99	7·58
12	3·074	3·57	4·18	4·40	5·23	6·30	7·81	8·44
13	3·565	4·11	4·76	5·01	5·89	7·04	8·63	9·30
14	4·075	4·66	5·37	5·63	6·57	7·79	9·47	10·17
15	4·601	5·23	5·98	6·26	7·26	8·55	10·31	11·04
16	5·142	5·81	6·61	6·91	7·96	9·31	11·15	11·91
17	5·697	6·41	7·26	7·56	8·67	10·09	12·00	12·79
18	6·265	7·02	7·91	8·23	9·39	10·86	12·86	13·68
19	6·844	7·63	8·57	8·91	10·12	11·65	13·72	14·56
20	7·434	8·26	9·24	9·59	10·85	12·44	14·58	15·45
21	8·034	8·90	9·92	10·28	11·59	13·24	15·44	16·34
22	8·643	9·54	10·60	10·98	12·34	14·04	16·31	17·24
23	9·26	10·20	11·29	11·69	13·09	14·85	17·19	18·14
24	9·89	10·86	11·99	12·40	13·85	15·66	18·06	19·04
25	10·52	11·52	12·70	13·12	14·61	16·47	18·94	19·94
26	11·16	12·20	13·41	13·84	15·38	17·29	19·82	20·84
27	11·81	12·88	14·12	14·57	16·15	18·11	20·70	21·75
28	12·46	13·56	14·85	15·31	16·93	18·94	21·59	22·66
29	13·12	14·26	15·57	16·05	17·71	19·77	22·48	23·57
30	13·79	14·95	16·31	16·79	18·49	20·60	23·36	24·48
40	20·71	22·16	23·81	24·43	26·51	29·05	32·34	33·66
50	27·99	29·71	31·63	32·36	34·76	37·69	41·41	42·94
60	35·53	37·48	39·66	40·48	43·19	46·46	50·61	52·29
70	43·28	45·44	47·86	48·76	51·74	55·33	58·99	61·70
80	51·17	53·54	56·04	57·15	60·39	64·28	68·23	71·14
90	59·20	61·75	64·45	65·65	69·13	73·29	77·49	80·62
100	67·33	70·06	73·90	74·22	77·93	82·36	86·76	90·13

Table A2 continued

D.F.	Probability of a larger value of χ^2							
	0·700	0·500	0·300	0·200	0·100	0·050	0·020	0·010
1	0·15	0·45	1·07	1·64	2·71	3·84	5·41	6·63
2	0·71	1·39	2·41	3·22	4·60	5·99	7·82	9·21
3	1·42	2·37	3·66	4·64	6·25	7·81	9·84	11·34
4	2·20	3·36	4·88	5·99	7·78	9·49	11·67	13·28
5	3·00	4·35	6·06	7·29	9·24	11·07	13·39	15·09
6	3·83	5·35	7·23	8·56	10·64	12·59	15·03	16·81
7	4·67	6·35	8·38	9·80	12·02	14·07	16·62	18·48
8	5·53	7·34	9·52	11·03	13·36	15·51	18·17	20·09
9	6·39	8·34	10·66	12·24	14·68	16·92	19·68	21·67
10	7·27	9·34	11·78	13·44	15·99	18·31	21·16	23·21
11	8·15	10·34	12·90	14·63	17·28	19·68	22·62	24·72
12	9·03	11·34	14·01	15·81	18·55	21·03	24·05	26·22
13	9·93	12·34	15·12	16·98	19·81	22·36	25·47	27·69
14	10·82	13·34	16·22	18·15	21·06	23·68	26·87	29·14
15	11·72	14·34	17·32	19·31	22·31	25·00	28·26	30·58
16	12·62	15·34	18·42	20·46	23·54	26·30	29·63	32·00
17	13·53	16·34	19·51	21·62	24·77	27·59	31·00	33·41
18	14·44	17·34	20·60	22·76	25·99	28·87	32·35	34·81
19	15·35	18·34	21·69	23·90	27·20	30·14	33·69	36·19
20	16·27	19·34	22·78	25·04	28·41	31·41	35·02	37·57
21	17·18	20·34	23·86	26·17	29·62	32·67	36·34	38·93
22	18·10	21·34	24·94	27·30	30·81	33·92	37·66	40·29
23	19·02	22·34	26·02	28·43	32·01	35·17	38·97	41·64
24	19·94	23·34	27·10	29·55	33·20	36·42	40·27	42·98
25	20·87	24·34	28·17	30·68	34·38	37·65	41·57	44·31
26	21·79	25·34	29·25	31·80	35·56	38·89	42·86	45·64
27	22·72	26·34	30·32	32·91	36·74	40·11	44·14	46·96
28	23·65	27·34	31·39	34·03	37·92	41·34	45·42	48·28
29	24·58	28·34	32·46	35·14	39·09	42·56	46·69	49·59
30	25·51	29·34	33·53	36·25	40·26	43·77	47·96	50·89
40	34·87	39·34	44·18	47·31	51·81	55·76	60·50	63·69
50	44·30	49·33	54·76	56·18	63·17	67·50	70·69	76·15
60	53·80	59·33	65·26	69·01	74·40	79·08	84·65	88·38
70	63·35	69·33	75·70	79·73	85·53	90·53	96·43	100·43
80	72·95	79·33	86·10	90·39	96·58	101·88	108·09	112·33
90	82·54	89·33	96·47	101·00	107·57	113·15	119·65	124·12
100	92·23	99·33	106·82	115·58	118·50	124·34	131·11	135·81

Table A3 (1) Percentage points of the F-distribution

D.F. of lesser mean square	Probability point	Degrees of freedom of the greater mean square										
		1	2	3	4	5	6	7	8	9	10	12
1	0·10	39·9	49·5	53·6	55·8	57·2	58·2	58·9	59·4	59·9	60·2	60·7
	0·05	161	199	216	225	230	234	237	239	241	242	244
	0·01	4,052	5,000	5,403	5,625	5,764	5,859	5,928	5,982	6,022	6,056	6,106
2	0·10	8·53	9·0	9·16	9·24	9·29	9·33	9·35	9·37	9·38	9·39	9·41
	0·05	18·5	19·0	19·2	19·2	19·3	19·3	19·4	19·4	19·4	19·4	19·4
	0·01	98·5	99·0	99·2	99·2	99·3	99·3	99·3	99·4	99·4	99·4	99·4
3	0·10	5·54	5·46	5·39	5·34	5·31	5·28	5·27	5·25	5·24	5·23	5·22
	0·05	10·13	9·55	9·28	9·12	9·01	8·94	8·88	8·84	8·81	8·78	8·74
	0·01	34·12	30·81	29·46	28·71	28·24	27·91	27·67	27·49	27·34	27·23	27·10
4	0·10	4·54	4·32	4·19	4·11	4·05	4·01	3·98	3·95	3·94	3·92	3·90
	0·05	7·71	6·94	6·59	6·39	6·26	6·16	6·09	6·04	6·00	5·96	5·91
	0·01	21·20	18·00	16·69	15·98	15·52	15·21	14·98	14·80	14·66	14·54	14·40
5	0·10	4·06	3·78	3·62	3·52	3·45	3·40	3·37	3·34	3·32	3·30	3·27
	0·05	6·61	5·79	5·41	5·19	5·05	4·95	4·88	4·82	4·77	4·74	4·68
	0·01	16·26	13·27	12·06	11·39	10·97	10·67	10·45	10·27	10·15	10·05	9·89
6	0·10	3·78	3·46	3·29	3·18	3·11	3·05	3·01	2·98	2·96	2·94	2·90
	0·05	5·99	5·14	4·76	4·53	4·39	4·28	4·21	4·15	4·10	4·06	4·00
	0·01	13·74	10·92	9·78	9·15	8·75	8·47	8·26	8·10	7·98	7·87	7·72
7	0·10	3·59	3·26	3·07	2·96	2·88	2·83	2·78	2·75	2·72	2·70	2·57
	0·05	5·59	4·74	4·35	4·12	3·97	3·87	3·79	3·73	3·68	3·64	3·57
	0·01	12·25	9·55	8·45	7·85	7·46	7·19	6·99	6·84	6·72	6·62	6·47
8	0·10	3·46	3·11	2·92	2·81	2·73	2·67	2·62	2·59	2·56	2·54	2·50
	0·05	5·32	4·46	4·07	3·84	3·69	3·58	3·50	3·44	3·39	3·35	3·28
	0·01	11·26	8·65	7·59	7·01	6·63	6·37	6·18	6·03	5·91	5·81	5·67
9	0·10	3·36	3·01	2·81	2·69	2·61	2·55	2·51	2·47	2·44	2·42	2·33
	0·05	5·12	4·26	3·86	3·63	3·48	3·37	3·29	3·23	3·18	3·14	3·07
	0·01	10·56	8·02	6·99	6·42	6·06	5·80	5·61	5·47	5·35	5·26	5·1·
10	0·10	3·28	2·92	2·73	2·61	2·52	2·46	2·41	2·38	2·35	2·32	2·28
	0·05	4·96	4·10	3·71	3·48	3·33	3·22	3·14	3·07	3·02	2·98	2·91
	0·01	10·04	7·56	6·55	5·99	5·64	5·39	5·20	5·06	4·94	4·85	4·71

Table A3 (2)

D.F. of lesser mean square	Probability point	Degrees of freedom of the greater mean square										
		15	20	24	30	40	50	60	100	120	500	∞
1	0·10	61·22	61·74	62·00	62·3	62·53	62·7	62·8	63·0	63·1	63·2	63·3
	0·05	246	248	249	250	251	252	252	253	253	254	254
	0·01	6,157	6,209	6,235	6,261	6,287	6,302	6,313	6,334	6,339	6,361	6,366
2	0·10	9·42	9·44	9·44	9·45	9·47	9·47	9·47	9·48	9·48	9·49	9·49
	0·05	19·43	19·45	19·45	19·46	19·47	19·47	19·48	19·48	19·49	19·49	19·50
	0·01	99·43	99·45	99·46	99·47	99·47	99·48	99·48	99·49	99·49	99·50	99·50
3	0·10	5·20	5·18	5·18	5·17	5·16	5·15	5·15	5·15	5·14	5·13	5·13
	0·05	8·70	8·66	8·64	8·62	8·60	8·58	8·57	8·56	8·55	8·54	8·53
	0·01	26·87	26·69	26·60	26·50	26·41	26·30	26·27	26·23	26·18	26·14	26·12
4	0·10	3·87	3·84	3·83	3·82	3·80	3·79	3·79	3·78	3·78	3·77	3·76
	0·05	5·86	5·80	5·77	5·74	5·71	5·70	5·69	5·66	5·65	5·64	5·63
	0·01	14·20	14·02	13·90	13·83	13·74	13·69	13·63	13·57	13·53	13·48	13·46
5	0·10	3·24	3·21	3·19	3·17	3·16	3·15	3·14	3·13	3·12	3·11	3·10
	0·05	4·62	4·56	4·53	4·50	4·46	4·44	4·43	4·40	4·40	4·37	4·36
	0·01	9·72	9·55	9·47	9·38	9·29	9·24	9·20	9·13	9·11	9·04	9·02
6	0·10	2·87	2·84	2·82	2·80	2·78	2·77	2·76	2·75	2·74	2·73	2·72
	0·05	3·94	3·87	3·84	3·81	3·77	3·75	3·74	3·71	3·70	3·68	3·67
	0·01	7·56	7·40	7·31	7·23	7·14	7·09	7·06	6·99	6·97	6·90	6·88
7	0·10	2·63	2·59	2·58	2·56	2·54	2·52	2·51	2·50	2·49	2·48	2·47
	0·05	3·51	3·44	3·41	3·38	3·34	3·32	3·30	3·28	3·27	3·24	3·23
	0·01	6·31	6·16	6·07	5·99	5·91	5·85	5·82	5·75	5·74	5·67	5·65
8	0·10	2·46	2·42	2·40	2·38	2·36	2·35	2·34	2·32	2·32	2·31	2·29
	0·05	3·22	3·15	3·12	3·08	3·04	3·03	3·01	2·98	2·97	2·94	2·93
	0·01	5·52	5·36	5·28	5·20	5·12	5·06	5·03	4·96	4·95	4·88	4·86
9	0·10	2·34	2·30	2·28	2·25	2·23	2·22	2·21	2·19	2·18	2·17	2·16
	0·05	3·01	2·94	2·90	2·86	2·83	2·80	2·79	2·76	2·75	2·72	2·71
	0·01	4·96	4·81	4·73	4·65	4·57	4·51	4·48	4·41	4·40	4·33	4·31
10	0·10	2·24	2·20	2·18	2·16	2·13	2·12	2·11	2·09	2·08	2·07	2·06
	0·05	2·85	2·77	2·74	2·70	2·66	2·64	2·62	2·59	2·58	2·55	2·54
	0·01	4·56	4·41	4·33	4·25	4·17	4·12	4·08	4·01	4·00	3·93	3·91

Table A3 (3)

D.F. of lesser mean square	Probability point	Degrees of freedom of the greater mean square										
		1	2	3	4	5	6	7	8	9	10	12
11	0·10	3·23	2·86	2·66	2·54	2·45	2·39	2·34	2·30	2·27	2·25	2·21
	0·05	4·84	3·98	3·59	3·36	3·20	3·09	3·01	2·95	2·90	2·85	2·79
	0·01	9·65	7·21	6·22	5·67	5·32	5·07	4·89	4·74	4·63	4·54	4·40
12	0·10	3·18	2·81	2·61	2·48	2·39	2·33	2·28	2·24	2·21	2·19	2·15
	0·05	4·75	3·89	3·49	3·26	3·11	3·00	2·91	2·85	2·80	2·75	2·69
	0·01	9·33	6·93	5·95	5·41	5·06	4·82	4·64	4·50	4·39	4·30	4·16
13	0·10	3·14	2·76	2·56	2·43	2·35	2·28	2·23	2·20	2·16	2·14	2·10
	0·05	4·67	3·81	3·41	3·18	3·03	2·92	2·83	2·77	2·72	2·67	2·60
	0·01	9·07	6·70	5·74	5·21	4·86	4·62	4·44	4·30	4·19	4·10	3·96
14	0·10	3·10	2·73	2·52	2·39	2·31	2·24	2·19	2·15	2·12	2·10	2·05
	0·05	4·60	3·74	3·34	3·11	2·96	2·85	2·76	2·70	2·65	2·60	2·53
	0·01	8·86	6·51	5·56	5·04	4·69	4·46	4·28	4·14	4·03	3·94	3·80
15	0·10	3·07	2·70	2·49	2·36	2·27	2·21	2·16	2·12	2·09	2·06	2·02
	0·05	4·54	3·68	3·29	3·06	2·90	2·79	2·71	2·64	2·59	2·54	2·48
	0·01	8·68	6·36	5·42	4·89	4·56	4·32	4·14	4·00	3·89	3·80	3·67
16	0·10	3·05	2·67	2·46	2·33	2·24	2·18	2·13	2·09	2·06	2·03	1·99
	0·05	4·49	3·63	3·24	3·01	2·85	2·74	2·66	2·59	2·54	2·49	2·42
	0·01	8·53	6·23	5·29	4·77	4·44	4·20	4·03	3·89	3·78	3·69	3·55
17	0·10	3·03	2·64	2·44	2·31	2·22	2·15	2·10	2·06	2·03	2·00	1·96
	0·05	4·45	3·59	3·20	2·96	2·81	2·70	2·61	2·55	2·49	2·45	2·38
	0·01	8·40	6·11	5·18	4·67	4·34	4·10	3·93	3·79	3·68	3·59	3·46
18	0·10	3·01	2·62	2·42	2·29	2·20	2·13	2·08	2·04	2·00	1·98	1·93
	0·05	4·41	3·55	3·16	2·93	2·77	2·66	2·58	2·51	2·46	2·41	2·34
	0·01	8·29	6·01	5·09	4·58	4·25	4·01	3·84	3·71	3·60	3·51	3·37
19	0·10	2·99	2·61	2·40	2·27	2·18	2·11	2·06	2·02	1·98	1·96	1·91
	0·05	4·38	3·52	3·13	2·90	2·74	2·63	2·54	2·48	2·42	2·38	2·31
	0·01	8·18	5·93	5·01	4·50	4·17	3·94	3·77	3·63	3·52	3·43	3·30
20	0·10	2·97	2·59	2·38	2·25	2·16	2·09	2·04	2·00	1·96	1·94	1·89
	0·05	4·35	3·49	3·10	2·87	2·71	2·60	2·51	2·45	2·39	2·35	2·23
	0·01	8·10	5·85	4·94	4·43	4·10	3·87	3·70	3·56	3·46	3·37	3·23

Table A3 (4)

D.F. of lesser mean square	Probability point	Degrees of freedom of the greater mean square										
		15	20	24	30	40	50	60	100	120	500	∞
11	0·10	2·17	2·12	2·10	2·08	2·05	2·04	2·03	2·01	2·00	1·98	1·97
	0·05	2·72	2·65	2·61	2·57	2·53	2·50	2·49	2·46	2·45	2·41	2·40
	0·01	4·25	4·10	4·02	3·94	3·86	3·80	3·78	3·70	3·69	3·62	3·60
12	0·10	2·10	2·06	2·04	2·01	1·99	1·97	1·96	1·94	1·93	1·91	1·90
	0·05	2·62	2·54	2·51	2·47	2·43	2·40	2·38	2·35	2·34	2·31	2·30
	0·01	4·01	3·86	3·78	3·70	3·62	3·56	3·54	3·46	3·45	3·38	3·36
13	0·10	2·05	2·01	1·98	1·96	1·93	1·91	1·90	1·89	1·88	1·86	1·85
	0·05	2·53	2·46	2·42	2·38	2·34	2·32	2·30	2·26	2·25	2·22	2·21
	0·01	3·82	3·66	3·59	3·51	3·43	3·37	3·34	3·27	3·25	3·18	3·17
14	0·10	2·01	1·96	1·94	1·91	1·89	1·87	1·86	1·84	1·83	1·81	1·80
	0·05	2·46	2·39	2·35	2·31	2·27	2·24	2·22	2·19	2·18	2·14	2·13
	0·01	3·66	3·51	3·43	3·35	3·27	3·21	3·18	3·11	3·09	3·02	3·00
15	0·10	1·97	1·92	1·90	1·87	1·85	1·83	1·82	1·80	1·79	1·77	1·76
	0·05	2·40	2·33	2·29	2·25	2·20	2·18	2·16	2·12	2·11	2·08	2·07
	0·01	3·52	3·37	3·29	3·21	3·13	3·07	3·05	2·97	2·96	2·89	2·87
16	0·10	1·94	1·89	1·87	1·84	1·81	1·79	1·78	1·76	1·75	1·73	1·72
	0·05	2·35	2·28	2·24	2·19	2·15	2·12	2·11	2·07	2·06	2·02	2·01
	0·01	3·41	3·26	3·18	3·10	3·02	2·97	2·92	2·86	2·84	2·78	2·75
17	0·10	1·91	1·86	1·84	1·81	1·78	1·76	1·75	1·73	1·72	1·70	1·69
	0·05	2·31	2·23	2·19	2·15	2·10	2·08	2·06	2·02	2·01	1·97	1·96
	0·01	3·31	3·16	3·08	3·00	2·92	2·87	2·83	2·76	2·75	2·68	2·65
18	0·10	1·89	1·84	1·81	1·78	1·75	1·74	1·72	1·70	1·69	1·67	1·66
	0·05	2·27	2·19	2·15	2·11	2·06	2·04	2·02	1·98	1·97	1·93	1·92
	0·01	3·23	3·08	3·00	2·92	2·84	2·78	2·75	2·68	2·66	2·59	2·57
19	0·10	1·86	1·81	1·79	1·76	1·73	1·71	1·70	1·67	1·67	1·64	1·63
	0·05	2·23	2·16	2·11	2·07	2·03	2·00	1·98	1·94	1·93	1·89	1·88
	0·01	3·15	3·00	2·92	2·84	2·76	2·71	2·67	2·60	2·58	2·51	2·49
20	0·10	1·84	1·79	1·77	1·74	1·71	1·69	1·68	1·65	1·65	1·62	1·61
	0·05	2·20	2·12	2·08	2·04	1·99	1·96	1·95	1·91	1·90	1·85	1·84
	0·01	3·09	2·94	2·86	2·78	2·69	2·63	2·61	2·53	2·52	2·44	2·42

Table A3 (5)

D.F. of lesser mean square	Probability point	Degrees of freedom of the greater mean square										
		1	2	3	4	5	6	7	8	9	10	12
21	0·10	2·96	2·57	2·36	2·23	2·14	2·08	2·02	1·98	1·95	1·92	1·87
	0·05	4·32	3·47	3·07	2·84	2·68	2·57	2·49	2·42	2·37	2·32	2·25
	0·01	8·02	5·78	4·87	4·37	4·04	3·81	3·64	3·51	3·40	3·31	3·17
22	0·10	2·95	2·56	2·35	2·22	2·13	2·06	2·01	1·97	1·93	1·90	1·86
	0·05	4·30	3·44	3·05	2·82	2·66	2·55	2·46	2·40	2·34	2·30	2·23
	0·01	7·95	5·72	4·82	4·31	3·99	3·76	3·59	3·45	3·35	3·26	3·12
23	0·10	2·94	2·55	2·34	2·21	2·11	2·05	1·99	1·95	1·92	1·89	1·85
	0·05	4·28	3·42	3·03	2·80	2·64	2·53	2·44	2·37	2·32	2·27	2·20
	0·01	7·88	5·66	4·76	4·26	3·94	3·71	3·54	3·41	3·30	3·21	3·07
24	0·10	2·93	2·54	2·33	2·19	2·10	2·04	1·98	1·94	1·91	1·88	1·83
	0·05	4·26	3·40	3·01	2·78	2·62	2·51	2·42	2·36	2·30	2·25	2·18
	0·01	7·82	5·61	4·72	4·22	3·90	3·67	3·50	3·36	3·26	3·17	3·03
25	0·10	2·92	2·53	2·32	2·18	2·09	2·02	1·97	1·93	1·89	1·87	1·82
	0·05	4·24	3·39	2·99	2·76	2·60	2·49	2·40	2·34	2·28	2·24	2·16
	0·01	7·77	5·57	4·68	4·18	3·86	3·63	3·46	3·32	3·23	3·13	2·99
26	0·10	2·91	2·52	2·31	2·17	2·08	2·01	1·96	1·92	1·88	1·86	1·81
	0·05	4·23	3·37	2·98	2·74	2·59	2·47	2·39	2·32	2·27	2·22	2·15
	0·01	7·72	5·53	4·64	4·14	3·82	3·59	3·42	3·29	3·18	3·09	2·96
27	0·10	2·90	2·51	2·30	2·17	2·07	2·00	1·95	1·91	1·87	1·85	1·80
	0·05	4·21	3·35	2·96	2·73	2·57	2·46	2·37	2·31	2·25	2·20	2·13
	0·01	7·68	5·49	4·60	4·11	3·78	3·56	3·39	3·26	3·15	3·06	2·93
28	0·10	2·89	2·50	2·29	2·16	2·06	2·00	1·94	1·90	1·87	1·84	1·79
	0·05	4·20	3·34	2·95	2·71	2·56	2·45	2·36	2·29	2·24	2·19	2·12
	0·01	7·64	5·45	4·57	4·07	3·75	3·53	3·36	3·23	3·12	3·03	2·90
29	0·10	2·89	2·50	2·28	2·15	2·06	1·99	1·93	1·89	1·86	1·83	1·78
	0·05	4·18	3·33	2·93	2·70	2·55	2·43	2·35	2·28	2·22	2·18	2·10
	0·01	7·60	5·42	4·54	4·04	3·73	3·50	3·33	3·20	3·09	3·00	2·87
30	0·10	2·88	2·49	2·28	2·14	2·05	1·98	1·93	1·88	1·85	1·82	1·77
	0·05	4·17	3·32	2·92	2·69	2·53	2·42	2·33	2·27	2·21	2·16	2·09
	0·01	7·56	5·39	4·51	4·02	3·70	3·47	3·30	3·17	3·07	2·98	2·84

Table A3 (6)

D.F. of lesser mean square	Probability point	Degrees of freedom of the greater mean square										
		15	20	24	30	40	50	60	100	120	500	∞
21	0·10	1·83	1·78	1·75	1·72	1·69	1·67	1·66	1·63	1·62	1·60	1·59
	0·05	2·18	2·10	2·05	2·01	1·96	1·94	1·92	1·88	1·87	1·82	1·81
	0·01	3·03	2·88	2·80	2·72	2·64	2·58	2·55	2·48	2·46	2·38	2·36
22	0·10	1·81	1·76	1·73	1·70	1·67	1·35	1·64	1·61	1·60	1·58	1·57
	0·05	2·15	2·07	2·03	1·98	1·94	1·91	1·89	1·85	1·84	1·80	1·78
	0·01	2·98	2·83	2·75	2·67	2·58	2·53	2·50	2·42	2·40	2·33	2·31
23	0·10	1·80	1·74	1·72	1·69	1·66	1·64	1·62	1·59	1·59	1·56	1·55
	0·05	2·13	2·05	2·00	1·96	1·91	1·88	1·86	1·82	1·81	1·77	1·76
	0·01	2·93	2·78	2·70	2·62	2·54	2·48	2·45	2·37	2·35	2·28	2·26
24	0·10	1·78	1·73	1·70	1·67	1·64	·62	1·61	1·58	1·57	1·54	1·53
	0·05	2·11	2·03	1·98	1·94	1·89	1·86	1·84	1·80	1·79	1·75	1·73
	0·01	2·89	2·74	2·66	2·58	2·49	2·44	2·40	2·33	2·31	2·24	2·21
25	0·10	1·77	1·72	1·69	1·66	1·63	1·60	1·59	1·57	1·56	1·53	1·52
	0·05	2·09	2·01	1·96	1·92	1·87	1·84	1·82	1·78	1·77	1·73	1·71
	0·01	2·85	2·70	2·62	2·54	2·45	2·40	2·36	2·29	2·27	2·19	2·17
26	0·10	1·76	1·71	1·68	1·65	1·61	1·59	1·58	1·55	1·54	1·51	1·50
	0·05	2·07	1·99	1·95	1·90	1·85	1·82	1·80	1·76	1·75	1·71	1·69
	0·01	2·82	2·66	2·58	2·50	2·42	2·36	2·33	2·25	2·23	2·16	2·13
27	0·10	1·75	1·70	1·66	1·64	1·60	1·58	1·57	1·54	1·53	1·50	1·49
	0·05	2·06	1·97	1·93	1·88	1·84	1·81	1·79	1·74	1·73	1·69	1·67
	0·01	2·78	2·63	2·55	2·47	2·38	2·33	2·29	2·22	2·20	2·12	2·10
28	0·10	1·74	1·69	1·66	1·63	1·59	1·57	1·56	1·53	1·52	1·49	1·48
	0·05	2·04	1·96	1·91	1·87	1·82	1·79	1·77	1·73	1·71	1·67	1·65
	0·01	2·75	2·60	2·52	2·44	2·35	2·30	2·26	2·19	2·17	2·09	2·06
29	0·10	1·73	1·68	1·65	1·62	1·58	1·56	1·55	1·52	1·51	1·48	1·47
	0·05	2·03	1·94	1·90	1·85	1·81	1·77	1·75	1·71	1·70	1·65	1·64
	0·01	2·73	2·57	2·49	2·41	2·33	2·27	2·23	2·16	2·14	2·06	2·03
30	0·10	1·72	1·67	1·64	1·61	1·57	1·55	1·54	1·51	1·50	1·47	1·46
	0·05	2·01	1·93	1·89	1·84	1·79	1·76	1·75	1·70	1·68	1·64	1·62
	0·01	2·70	2·55	2·47	2·39	2·30	2·25	2·21	2·13	2·11	2·03	2·01

Table A3 (T)

D.F. of lesser mean square	Probability point	Degrees of freedom of the greater mean square										
		1	2	3	4	5	6	7	8	9	10	12
40	0·10	2·84	2·44	2·23	2·09	2·00	1·93	1·87	1·83	1·79	1·76	1·71
	0·05	4·08	3·23	2·84	2·61	2·45	2·34	2·25	2·18	2·12	2·08	2·00
	0·01	7·31	5·18	4·31	3·83	3·51	3·29	3·12	2·99	2·89	2·80	2·66
50	0·10	2·81	2·41	2·20	2·06	1·97	1·90	1·84	1·80	1·76	1·73	1·68
	0·05	4·03	3·18	2·79	2·56	2·40	2·29	2·20	2·13	2·07	2·02	1·95
	0·01	7·17	5·06	4·20	3·72	3·41	3·18	3·02	2·88	2·78	2·70	2·56
60	0·10	2·79	2·39	2·18	2·04	1·95	1·87	1·82	1·77	1·74	1·71	·66
	0·05	4·00	3·15	2·76	2·53	2·37	2·25	2·17	2·10	2·04	1·99	·92
	0·01	7·08	4·98	4·13	3·65	3·34	3·12	2·95	2·82	2·72	2·63	2·50
70	0·10	2·78	2·38	2·17	2·03	1·94	1·86	1·80	1·76	1·73	1·70	1·65
	0·05	3·98	3·13	2·74	2·50	2·35	2·23	2·14	2·07	2·01	1·97	1·89
	0·01	7·01	4·92	4·08	3·60	3·29	3·07	2·91	2·77	2·67	2·59	2·45
80	0·10	2·77	2·37	2·15	2·02	1·92	1·85	1·79	1·75	1·71	1·68	1·53
	0·05	3·96	3·11	2·72	2·48	2·33	2·21	2·12	2·05	1·99	1·95	1·38
	0·01	6·96	4·88	4·04	3·56	3·25	3·04	2·87	2·74	2·64	2·55	2·42
100	0·10	2·76	2·36	2·14	2·00	1·91	1·83	1·78	1·73	1·70	1·66	1·61
	0·05	3·94	3·09	2·70	2·46	2·30	2·19	2·10	2·03	1·97	1·92	1·85
	0·01	6·90	4·82	3·98	3·51	3·20	2·99	2·82	2·69	2·59	2·51	2·37
120	0·10	2·75	2·35	2·13	1·99	1·90	1·82	1·77	1·72	1·68	1·65	1·60
	0·05	3·92	3·07	2·68	2·45	2·29	2·18	2·09	2·02	1·96	1·91	1·83
	0·01	6·85	4·79	3·95	3·48	3·17	2·96	2·79	2·66	2·56	2·47	2·33
400	0·10	2·74	2·33	2·11	1·97	1·88	1·80	1·75	1·70	1·66	1·63	1·55
	0·05	3·86	3·02	2·62	2·39	2·23	2·12	2·03	1·96	1·90	1·85	1·77
	0·01	6·70	4·66	3·83	3·36	3·06	2·85	2·69	2·55	2·46	2·37	2·23
1,000	0·10	2·72	2·31	2·09	1·95	1·86	1·78	1·73	1·68	1·64	1·61	1·56
	0·05	3·85	3·00	2·61	2·38	2·22	2·10	2·02	1·95	1·89	1·84	1·76
	0·01	6·66	4·62	3·80	3·34	3·04	2·82	2·66	2·53	2·43	2·34	2·20
∞	0·10	2·71	2·30	2·08	1·94	1·85	1·77	1·72	1·67	1·63	1·60	1·55
	0·05	3·84	3·00	2·60	2·37	2·21	2·10	2·01	1·94	1·88	1·83	1·75
	0·01	6·63	4·61	3·78	3·32	3·02	2·80	2·64	2·51	2·41	2·32	2·18

Table A3 (8)

D.F. of lesser mean square	Probability point	Degrees of freedom of the greater mean square										
		15	20	24	30	40	50	60	100	120	500	∞
40	0·10	1·66	1·61	1·57	1·54	1·51	1·48	1·47	1·44	1·42	1·39	1·38
	0·05	1·92	1·84	1·79	1·74	1·69	1·66	1·64	1·59	1·58	1·53	1·51
	0·01	2·52	2·37	2·29	2·20	2·11	2·05	2·02	1·94	1·92	1·84	1·80
50	0·10	1·63	1·57	1·54	1·50	1·47	1·44	1·43	1·39	1·37	1·34	1·33
	0·05	1·87	1·78	1·74	1·69	1·63	1·60	1·58	1·52	1·51	1·46	1·44
	0·01	2·42	2·26	2·18	2·10	2·00	1·94	1·91	1·82	1·80	1·71	1·68
60	0·10	1·60	1·54	1·51	1·48	1·44	1·41	1·40	1·37	1·35	1·31	1·29
	0·05	1·84	1·75	1·70	1·65	1·59	1·56	1·53	1·48	1·47	1·41	1·39
	0·01	2·35	2·20	2·12	2·03	1·94	1·86	1·84	1·74	1·73	1·63	1·60
70	0·10	1·58	1·52	1·49	1·46	1·42	1·39	1·38	1·35	1·33	1·29	1·27
	0·05	1·81	1·72	1·67	1·62	1·56	1·53	1·50	1·45	1·43	1·37	1·35
	0·01	2·31	2·15	2·07	1·96	1·88	1·82	1·78	1·69	1·67	1·56	1·53
80	0·10	1·57	1·51	1·47	1·44	1·40	1·38	1·36	1·32	1·30	1·26	1·24
	0·05	1·79	1·70	1·65	1·60	1·54	1·51	1·48	1·42	1·40	1·35	1·32
	0·01	2·27	2·11	2·03	1·94	1·84	1·78	1·75	1·65	1·62	1·52	1·49
100	0·10	1·56	1·49	1·46	1·42	1·38	1·35	1·33	1·29	1·27	1·23	1·21
	0·05	1·77	1·68	1·63	1·57	1·51	1·48	1·45	1·39	1·37	1·30	1·28
	0·01	2·22	2·06	1·98	1·89	1·79	1·73	1·69	1·59	1·56	1·46	1·43
120	0·10	1·54	1·48	1·45	1·41	1·37	1·34	1·32	1·28	1·26	1·22	1·19
	0·05	1·75	1·66	1·61	1·55	1·50	1·47	1·43	1·37	1·35	1·27	1·25
	0·01	2·19	2·03	1·95	1·86	1·76	1·70	1·66	1·55	1·53	1·42	1·38
400	0·10	1·52	1·45	1·42	1·38	1·34	1·30	1·28	1·22	1·20	1·12	1·07
	0·05	1·70	1·60	1·55	1·49	1·42	1·38	1·35	1·28	1·26	1·16	1·13
	0·01	2·09	1·92	1·84	1·74	1·64	1·57	1·53	1·42	1·39	1·24	1·19
1,000	0·10	1·50	1·43	1·39	1·35	1·31	1·27	1·25	1·19	1·18	1·09	1·02
	0·05	1·68	1·58	1·53	1·47	1·41	1·36	1·33	1·26	1·24	1·13	1·08
	0·01	2·06	1·89	1·81	1·71	1·61	1·54	1·50	1·38	1·34	1·19	1·10
∞	0·10	1·49	1·42	1·38	1·34	1·30	1·26	1·24	1·18	1·17	1·08	1·00
	0·05	1·67	1·57	1·52	1·46	1·39	1·35	1·32	1·24	1·22	1·11	1·00
	0·01	2·04	1·88	1·79	1·70	1·59	1·52	1·47	1·36	1·32	1·15	1·00

Table A4 Double-sided values of 't'

D.F.	Probability 0·9	0·8	0·7	0·6	0·5	0·4	0·3	0·2
1	0·158	0·325	0·510	0·727	1·000	1·376	1·963	3·078
2	0·142	0·289	0·445	0·617	0·816	1·061	1·386	1·886
3	0·137	0·277	0·424	0·585	0·765	0·978	1·250	1·638
4	0·134	0·271	0·414	0·569	0·741	0·941	1·190	1·533
5	0·132	0·267	0·408	0·559	0·727	0·920	1·156	1·476
6	0·131	0·265	0·404	0·553	0·718	0·906	1·134	1·440
7	0·130	0·263	0·402	0·549	0·711	0·896	1·119	1·415
8	0·130	0·262	0·399	0·546	0·706	0·889	1·108	1·397
9	0·129	0·261	0·398	0·543	0·703	0·883	1·100	1·383
10	0·129	0·260	0·397	0·542	0·700	0·879	1·093	1·372
11	0·129	0·260	0·396	0·540	0·697	0·876	1·088	1·363
12	0·128	0·259	0·395	0·539	0·695	0·873	1·083	1·356
13	0·128	0·259	0·394	0·538	0·694	0·870	1·079	1·350
14	0·128	0·258	0·393	0·537	0·692	0·868	1·076	1·345
15	0·128	0·258	0·393	0·536	0·691	0·866	1·074	1·341
16	0·128	0·258	0·392	0·535	0·690	0·865	1·071	1·337
17	0·128	0·257	0·392	0·534	0·689	0·863	1·069	1·333
18	0·127	0·257	0·392	0·534	0·688	0·862	1·067	1·330
19	0·127	0·257	0·391	0·533	0·688	0·861	1·066	1·328
20	0·127	0·257	0·391	0·533	0·687	0·860	1·064	1·325
21	0·127	0·257	0·391	0·532	0·686	0·859	1·063	1·323
22	0·127	0·256	0·390	0·532	0·686	0·858	1·061	1·321
23	0·127	0·256	0·390	0·532	0·685	0·858	1·060	1·319
24	0·127	0·256	0·390	0·531	0·685	0·857	1·059	1·318
25	0·127	0·256	0·390	0·531	0·684	0·856	1·058	1·316
26	0·127	0·256	0·390	0·531	0·684	0·856	1·058	1·315
27	0·127	0·256	0·389	0·531	0·684	0·855	1·057	1·314
28	0·127	0·256	0·389	0·530	0·683	0·855	1·056	1·313
29	0·127	0·256	0·389	0·530	0·683	0·854	1·055	1·311
30	0·127	0·256	0·389	0·530	0·683	0·854	1·055	1·310
40	0·126	0·255	0·388	0·529	0·681	0·851	1·050	1·303
60	0·126	0·254	0·387	0·527	0·679	0·848	1·046	1·296
120	0·126	0·254	0·386	0·526	0·677	0·845	1·041	1·289
∞	0·126	0·253	0·385	0·524	0·674	0·842	1·036	1·282

Table A4 continued

D.F.	Probability 0·1	0·05	0·02	0·01	0·005	0·002	0·001
1	6·314	12·706	31·821	63·657	127·320	318·310	636·619
2	2·920	4·303	6·965	9·925	14·089	22·326	31·598
3	2·353	3·182	4·541	5·841	7·453	10·213	12·941
4	2·132	2·776	3·747	4·604	5·598	7·173	8·610
5	2·015	2·571	3·365	4·032	4·773	5·893	6·859
6	1·943	2·447	3·143	3·707	4·317	5·208	5·959
7	1·895	2·365	2·998	3·499	4·029	4·785	5·405
8	1·860	2·306	2·896	3·355	3·833	4·501	5·041
9	1·833	2·262	2·821	3·250	3·690	4·297	4·781
10	1·812	2·228	2·764	3·169	3·581	4·144	4·587
11	1·796	2·201	2·718	3·106	3·497	4·025	4·437
12	1·782	2·179	2·681	3·055	3·428	3·930	4·318
13	1·771	2·160	2·650	3·012	3·372	3·852	4·221
14	1·761	2·145	2·624	2·977	3·326	3·787	4·140
15	1·753	2·131	2·602	2·947	3·286	3·733	4·073
16	1·746	2·120	2·583	2·921	3·252	3·686	4·015
17	1·740	2·110	2·567	2·898	3·222	3·646	3·965
18	1·734	2·101	2·552	2·878	3·197	3·610	3·922
19	1·729	2·093	2·539	2·861	3·174	3·579	3·883
20	1·725	2·086	2·528	2·845	3·153	3·552	3·850
21	1·721	2·080	2·518	2·831	3·135	3·527	3·819
22	1·717	2·074	2·508	2·819	3·119	3·505	3·792
23	1·714	2·069	2·500	2·807	3·104	3·485	3·767
24	1·711	2·064	2·492	2·797	3·001	3·467	3·745
25	1·708	2·060	2·485	2·787	3·078	3·450	3·725
26	1·706	2·056	2·479	2·779	3·067	3·435	3·707
27	1·703	2·052	2·473	2·771	3·057	3·421	3·690
28	1·701	2·048	2·467	2·763	3·047	3·408	3·674
29	1·699	2·045	2·462	2·756	3·038	3·396	3·659
30	1·697	2·042	2·457	2·750	3·030	3·385	3·646
40	1·684	2·021	2·423	2·704	2·971	3·307	3·551
60	1·671	2·000	2·390	2·660	2·915	3·232	3·460
120	1·658	1·980	2·358	2·617	2·860	3·160	3·373
∞	1·645	1·960	2·326	2·576	2·807	3·090	3·291

300 INDUSTRIAL STATISTICS

Table A5 (1) Values of u exceeded with probability 0·01. Lord's test

Smaller number n_2 \\ Larger number n_1	2	3	4	5	6	7	8	9	10	11	12	13	14	15	16	17	18	19	20
2	3·958	1·557	1·242	1·008	0·865	0·776	0·713	0·666	0·630	0·601	0·577	0·557	0·541	0·526	0·513	0·502	0·492	0·483	0·475
3		1·050	0·814	0·660	0·590	0·536	0·498	0·469	0·446	0·427	0·412	0·399	0·388	0·378	0·370	0·362	0·356	0·350	0·344
4			0·620	0·528	0·469	0·429	0·399	0·377	0·359	0·345	0·333	0·322	0·314	0·306	0·299	0·293	0·288	0·283	0·279
5				0·450	0·402	0·368	0·343	0·323	0·309	0·296	0·286	0·277	0·270	0·263	0·257	0·252	0·248	0·244	0·240
6					0·359	0·329	0·307	0·289	0·276	0·265	0·255	0·247	0·241	0·235	0·229	0·225	0·221	0·217	0·214
7						0·301	0·281	0·265	0·252	0·242	0·233	0·226	0·220	0·214	0·209	0·205	0·201	0·198	0·195
8							0·262	0·247	0·235	0·225	0·217	0·210	0·204	0·199	0·194	0·190	0·186	0·183	0·180
9								0·223	0·221	0·212	0·204	0·197	0·192	0·187	0·182	0·178	0·175	0·172	0·169
10									0·210	0·201	0·194	0·187	0·182	0·177	0·173	0·169	0·165	0·162	0·160
11										0·193	0·185	0·179	0·174	0·169	0·165	0·161	0·158	0·155	0·152
12											0·178	0·172	0·167	0·162	0·158	0·154	0·151	0·149	0·146
13												0·166	0·161	0·156	0·152	0·149	0·146	0·143	0·140
14													0·156	0·151	0·147	0·144	0·141	0·138	0·135
15														0·147	0·143	0·140	0·137	0·134	0·131
16															0·139	0·136	0·133	0·130	0·128
17																0·132	0·130	0·127	0·124
18																	0·126	0·124	0·121
19																		0·121	0·119
20																			0·116

Table A5 (2) Values of u exceeded with probability 0·02. Lord's test

Smaller number n_2 \ Larger number n_1	2	3	4	5	6	7	8	9	10	11	12	13	14	15	16	17	18	19	20
2	2·776	1·255	1·002	0·827	0·721	0·652	0·603	0·567	0·538	0·515	0·496	0·480	0·467	0·455	0·445	0·436	0·428	0·420	0·414
3		0·860	0·663	0·556	0·501	0·458	0·427	0·404	0·385	0·370	0·358	0·347	0·338	0·330	0·323	0·317	0·311	0·306	0·302
4			0·526	0·450	0·403	0·370	0·346	0·327	0·313	0·301	0·291	0·282	0·275	0·268	0·263	0·258	0·253	0·249	0·246
5				0·387	0·347	0·319	0·299	0·282	0·270	0·260	0·251	0·244	0·237	0·232	0·227	0·222	0·218	0·215	0·212
6					0·312	0·287	0·268	0·254	0·242	0·233	0·225	0·218	0·212	0·207	0·203	0·199	0·195	0·192	0·189
7						0·263	0·246	0·233	0·222	0·213	0·206	0·199	0·194	0·189	0·185	0·181	0·178	0·175	0·172
8							0·213	0·217	0·207	0·199	0·192	0·186	0·180	0·176	0·172	0·168	0·165	0·162	0·160
9								0·205	0·195	0·187	0·180	0·175	0·170	0·165	0·162	0·158	0·155	0·152	0·150
10									0·186	0·178	0·171	0·166	0·161	0·157	0·153	0·150	0·147	0·144	0·142
11										0·170	0·164	0·159	0·154	0·150	0·146	0·143	0·140	0·138	0·135
12											0·158	0·153	0·148	0·144	0·140	0·137	0·134	0·132	0·130
13												0·147	0·143	0·139	0·135	0·132	0·130	0·127	0·125
14													0·138	0·135	0·131	0·128	0·125	0·123	0·121
15														0·131	0·127	0·124	0·122	0·119	0·117
16															0·124	0·121	0·118	0·116	0·114
17																0·118	0·115	0·113	0·111
18																	0·113	0·111	0·108
19																		0·108	0·106
20																			0·104

Table A5 (3) Values of u exceeded with probability 0·05. Lord's test

Smaller number n_2 \ Larger number n_1	2	3	4	5	6	7	8	9	10	11	12	13	14	15	16	17	18	19	20
2	1·714	0·915	0·732	0·619	0·549	0·502	0·469	0·443	0·423	0·407	0·393	0·382	0·372	0·363	0·356	0·349	0·343	0·338	0·333
3		0·635	0·511	0·429	0·391	0·360	0·338	0·321	0·307	0·296	0·287	0·279	0·272	0·266	0·261	0·256	0·252	0·248	0·245
4			0·407	0·353	0·319	0·294	0·276	0·263	0·252	0·242	0·235	0·228	0·223	0·218	0·213	0·210	0·206	0·203	0·200
5				0·307	0·277	0·256	0·240	0·228	0·218	0·210	0·204	0·198	0·193	0·189	0·185	0·182	0·179	0·176	0·173
6					0·250	0·240	0·217	0·206	0·197	0·189	0·183	0·178	0·173	0·169	0·166	0·163	0·160	0·157	0·155
7						0·213	0·200	0·189	0·181	0·174	0·168	0·163	0·159	0·155	0·152	0·149	0·146	0·144	0·142
8							0·187	0·177	0·169	0·162	0·157	0·152	0·148	0·144	0·141	0·138	0·136	0·134	0·132
9								0·167	0·160	0·153	0·148	0·143	0·139	0·136	0·133	0·130	0·128	0·126	0·124
10									0·152	0·146	0·141	0·136	0·133	0·129	0·126	0·124	0·121	0·119	0·117
11										0·140	0·135	0·131	0·127	0·123	0·121	0·118	0·116	0·114	0·112
12											0·130	0·126	0·122	0·119	0·116	0·113	0·111	0·109	0·107
13												0·121	0·118	0·115	0·112	0·109	0·107	0·105	0·103
14													0·114	0·111	0·108	0·106	0·104	0·102	0·101
15														0·108	0·105	0·103	0·101	0·099	0·097
16															0·103	0·100	0·098	0·096	0·094
17																0·098	0·096	0·094	0·092
18																	0·094	0·092	0·090
19																		0·090	0·088
20																			0·086

Table A5 (4) Values of u exceeded with probability 0·1. Lord's test

Larger number n_1 → Smaller number n_2 ↓	2	3	4	5	6	7	8	9	10	11	12	13	14	15	16	17	18	19	20
2	1·161	0·693	0·556	0·478	0·429	0·396	0·372	0·353	0·338	0·326	0·316	0·307	0·300	0·294	0·287	0·282	0·278	0·274	0·270
3		0·487	0·398	0·339	0·311	0·288	0·271	0·258	0·248	0·240	0·232	0·226	0·221	0·216	0·212	0·209	0·205	0·202	0·200
4			0·322	0·282	0·256	0·237	0·224	0·213	0·204	0·197	0·191	0·186	0·182	0·178	0·175	0·172	0·169	0·166	0·164
5				0·247	0·224	0·208	0·195	0·186	0·178	0·172	0·167	0·162	0·158	0·155	0·152	0·149	0·147	0·144	0·142
6					0·203	0·188	0·177	0·168	0·161	0·155	0·150	0·146	0·142	0·139	0·136	0·134	0·131	0·129	0·128
7						0·174	0·163	0·155	0·148	0·143	0·138	0·134	0·131	0·128	0·125	0·123	0·121	0·119	0·117
8							0·153	0·145	0·139	0·133	0·129	0·125	0·122	0·119	0·116	0·114	0·112	0·110	0·109
9								0·137	0·131	0·125	0·122	0·118	0·115	0·112	0·110	0·107	0·106	0·104	0·102
10									0·125	0·120	0·116	0·112	0·109	0·107	0·104	0·102	0·100	0·098	0·097
11										0·115	0·111	0·108	0·105	0·102	0·100	0·098	0·096	0·094	0·092
12											0·107	0·104	0·101	0·098	0·096	0·094	0·092	0·090	0·089
13												0·100	0·097	0·095	0·092	0·090	0·089	0·087	0·086
14													0·094	0·092	0·090	0·088	0·086	0·084	0·083
15														0·089	0·087	0·085	0·083	0·082	0·080
16															0·085	0·083	0·081	0·080	0·078
17																0·081	0·079	0·078	0·076
18																	0·077	0·076	0·074
19																		0·074	0·073
20																			0·071

Table A6 Critical values for Lord's test for a single mean

Sample size	Level of probability, per cent			
	95	97·5	99	99·5
2	3·16	6·35	15·91	31·83
3	0·885	1·30	2·11	3·01
4	0·529	0·717	1·02	1·32
5	0·388	0·507	0·685	0·843
6	0·312	0·399	0·523	0·628
7	0·263	0·333	0·429	0·507
8	0·230	0·288	0·366	0·429
9	0·205	0·255	0·322	0·374
10	0·186	0·230	0·288	0·333

Table A7 95 per cent probability critical values for range ratios

Number of Tests included in ratio denominator	Number of Tests included in ratio numerator								
	2	3	4	5	6	7	8	9	10
2	12·7	19·1	25·0	28·0	29·0	31·0	32·0	34·0	36·0
3	3·19	4·4	5·0	5·7	6·2	6·6	6·9	7·2	7·4
4	2·02	2·7	3·1	3·4	3·6	3·8	4·0	4·2	4·4
5	1·61	2·1	2·4	2·6	2·8	2·9	3·0	3·1	3·2
6	1·36	1·8	2·0	2·2	2·3	2·4	2·5	2·6	2·7
7	1·26	1·6	1·8	1·9	2·0	2·1	2·2	2·3	2·4
8	1·17	1·4	1·6	1·8	1·9	1·9	2·0	2·1	2·1
9	1·10	1·3	1·5	1·6	1·7	1·8	1·9	1·9	2·0
10	1·05	1·3	1·4	1·5	1·6	1·7	1·8	1·8	1·9

Table A8 For unpaired replicates

N	$P = 0·05$	$P = 0·02$	$P = 0·01$
5	18	16	15
6	27	24	23
7	37	34	32
8	49	46	43
9	63	59	56
10	79	74	71
11	97	91	87
12	116	110	105
13	137	130	125
14	160	152	147
15	185	176	170
16	212	202	196
17	241	230	223
18	271	259	252
19	303	291	282
20	338	324	315

Table gives the probability (P) of chance occurrence of a rank total equal to or less than T tor N replicates. Values of T are given in the body of the table to the nearest whole number.

Table A9 For paired replicates

N	P = 0·05	P = 0·02	P = 0·01
6	1	0	—
7	2	1	—
8	4	2	0
9	6	3	2
10	8	5	3
11	11	7	5
12	14	10	7
13	18	13	9
14	22	16	12
15	26	20	15
16	31	24	19
17	36	28	23
18	41	33	27
19	47	38	32
20	53	43	37

Table gives the probability (P) of chance occurrence of a rank total of one sign, $+$ or $-$, whichever is the less, equal to or less than T for N replicates. Values of T are given in the body of the table to the nearest whole number.

Table A10 For grouped data

N	P	n = 2	n = 3	n = 4	n = 5	n = 6	n = 7
2	0·01	—	9	13	17	22	26
	0·02	—	10	14	18	23	27
	0·05	6	11	15	19	24	28
3	0·01	13	21	30	39	49	58
	0·02	14	22	31	41	50	59
	0·05	15	24	33	42	52	62
4	0·01	24	39	54	70	86	102
	0·02	25	40	56	72	88	105
	0·05	26	42	58	75	91	108
5	0·01	38	61	85	110	135	160
	0·02	39	63	88	112	138	163
	0·05	42	66	91	116	142	168
6	0·01	55	89	124	159	195	231
	0·02	57	92	127	162	198	235
	0·05	61	96	131	168	204	241
7	0·01	77	123	170	218	266	314
	0·02	79	126	174	222	270	319
	0·05	83	131	179	228	277	327

Table gives the probability (P) of chance occurrence of a rank total equal to or less than T for N replicates in each of n groups. Values of T are given in the body of the table to the nearest whole number.

Table A11 Table of random numbers

83	28	78	05	18	98	49	22	54	11	92	37	45	11	63	60	19	05	91	26
84	73	82	58	01	90	55	37	85	68	98	15	99	52	99	84	51	91	73	81
00	79	20	99	42	57	55	67	93	39	99	25	65	10	94	54	84	65	16	23
94	48	02	99	71	08	50	84	66	10	10	34	92	30	89	28	30	74	24	24
54	37	52	43	87	22	21	34	20	15	07	67	64	98	36	01	33	34	04	42
47	68	59	90	98	90	27	71	89	89	98	20	24	19	85	02	34	38	26	71
76	16	58	55	51	85	44	00	28	28	38	91	70	70	16	81	13	49	46	54
37	64	90	35	64	45	47	72	82	03	01	65	05	97	13	90	90	57	51	97
92	78	39	12	48	01	83	46	39	29	98	71	39	56	97	66	97	70	05	77
24	50	29	02	71	28	53	99	75	07	13	18	76	97	72	54	85	79	71	60
01	72	71	23	86	40	70	05	35	36	15	64	11	01	11	18	90	14	95	05
43	28	52	77	22	80	49	89	79	65	91	17	80	94	34	02	17	61	00	42
29	09	19	54	67	67	88	54	62	09	07	97	35	19	31	25	06	92	25	02
27	95	74	89	62	45	75	39	06	89	58	96	64	65	81	84	85	20	01	47
52	43	54	97	75	80	00	38	20	38	57	46	57	33	87	19	66	06	40	32
78	11	60	42	09	83	28	40	93	57	61	22	27	27	47	80	44	34	47	27
03	74	36	27	13	19	14	76	35	73	66	29	95	65	12	87	61	91	34	30
82	25	35	57	16	29	21	27	51	23	06	52	40	00	28	11	47	23	63	01
09	91	87	20	33	76	61	55	79	21	74	36	21	36	05	47	28	42	92	51
19	82	00	40	15	52	45	35	13	48	74	10	97	36	22	85	44	57	91	72
69	41	17	07	11	54	36	81	57	38	55	39	85	74	48	05	06	43	10	63
48	80	36	26	28	95	03	79	54	31	41	55	48	84	78	63	09	05	69	07
80	02	51	78	94	07	88	62	85	82	80	37	56	15	59	30	46	42	84	02
19	51	95	22	72	72	95	51	57	73	04	68	00	95	04	30	66	52	60	74
50	36	31	76	75	39	04	95	69	47	95	23	01	70	95	04	04	18	68	14
60	03	34	57	41	76	35	06	75	60	21	58	86	36	02	33	00	59	63	13
59	40	60	83	61	73	45	18	08	23	54	86	64	57	76	70	00	89	43	24
29	51	12	43	14	24	35	78	76	22	82	50	68	02	13	19	07	00	19	07
57	07	34	86	57	96	99	57	44	54	90	87	33	76	71	71	23	28	88	37
81	73	29	08	96	62	34	26	52	32	23	74	17	49	45	62	17	88	50	50
40	20	21	54	17	65	99	31	09	72	67	87	16	34	00	76	26	23	42	40
81	26	86	30	79	17	93	45	74	50	50	24	65	52	06	59	04	60	73	63
13	65	31	57	36	88	98	35	04	96	41	37	45	87	57	57	21	15	34	59
23	41	47	66	24	73	31	96	72	07	09	43	88	63	33	80	54	79	84	18
79	62	53	27	85	43	51	69	83	81	90	85	84	72	18	48	41	20	81	59
13	40	75	73	19	92	12	01	91	95	23	99	99	30	30	58	46	22	64	41
54	87	97	55	83	91	42	61	41	02	40	18	39	20	56	19	56	35	04	32
09	29	30	63	75	86	85	29	15	34	68	92	34	06	81	60	32	16	05	37
61	99	27	99	73	18	94	29	25	74	22	20	70	46	30	38	26	91	59	16
31	84	93	27	40	23	25	86	68	30	10	11	91	59	61	07	41	97	10	39
35	86	11	25	98	38	27	14	79	68	77	60	63	34	23	80	75	43	48	79
40	42	68	85	23	40	27	56	54	56	75	65	70	49	24	08	10	44	75	59
25	14	94	00	99	80	81	44	49	08	98	93	71	74	11	14	54	69	71	66
56	18	75	63	56	68	25	36	75	98	00	18	19	15	24	28	56	80	75	97
79	61	54	67	58	38	93	69	45	95	61	19	17	35	89	90	98	70	26	20
92	91	85	49	33	32	46	67	28	20	40	99	88	73	56	33	29	13	41	89
01	79	85	45	45	36	05	67	56	17	59	77	59	34	35	01	15	21	00	35
55	84	71	36	40	39	47	25	25	73	69	14	55	73	35	86	61	17	98	69
38	36	66	66	19	40	90	83	06	31	24	67	91	74	54	14	87	24	61	80
01	69	50	70	31	02	98	86	42	01	94	98	07	85	28	38	37	30	72	76

Table A12 Random normal numbers $\mu = 0$; $\sigma = 1$

	(1)	(2)	(3)	(4)	(5)	(6)	(7)
1	0·464	0·137	2·455	−0·323	−0·068	0·296	−0·288
2	0·060	−2·526	−0·531	−1·940	0·543	−1·558	0·187
3	1·486	−0·354	−0·634	0·697	0·926	1·375	0·785
4	1·022	−0·472	1·279	3·521	0·571	−1·851	0·194
5	1·394	−0·555	0·046	0·321	2·945	1·974	−0·258
6	0·906	−0·513	−0·525	0·595	0·881	−0·934	1·579
7	1·179	−1·055	0·007	0·769	0·971	0·712	1·090
8	−1·501	−0·488	−0·162	−0·136	1·033	0·203	0·448
9	−0·690	0·756	−1·618	−0·445	−0·511	−2·051	−0·457
10	1·372	0·225	0·378	0·761	0·181	−0·736	0·960
11	−0·482	1·677	−0·057	−1·229	−0·486	0·856	−0·491
12	−1·376	−0·150	1·356	−0·561	−0·256	0·212	0·219
13	−1·010	0·508	0·918	1·598	0·065	0·415	−0·169
14	−0·005	−0·899	0·012	−0·725	1·147	−0·121	−0·096
15	1·393	−1·163	−0·911	1·231	−0·199	−0·246	1·239
16	−1·787	−0·261	1·237	1·046	−0·508	−1·630	−0·146
17	−0·105	−0·357	−1·384	0·360	−0·992	−0·116	−1·698
18	−1·339	1·827	−0·959	0·424	0·969	−1·141	−1·041
19	1·041	0·535	0·731	1·377	0·983	−1·330	1·620
20	0·279	−2·056	0·717	−0·873	−1·096	−1·396	1·047
21	−1·805	−2·008	1·633	0·542	0·250	0·166	0·032
22	−1·186	1·180	1·114	0·882	1·265	−0·202	0·151
23	0·658	−1·141	1·151	−1·210	−0·927	0·425	0·290
24	−0·439	0·358	−1·939	0·891	−0·227	0·602	0·973
25	1·398	−0·230	0·385	−0·649	−0·577	0·237	−0·289
26	0·199	0·208	−1·083	−0·219	−0·291	1·221	1·119
27	0·159	0·272	−0·313	0·084	−2·828	−0·439	−0·792
28	2·273	0·606	0·606	−0·747	0·247	1·291	0·063
29	0·041	−0·307	0·121	0·790	−0·584	0·541	0·484
30	−1·132	−2·098	0·921	0·145	0·446	−2·661	1·045
31	0·768	0·079	−1·473	0·034	−2·127	0·665	0·084
32	0·375	−1·658	−0·851	0·234	−0·656	0·340	−0·086
33	−0·513	−0·344	0·210	−0·736	1·041	0·008	0·427
34	0·292	−0·521	1·266	−1·206	−0·899	0·110	−0·528
35	1·026	2·990	−0·574	−0·491	−1·114	1·297	−1·433
36	−1·334	1·278	−0·568	−0·109	−0·515	−0·566	2·923
37	−0·287	−0·144	−0·254	0·574	−0·451	−1·181	−1·190
38	0·161	−0·886	−0·921	−0·509	1·410	−0·518	0·192
39	−1·346	0·193	−1·202	0·394	−1·045	0·843	0·942
40	1·250	−0·199	−0·288	1·810	1·378	0·584	1·216

BIBLIOGRAPHY

1 E. S. PEARSON and H. O. HARTLEY, *Biometrika Tables for Statisticians*, Volume 1, Cambridge University Press, 1958.
2 G. U. YULE and M. G. KENDALL, *An Introduction to the Theory of Statistics*, Griffin, London, 1958.
3 C. A. BENNETT and N. L. FRANKLIN, *Statistical Analysis in Chemistry and the Chemical Industry*, Wiley, New York, 1954.
4 O. L. DAVIES (ed.), *The Design and Analysis of Industrial Experiments*, Oliver & Boyd, London, 1956.
5 O. L. DAVIES (ed.), *Statistical Methods in Research and Production*, Oliver & Boyd, London, 1958.
6 L. M. DEBING (ed.), *Quality Control for Plastics Engineers*, Reinhold Publishing Corporation, New York, 1957.
7 J. E. FREUND and F. J. WILLIAMS, *Modern Business Statistics*, Pitman & Sons, London, 1959.
8 K. A. BROWNLEE, *Industrial Experimentation*, HMSO, London, 1957.
9 K. A. BROWNLEE, *Statistical Theory and Methodology in Science and Engineering*, Wiley, New York and London, 1960.
10 H. SCHEFFÉ, *The Analysis of Variance*, Wiley, New York and London, 1959.
11 W. G. COCHRAN, *Sampling Techniques*, Wiley, New York and London, 1964.
12 B. C. BROOKES and W. F. L. DICK, *An Introduction to Statistical Method*, Heinemann, London, 1963.
13 DEFENCE SPECIFICATION DEF-131-A, Sampling Procedures and Tables for Inspection by Attributes, HMSO, London, 1966.
14 MILITARY STANDARD MIL-STD-414, *Sampling Procedures and Tables for Inspection by Variables for Percent Defective*, U.S. Government Printing Office, Washington, 1957.
15 R. H. WOODWARD and P. L. GOLDSMITH, *Cumulative Sum Techniques*, I.C.I. Monograph No. 3, Oliver & Boyd, London, 1964.
16 O. L. LACEY, *Statistical Methods in Experimentation*, The MacMillan Company, New York, 1953.
17 W. A. SHEWHART, *Economic Control of the Quality of Manufactured Product*, Van Nostrand, New York, 1941.
18 E. S. PEARSON, *The Application of Statistical Methods to Industrial Standardisation and Quality Control*, B.S. 600, HMSO, London, 1935.
19 B. P. DUDDING and W. J. JENNETT, *Control Chart Technique when manufacturing to a Specification*, B.S. 2564, HMSO, London, 1955.
20 M. G. KENDALL, *Rank Correlation Methods*, Griffin, London, 1948.
21 M. H. QUENOUILLE, *Rapid Statistical Calculations*, Griffin, London, 1960.
22 A. BRADFORD HILL, *Principles of Medical Statistics*, The Lancet Limited, London, 1961.
23 A. HUITSON, *The Analysis of Variance*, Griffin, London, 1966.
24 E. S. PEARSON and J. WISHART, *Students' Collected Papers*, Cambridge University Press, 1958.

25 C. V. DURELL, *Advanced Algebra*, Volume 1, G. Bell and Sons, London, 1963.
26 R. A. FISHER, *The Design of Experiments*, Oliver & Boyd, London, 1939.
27 O. L. DAVIES and E. S. PEARSON, 'Methods of Estimating from Samples the Population Standard Deviation', *J.R.S.S.* (Supplement) **1**, 76, 1934.
28 R. H. WILSON, *A Scientific Routine for Stock Control*, Harvard Business Review, 1935.
29 F. YATES, 'Some Examples of Biased Sampling', *Ann. Eugenics*, **6**, 202, 1935.
30 M. FRIEDMAN, 'The Use of Ranks to avoid the assumption of Normality', *J. Am. Stat. Ass.*, **32**, 675, 1937.
31 A. WALD, 'The fitting of straight lines if both variables are subject to error', *Ann. Math. Stat.* **xi**, 284, 1940.
32 D. V. LINDLEY, 'Regression Lines and Linear Functional Relationships', *J.R.S.S.* (B) **16**, 151, 1947.
33 E. LORD, 'The use of the Range in place of the standard deviation in the *t*-test', *Biometrika* **34**, 41, 1947.
34 J. M. BUIST and O. L. DAVIES, 'Methods of averaging Physical Test Results: Use of Median', *Rubber Journal* **cxii**, 447, 1947.
35 M. S. BARTLETT, 'The Use of Transformations', *Biometrics* **3**, 39, 1947.
36 F. WILCOXON, 'Probability Tables for Individual Comparisons by Ranking Methods', *Biometrics* **3**, 119, 1947.
37 H. OLMSTEED and J. W. TUKEY, 'A Corner Test for Association', *Ann. Math. Stat.* **18**, 495.
38 S. S. WILKS, 'Order Statistics', *Bull. Am. M.S.* **54**, 6, 1948.
39 M. S. BARTLETT, 'Fitting a Straight Line when both variables are subject to error', *Biometrics* **5**, 203, 1949.
40 J. W. TUKEY, 'The Simplest Signed Rank Tests', *Memorandum Report* 17, SRG, Princeton University, 1949.
41 J. W. TUKEY, 'Comparing Individual Means in the Analysis of Variance', *Biometrics* **5**, 99, 1949.
42 A. G. BAKER, 'Properties of Some Tests in Sequential Analysis', *Biometrika* **37**, 334, 1950.
43 F. WILCOXON, *Some Rapid Approximate Statistical Procedures*, Am. Cyanamid Co., Stamford, Conn., 1950.
44 B. WOOLF, 'Computation and Interpretation of Multiple Regressions', *J.R.S.S.* (B) **13**, 100, 1951.
45 W. J. DIXON, 'Processing Data for Outliers, *Biometrics* **9**, 74, 1953.
46 EHRENBERG and SHEWAN, 'The objective approach to sensory tests of food', *J. Sci. Food Agric.* **4**, 482, 1953.
47 G. A. BARNARD, 'Sampling Inspection and Statistical Decisions', *J.R.S.S.* (B) **16**, 151, 1954.
48 D. B. DUNCAN, 'Multiple Range and Multiple *F*-tests', *Biometrics* **11**, 1–42, 1955.
49 DUCKWORTH and WYATT, 'Rapid Statistical Techniques for Operational Research Workers', *O.R.Q.* **9**, 218, 1958.
50 O. L. DAVIES, 'Some Statistical Aspects of the Economics of Analytical Testing', *Technometrics* **1**, 49, 1959.
51 J. S. JAMES, 'A Statistical Approach to Stores Auditing', *App. Stat.* **8**, 145, 1959.
52 P. G. MOORE, 'Some Approximate Statistical Tests', *O.R.Q.* **10**, 1, 1959.
53 M. R. BRYSON, 'Physical Inventory using Sampling Methods', *App. Stat.* **9**, 178, 1960.
54 N. T. GRIDGEMAN, 'Statistics and Taste Testing', *App. Stat.* **9**, 103, 1960.
55 E. S. PAGE, 'Cumulative Sum Charts', *Technometrics* **3**, 11, 1961.
56 P. G. MOORE, 'A Statistical Approach to the Allocation of Technical Effort in some Industrial Situations', *J.R.S.S.* **126**, 493, 1963.
57 DIXON and MOOD, 'The Statistical Sign Test', *J. Am. Stat. Ass.* **41**, 557, 1946.

INDEX